PF

PROCEEDINGS OF A SYMPOSIUM
IN APPLIED MATHEMATICS
OF THE AMERICAN MATHEMATICAL SOCIETY

Held in New York City
April 5-7, 1966

J. T. SCHWARTZ
EDITOR

VOLUME XIX

PROCEEDINGS OF
SYMPOSIA IN APPLIED MATHEMATICS

MATHEMATICAL ASPECTS
OF COMPUTER SCIENCE

AMERICAN MATHEMATICAL SOCIETY

PROVIDENCE, RHODE ISLAND

1967

Prepared by the American Mathematical Society with the support of the Air Force Office of Scientific Research of the Office of Aerospace Research, under Contract No. AF 49(638)-1667 and the Institute for Defense Analyses.

Library of Congress Catalog Number 67-16554

CONTENTS

v

J. A. Robinson

A REVIEW
OF AUTOMATIC THEOREM-PROVING

1. **Introduction. The basic formalism.** By a *theorem-proving problem* we mean a problem which has the form: *show that B follows from* $A_1, \cdots, A_n$, where $A_1, \cdots, A_n$ and B are *statements*. It may well be that $A_1, \cdots, A_n$ are the *axioms* or *postulates* of some theory, and that B is a (presumed) *theorem* of that theory; in that case the problem is that of *proving* the given theorem from the given axioms.

It is usually thought that such problems require a certain amount of ingenuity for their solution, and indeed it is by using mathematical skill and ingenuity in reasoning that people usually solve them. However, under very general conditions on the language in which the statements $A_1, \cdots, A_n$ and B are expressed (so general that, as far as one can tell, any statement ever uttered, or ever likely to be uttered, in a mathematical context, can be expressed suitably in a language which meets them), a theorem-proving problem can be solved *automatically* if it can be solved at all. That is to say, if the given B *does* follow from the given $A_1, \cdots, A_n$ then this fact can be detected, automatically, by executing a certain purely clerical algorithm on $A_1, \cdots, A_n$ and B as input. As a by-product of the ensuing computation there will be constructed a *proof* (in a suitable sense) of B from $A_1, \cdots, A_n$.

These very general conditions are those that characterize the so-called *first-order predicate calculus*. In order that this paper may be read more or less independently, this formalism will now be briefly described, in a *quantifier-free* version which avoids several complications which are not really germane to our present purposes. The relationship between this version of the first-order predicate calculus and versions which contain quantifiers is well discussed in Davis and Putnam [2] and in Davis [3].

A single nonempty collection D of entities, the so-called *universe of discourse*, is supposed to be understood; symbols, called *relation symbols*, are available to denote *relations over* D, i.e., functions from D^n, the set of all n-tuples of elements of D, (where n is the *degree* of the relation and of the

1

relation symbol that denotes it) to the set of truth values: *true, false*. Other symbols, called *function symbols*, are available to denote functions from D^n to D, where n is the *degree* of the function and of the symbol that denotes it. Function symbols of degree zero, in particular, are in effect *names* of fixed elements of D, while relation symbols of degree zero in effect are statements whose truth values are already determined. In addition to the relation symbols and function symbols there are available symbols, called *variables*, which are thought of as denoting arbitrary elements of D.

The usual conventions are that relation symbols are written as upper-case letters, with numeric subscripts if need be, that function symbols are written as lowercase letters chosen from among the first twenty in the alphabet, with numeric subscripts if need be, and that variables are written as lowercase letters chosen from among the last six in the alphabet, with numeric subscripts if need be. We shall assume these conventions.

Using this much of the symbolic apparatus, one can construct *terms* from the variables x, y, z, etc., and function symbols a, b, c, etc., by *composition* using parentheses and commas in the familiar style of mathematical notation for the application of functions to their arguments: $f(x,y)$, $g(a,b(x,y,f(x)))$, etc., obtaining thereby expressions which denote entities in D which can be recursively determined by applying the functions denoted by the function symbols to the elements of D which are denoted by the respective expressions found in the parenthesized list immediately following the function symbols. In like manner one can express simple statements by constructing so-called *atomic formulae*, or *atoms*, which consist of a relation symbol followed by a parenthesized list of terms, and which are *true* or *false* according as the relation denoted by the relation symbol, when applied to the elements of D denoted by the respective expressions in the parenthesized list, gives the value *true* or the value *false*.

Finally, compound statements can be constructed, starting from the atoms described above, by means of the *statement connectives*. These are the symbols for *negation*, $\neg$, *conjunction*, $\wedge$, and *disjunction*, $\vee$. Thus the statement $\neg A$ is *true* when A is *false*, and conversely, and is called the *negation of A*; the *conjunction of $A_1, \cdots, A_n$* is written $(A_1 \wedge \cdots \wedge A_n)$ and is *true* when each of the A_i is *true*, otherwise it is *false*; the *disjunction of $A_1, \cdots, A_n$* is written $(A_1 \vee \cdots \vee A_n)$ and is *false* when each of the A_i is *false*, otherwise it is *true*.

In general, any statement which can be constructed in this way will contain zero, one, or more variables, and it is then *true* if it is *true* no matter what elements of D these variables are taken to denote.

Within this formalism, a statement B is said to *follow from* the statements $A_1, \cdots, A_n$ if and only if there is no way of choosing D, and a denotation over D for each relation symbol and function symbol as explained above, so that $(A_1 \wedge \cdots \wedge A_n \wedge \neg B)$ is *true*. A statement which cannot be *true* no matter what D and the denotations within D of the relation symbols and function symbols are taken to be, is said to be *unsatisfiable*, whereas it is said to be *satisfiable* if there is a choice of D, and of denotations within D for the relation symbols and function symbols, for which it is *true*, and it is said to be *satisfied by* such a choice.

It will be seen that this definition of the relationship of *following from* is in accord with one's intuitive understanding of it: something follows logically from something else if it could not possibly be false given that the something else is not.

In preparation for the fundamental result explained in the next section, which is due to Skolem [15, 16], Herbrand [7], and Gödel [5], it should be noted that, in general, the statement that S is unsatisfiable is of absolutely enormous scope. It is saying something quite definite about all nonempty sets D (of however high a cardinality) as possible choices of universe of discourse, and about all possible denotations within each such D for the relation symbols and function symbols occurring in S.

From this point onwards we shall be discussing methods for showing, given an unsatisfiable S in the present formalism, that S is indeed unsatisfiable. It will be easier if we treat this problem purely as a combinatorial problem involving certain well-defined properties of certain well-defined symbolic objects. We will therefore take this point of view.

2. **A quick summary of the background theory.** The general theorem-proving problem is then that of showing that a statement S of our formalism, containing $n \geq 0$ variables, is unsatisfiable. S is in fact some combination of atoms, of an arbitrarily complicated structure, but we shall for the time being neglect this fact, concentrating simply on the variables which occur in S. We may take these to be, say, $x_1, \cdots, x_n$, and represent S accordingly as:

(2.1) $$S(x_1, \cdots, x_n).$$

We must then show that there is no interpretation of the *vocabulary*

(2.2) $$R_1, \cdots, R_k, \qquad f_1, \cdots, f_m$$

of S which makes S *true*. Each R_i is a relation symbol of degree (say) p_i, and each f_j is a function symbol of degree (say) q_j which occurs in S, and the list (2.2) is a list of all such.

The universe of discourse for the interpretation may, as was stressed in the previous section, be any nonempty set D whatsoever; but in particular it may be taken to be the set H of all *terms* which can be constructed from the variables $x_1, \cdots, x_n$ and function symbols $f_1, \cdots, f_m$ which appear in S itself. This particular choice of universe, which is uniquely determined by S, is called *the Herbrand universe of S.*

With H as the choice of universe of discourse, we may then specify, as the denotation of each function symbol f_j, the function $\mathbf{f}_j$ whose value, for the *terms* $t_1, \cdots, t_{q_j}$ as arguments, is simply the *term* $f_j(t_1, \cdots t_{q_j})$.

For each relation symbol R_i a relation $\mathbf{R}_i$ may then be specified by assigning the truth value *true* or the truth value *false* to each atom $R_i(t_1, \cdots, t_{p_i})$, where $t_1, \cdots, t_{p_i}$ are any terms in H.

Evidently, this is indeed an interpretation of S. Whether or not it actually satisfies S will now turn on the question whether every *instance* of S

(2.3) $$S(t_1, \cdots, t_n)$$

over H, i.e., every formula which comes from S by substitution of terms $t_1, \cdots, t_n$ from H for the respective variables $x_1, \cdots, x_n$, is *true* under that particular assignment of truth values to the atoms.

Let us suppose that the (at most denumerably many) atoms $R_i(t_1, \cdots, t_{p_i})$ are enumerated without repetitions in the sequence

(2.4) $$A_1, A_2, \cdots,$$

and that the (at most denumerably many) instances $S(t_1, \cdots, t_n)$ are enumerated without repetitions in the sequence

(2.5) $$S_1, S_2, \cdots,$$

and let us ask simply whether there is any assignment of truth values to

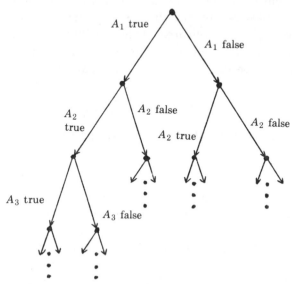

FIGURE 1

the A_i in (2.4) such that every combination S_j of them in (2.5) is *true* under that assignment.

By noting that each different assignment of truth values to the A_i corresponds to a distinct branch of the infinite binary tree shown in Figure 1, we may construct a tree T which represents the effect of each assignment on $S_1, S_2, \cdots$, as follows: *terminate* the corresponding branch of the infinite binary tree at the node at which, for the first time, all of the atoms occurring in some S_j have been given truth values and S_j is thereby made *false*, and write, immediately below that node, the index of the earliest such S_j. This uniquely determines a subtree T of the infinite binary tree whose branches correspond to interpretations which satisfy S only if they do not terminate.

Using this tree T, we can now easily prove the so-called *fundamental theorem of logic*, or the

SKOLEM-HERBRAND-GÖDEL THEOREM. *If S is unsatisfiable then some finite set of instances in the sequence $S_1, S_2, \cdots$, is truth-functionally unsatisfiable, and conversely.*

For, if S is unsatisfiable, then in particular no "symbolic" interpretation of the sort described above, with the Herbrand universe of S as universe of discourse, satisfies S. Therefore no assignment of truth values to the atoms $A_1, A_2, \cdots$, will make *every* $S_1, S_2, \cdots$, *true*, and therefore *every branch in the tree T terminates*. But, if each branch of a tree which splits into at most two branches at each node terminates, there can be only finitely many nodes in the tree. (Otherwise, there would be a nonterminating branch in the tree, consisting of *nodes with infinitely many descendants*; for the initial node of the tree would be such a node, and if any node is such a node it must have at least one immediate successor which also is.) Therefore T has only finitely many nodes, and hence only finitely many terminal nodes. The indices $j_1, j_2, \cdots, j_N$ written below these terminal nodes then provide a finite set

(2.6) $$S_{j_1}, S_{j_2}, \cdots, S_{j_N}$$

of instances of S which is truth-functionally unsatisfiable. For, if M is the largest index among those of the atoms A_i which actually occur in the instances (2.6), then each of the 2^M distinct assignments of truth values to $A_1, A_2, \cdots, A_M$ will falsify at least one instance in the set (2.6). The converse is trivial. Q.E.D.

Thus, by mechanizing the process of generating, given S, the successive instances $S_1, S_2, \cdots$, of S over its Herbrand universe in some enumeration thereof, and by testing the successive finite sequences $S_1, S_2, \cdots, S_n$ for truth-functional satisfiability, we obtain an automatic theorem-proving process which is guaranteed, by the theorem just proved, to *show* that the given S is unsatisfiable if in fact it is.

The entire field of automatic theorem-proving research is really concerned with this basic procedure, and in particular with designing versions of it which will be computationally practicable.

3. **Implementing the raw procedure is not practicable.** The fundamental procedure suggested by the Skolem-Herbrand-Gödel theorem is computationally impracticable because, given a uniform method of enumerating the instances $S_1, S_2, \cdots$, of a statement S over its Herbrand universe, the earliest K such that the set of instances $S_1, S_2, \cdots, S_K$ is truth-functionally unsatisfiable turns out in general to be a very large number indeed.

It is very natural to enumerate the instances of S in the order of their increasing complexity. All procedures in the literature which are of this general type follow this plan. Then in order to accumulate the members of the set (2.6) it is necessary, roughly speaking, to generate *all instances which are no more complex than the most complex instance in* (2.6). For even a low level L of complexity, the number of instances whose complexity does not exceed L is in general enormous. And for problems of reasonable mathematical interest the most complex instance in (2.6) may in fact be quite complex. The irony of the situation is that almost all of the instances which for this reason must be generated are irrelevant to the problem, and the number of those which are relevant is quite small.

There has emerged, over the past five years or so, a collection of ideas which are aimed at improving this situation. A certain unity underlies them, which will, it is hoped, be apparent from the discussion of them in the remaining part of this paper.

Given S, consider the truth-functionally unsatisfiable set (2.6) of instances of S which is known to exist if S is unsatisfiable. It is not difficult to see that the set (2.6) of instances is obtainable, abstractly considered, by taking a set C containing N variants of S, a substitution θ, and forming the result $C\theta$ of carrying out the substitution θ on each formula in C.

By a *variant* of a formula S is meant any formula exactly like S except perhaps for the choice of letters for the variables, if any, in S. By a *substitution* is meant a finite set $\{ T_1/V_1, \cdots, T_k/V_k \}$ of *substitution components* T_i/V_i, where V_i is a variable and T_i is a term different from V_i, no two components in the set having the same variable after the stroke symbol. We use Greek letters to represent substitutions. The result of carrying out the substitution θ on the expression (e.g., term or atom or formula) E is represented by $E\theta$ and is obtained from E by replacing each occurrence of the variable V_i by an occurrence of the term T_i, for each substitution component in the substitution θ. If C is a *set* of expressions, we write $C\theta$ to represent the set of all expressions $E\theta$, for E in C. As a special case of a set of substitution components we have the *empty* set thereof, written as ϵ, and having no effect when carried out on any expression.

Dag Prawitz [11] was the first to observe that, given a finite set C of formulas, the question whether or not there exists a substitution θ such that $C\theta$ is truth-functionally unsatisfiable *can be settled by an algorithm, which actually computes, given C as input, such a θ if there is one, and indicates that there is none, if there is none.* This algorithm lies at the heart of the theory of automatic theorem-proving as it stands at present. Given that there is such an algorithm, one can clearly use it to design an automatic theorem-proving procedure as follows: investigate successively larger sets $C_1, C_2, \cdots$, of $1, 2, \cdots$, variants of the given S with the algorithm until, with C_N, the algorithm constructs, for the first time, a substitution θ such that $C_N\theta$ is truth-functionally unsatisfiable. Since N is in general a *reasonably small* number, we clearly have here an extremely attractive improvement over the raw method based on the enumeration of instances of S over its Herbrand universe.

In the next section we develop the theory of the required algorithm.

4. Unification of partitions of sets of atoms. Suppose that C is a finite set of variants of S; and consider the set A of all the *atoms* which occur in the formulas in C. Now any substitution θ determines a *partition* P of A in a very natural way: two atoms X, Y in A are in the same class of P if and only if $X\theta = Y\theta$.

For the purpose of deciding whether or not $C\theta$ is truth-functionally unsatisfiable, we actually need only know the partition P that θ imposes on A, and not any of the details of θ itself. For, given any partition P of A, we can investigate, and effectively determine, whether or not C is *truth-functionally unsatisfiable modulo P,* i.e., whether or not the conjunction of formulas in C comes out false under every assignment of truth values to the atoms in A *in which atoms in the same class of P are assigned the same truth value.* And if C is truth-functionally unsatisfiable modulo the partition determined by θ, then of course $C\theta$ is truth-functionally unsatisfiable, and conversely.

Evidently, given any finite set C of formulas, we can make a complete census of the partitions of the finite set A of atoms which occur in the formulas in C, and we can determine which of these, if any, are those modulo which C is truth-functionally unsatisfiable.

If P is one such, then the remaining question will simply be: does there exist a substitution such that P is the partition of A determined by it?

We can ask this question in general about any set P of nonempty, finite, disjoint sets of atoms $A_1, A_2, \cdots, A_n$: the question is simply this: is there a substitution θ such that $A_1\theta, \cdots, A_n\theta$ are each *singletons*? (By a *singleton* is meant a set having exactly one element.)

The following *unification algorithm* completely solves this problem. In order to state it properly, we need to introduce some new notions. First, the *composition* $\theta\lambda$ of two substitutions, called for in the algorithm, is the substitution which contains the component $T\lambda / V$ whenever θ contains the component T/V, unless $T\lambda$ is V itself; and which also contains all the components of λ whose variables are different from those of the components of θ. This composition is associative, and corresponds correctly to iterated application of the two substitutions, i.e., $(E\theta)\lambda = E(\theta\lambda)$ for all E, θ, and λ. A detailed treatment may be found in [13].

Second, the *disagreement set* of a nonempty set A of atoms, called for in the algorithm, is obtained by locating the first symbol position, counting from the left, at which not all the atoms in A have exactly the same symbol, and then extracting, from each atom, the well-formed subexpression of it which begins with the symbol occupying that position. The set of these respective subexpressions is the disagreement set of A.

EXAMPLE: If A is $\{P(x,f(y,z)),\ P(x,a),\ P(x,g(h(k(x))))\}$ then the first symbol position at which not all atoms in A have exactly the same symbol is the *fifth*, since they all have the first *four* symbols P (x , in common. Thus the disagreement set consists of the respective subexpressions which begin in symbol position number five, and it is in fact the set $\{f(y,z),a,g(h(k(x)))\}$.

Finally, the *lexical ordering* of a set of expressions is assumed to be an ordering of the expressions in which *variables* precede all other expressions (any other details of the ordering being immaterial); it can therefore be safely assumed that the expression V_k specified in Step 2 of the algorithm is always a variable if there are any variables at all in the set from which it is being chosen.

With these explanations, we can now state the algorithm:

Unification Algorithm. Given any finite set $P = \{A_1, \cdots, A_n\}$ of finite, nonempty pairwise disjoint sets of atoms as *input*, proceed as follows:

Step 1. Put $k = 0$, $\sigma_0 = \epsilon$, and go to Step 2.

Step 2. If $A_1\sigma_k, \cdots, A_n\sigma_k$ are all singletons, *stop.* Otherwise, let h be the smallest index for which $A_h\sigma_k$ is *not* a singleton, and let V_k be the earliest and U_k the next earliest expressions in the lexical ordering of the disagreement set of $A_h\sigma_k$. Go to Step 3.

Step 3. If V_k is a variable which does not occur in U_k, put $\sigma_{k+1} = \sigma_k\{U_k/V_k\}$, add 1 to k, and return to Step 2. Otherwise, *stop.*

End of unification algorithm.

If the computation stops in Step 2 the partition P is said to be *unifiable* and the substitution $\sigma = \sigma_k$ then available as output is called *the most general unifier of P*. If the process stops in Step 3 then there does not exist any substitution θ such that $A_1\theta, \cdots, A_n\theta$ are all singletons.

The unification algorithm is justified by the theorem which states that if θ is any substitution and P is any partition such that $P\theta$ is a set of singletons then the unification algorithm will stop in Step 2 if given P as input and the most general unifier σ of P will satisfy the equation $\theta = \sigma\lambda$ for some substitution λ. The proof of this theorem is somewhat tedious and will not be given here. It may be found, in a slightly less general form, in [13].

The unification algorithm is essentially a cleaned-up and simplified version of the process described somewhat obscurely by Prawitz in [11]. Recently it came to my attention that essentially the same procedure was found by the late Emil Post and called by him the "L.C.M. process," but was never published. (See Davis [4, p. 370].)

To summarise this section: the existence of the unification algorithm allows one to contemplate automatic theorem-proving procedures of the general character proposed by Prawitz [11]: given S, generate sets $C_1, C_2, \cdots$, of $1, 2, \cdots$, variants of S which have no variables in common with each other; and, for each partition P (if any) of the atoms of C_i such that C_i is truth-functionally unsatisfiable modulo P, use the unification algorithm to determine whether or not P is unifiable. (Alternatively, for each unifiable partition P of the atoms of C_i, determine whether C_i is truth-functionally satisfiable modulo P.)

Davis [3] has proposed a procedure of this kind, which has been investigated and further elaborated in Chinlund, et al. [1], and also with more refinements in Loveland [8].

5. **Discussion of this method.** The computational bottleneck with which the Prawitz family of automatic theorem-proving procedures has to contend arises from the fact that the number of unifiable partitions of a set of atoms in general goes up very rapidly as the number of atoms in the set increases. Nothing can be done about this fundamental combinatorial fact of life, but one might hope to palliate its effect somewhat by exploiting, as far as possible, the properties of the structures involved.

Note, for example, that if P and Q are both partitions of the atoms of C, and $P \leq Q$ (i.e., each class in P is included in a class of Q), then C is truth-functionally unsatisfiable modulo Q whenever C is truth-functionally unsatisfiable modulo P. Hence only those partitions need be considered which are *maximal unifiable*, i.e., partitions P which are unifiable but for which no unifiable Q exists, other than P, such that $P \leq Q$.

Many computing processes suggest themselves for the task of obtaining all maximal unifiable partitions of a given set A of atoms, ranging from the overtly brute-force plan of starting at the top of the lattice of all partitions of A and working down each branch until the first unifiable partition along that branch is encountered, to highly complex and sophisticated schemes involving climbing up the lattice from the bottom, building up compound substitutions by successive pairwise unification operations. None of these inspire much hope that, when A is fairly large, the computational requirements will remain at all reasonable. This task seems, as far as one can tell at the present time, to be practicable computationally only when A is fairly small.

6. **Clashes and their resolution.** So far in the discussion we have assumed nothing more about the structure of S than that it is some truth-functional combination of atoms. As is well known, we can in fact assume with no loss of generality that this truth-functional combination has the special form of a *conjunction* of *disjunctions* of *literals*, where *literals* are simply atoms or negated atoms. Since tautologous components may be dropped from a conjunction without affecting its satisfiability or unsatisfiability, and since the order and multiplicity of literals in a disjunction do not affect its truth value, we may further assume that each conjunct is simply a *clause*, i.e., a finite set of literals, no two of which are complementary (i.e., exactly alike except for one of them being negated). The basic theory of §2 then leads directly to the result that if S is unsatisfiable and is in this special form, then there is some finite set C of variants of *clauses* of S, and some substitution θ, such that $C\theta$ is truth-functionally unsatisfiable.

Now, as before, this could simply lead us to study computationally, with the aid of the unification algorithm, the partitions of the atoms in successively wider collections of variants of clauses of S. This would not be any different from the method we have already considered. However, it is now possible to take into account the special structure which sets of clauses exhibit, and exploit its properties so as to improve that method quite considerably.

Let $K = C\theta$ be the set of clauses which comes from the set C of clauses by the substitution θ, and suppose that K is truth-functionally unsatisfiable.

We shall investigate the question: *what does the truth-functional unsatisfiability of K tell us about C?* First, we need to ask what this tells us about K itself, and in order to answer this question most appropriately we now introduce the notion of a *clash*.

A *clash* is a finite set of clauses $\{A_1, \cdots, A_n, B\}$ satisfying the following conditions:

(6.1) B contains at least $n > 0$ literals $L_1, \cdots, L_n$;

(6.2)   for each i, $1 \leq i \leq n$, A_i contains the *complement* $\overline{L_i}$ of the literal L_i, *but does not contain the complement of any other literal which occurs in B, nor the complement of any literal which occurs in any A_j, $1 \leq j \leq n$.*

(It is to be understood, in this definition and henceforth, that the *complement* of a literal L is obtained by negating L if L is unnegated, i.e., is an atom, and by "unnegating" L if L is negated, i.e., by removing its negation symbol; in either case, we shall denote the complement of L by $\overline{L}$.)

If the set $\{A_1, \cdots, A_n, B\}$ is a clash, then there is a unique clause, called the *resolvent* of the clash $\{A_1, \cdots, A_n, B\}$, and written: $[A_1, \cdots, A_n, B]$. This clause is the set

(6.3) $(A_1 - \{\overline{L}_1\}) \cup \cdots \cup (A_n - \{\overline{L}_n\}) \cup (B - \{L_1, \cdots, L_n\})$.

It should be noted that because of the conditions (6.1) and (6.2) there is exactly one way in which a finite set of clauses is a clash, if it is a clash at all.

According to our definition of resolvents, it is quite possible that a resolvent (6.3) should be the empty set of literals (e.g., this will happen for any clash in which $n = 1$, $A_1 = \{\overline{L}\}$, and $B = \{L\}$). For convenience the empty set of literals is considered to be a (special case of a) clause, called *the empty clause*, denoted by $\square$, and having the truth value *false* under all assignments of truth values to atoms.

It is quite straightforward to see that the resolvent of a clash *follows from* the clauses constituting the clash. (Simply note that there can be no assignment of truth values to atoms, under which at least one literal in each of $A_1, \cdots, A_n$ and B is true, which makes each literal in $[A_1, \cdots, A_n, B]$ false.)

By a *deduction* we shall mean a tree figure, as shown in Figure 2, to each node of which is attached a clause. The clauses attached to noninitial nodes are the resolvents of the sets of clauses attached to their immediate predecessor nodes. A deduction *of* a clause X *from* a set Y of clauses is then just a deduction at whose terminal node is X, and at whose initial nodes are clauses from the set Y.

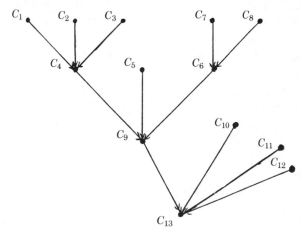

FIGURE 2. C_4 is the resolvent of $\{C_1, C_2, C_3\}$, C_6 of $\{C_7, C_8\}$, C_9 of $\{C_4, C_5, C_6\}$, and C_{13} of $\{C_9, C_{10}, C_{11}, C_{12}\}$. The whole tree figure is a deduction of C_{13} from any set of clauses which includes $\{C_1, C_2, C_3, C_5, C_7, C_8, C_{10}, C_{11}, C_{12}\}$.

It is now easy to see that for a finite set K of clauses:

(6.4)   if there is a deduction of $\square$ from K, then K is truth-functionally unsatisfiable.

The converse of (6.4),

(6.5)   if K is truth-functionally unsatisfiable, then there is a deduction of $\square$ from K, is also true, but requires rather more reasoning. In fact, (6.5) follows easily from the following lemma:

(6.6)   if K is a finite truth-functionally unsatisfiable set of clauses, then either $\square$ is in K or there is at least one clash $N \subseteq K$ whose resolvent is not in K.

For let K_0 be K; and in general, if $\square$ is not in K_j, for $j \geq 0$, let K_{j+1} be the result of adding to K_j the resolvent of any one of the clashes provided by (6.6). This gives a nested sequence $K_0, K_1, \cdots$, of sets of clauses which cannot continue indefinitely to grow, since the successive resolvents are all constructed from the same fixed finite set of literals (namely, those which occur in members of K); hence there are only finitely many such resolvents which can be added. The lemma therefore guarantees that, for some $j \geq 0$, we will have $\square$ in K_j. Tracing the genesis of $\square$ from K then gives the required deduction.

It suffices then to prove the lemma (6.6) in order to establish (6.5), and to that end we reason as follows.

Let K be a finite truth-functionally unsatisfiable set of clauses. If $\square$ is in K, the lemma holds. Assume $\square$ is not in K. Let A be a nonempty subset of K such that no literal in any clause of A occurs complemented in any clause in A, while each clause in $K - A$ does contain the complement of at least one literal which occurs in some clause in A. To construct such a subset A, choose any clause in K as A_1, and then, for $n \geq 1$, $A_1, \cdots, A_n$ having been chosen, choose as A_{n+1} any clause in the set $K - \{A_1, \cdots, A_n\}$ none of whose literals occurs complemented in any clause in the list $A_1, \cdots, A_n$. If no clause A_{n+1} can be chosen satisfying this condition, take A to be $\{A_1, \cdots, A_n\}$. A will clearly have the desired properties. Note that any such "maximal clash-free" subset A of K cannot actually exhaust K, since K is truth-functionally unsatisfiable, while any such A is truth-functionally satisfiable (e.g., by the assignment of *true* to each atom which occurs unnegated, of *false* to each atom which occurs negated, in some clause in A). Let us call the literals which occur in the clauses of A, *A-literals*. Let M be an assignment of truth values to the atoms which satisfies A, but which, among all such assignments, is one of those which causes the *fewest* A-literals to take on the value *true*. Then M must falsify one or more nonempty clauses in $K - A$ (since K is truth-functionally unsatisfiable and does not contain $\square$). Let us choose B to be such a clause, and let us make our choice so that B contains the *fewest* complements of A-literals. Let $L_1, \cdots, L_n$ be all the complements of A-literals in B. For each i, $1 \leq i \leq n$, let M_i be the assignment of truth values which is exactly like M except that L_i is *true* under M_i (L_i is of course *false* under M). Then M_i cannot satisfy A, since M_i causes fewer A-literals to be true than does M. Hence at least one clause A_i in A is *false* under M_i but *true* under M. Therefore A_i contains $\overline{L_i}$, and every literal in $A_i - \{\overline{L_i}\}$ is false under M. It is immediate that $N = \{A_1, \cdots, A_n, B\}$ is a clash whose resolvent is false under M and hence is not in K (since it contains fewer complements of A-literals than B). Thus the lemma is proved.

The conjunction of (6.4) and (6.5) constitutes what we shall call the *Clash Theorem*:

$$K \text{ is truth-functionally unsatisfiable}$$

(6.7) $\Leftrightarrow$

$$\text{there is a deduction of } \square \text{ from } K$$

which holds for every finite set K of clauses.

By analysing the reasoning in the proof of the lemma, one sees that any subset of the set N which contains B and at least one of the A_i is also a clash whose resolvent cannot be in K. Indeed, the clashes $\{A_i, B\}$ which contain only *one* of the A's give rise to the resolvents which are essentially those originally introduced in [13]. When the set A is taken to be the set of all "positive" clauses in K (i.e., the clauses which do not contain any negated atoms) then the resolvent of the clash N is essentially what in [14] was called a *hyper-resolvent*.

Now in order to formulate the main result of the theory of clashes and their resolution, we introduce the concept of a *latent clash*, as follows: if N is a set of clauses and θ is a substitution, such that $N\theta$ is a clash, then N is said to be a *latent clash*. Moreover, if σ is the most general unifier of the partition P of the atoms of N which θ determines, the resolvent of the clash $N\sigma$ is said to be *a resolvent of the latent clash N*.

Thus, given a set N of clauses, we determine all of its resolvents (if any) by getting all the unifiable partitions $P_1, \cdots, P_k$ of the atoms of N, and for each $N\sigma_i$ which is a clash (where σ_i is the most general unifier of P_i), forming the resolvent of $N\sigma_i$.

Now the crucial property on which the main result depends is this: *the resolvent $[N\theta]$ of the clash $N\theta$ is an instance of one of the resolvents of the latent clash N*. This can readily be shown by using the fact that $\theta = \sigma\lambda$, for some λ, where σ is the most general unifier of the partition determined by θ. The situation is best shown by means of the diagram:

(6.8)

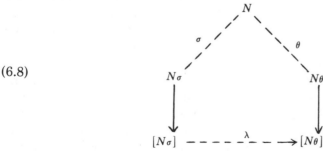

in which dotted arrows signify instantiation and solid arrows signify resolution. σ, θ and λ are assumed related as above.

Using this property, we can always produce, given a deduction of □ from *instances* of clauses in a set C of clauses, a deduction of □ *from C*, in which the resolutions are now in general resolutions of *latent* clashes. To see this, one merely envisions the attachment, to each node of the given tree, a further clause over and above the clause already there, as follows: to each initial node attach the corresponding clause in C of which the clause already there is an instance; then, for each noninitial node, if clauses have been attached in this way to each of its immediate predecessor nodes and constitute the set N, attach to it that resolvent of the latent clash N of which the clause already there is an instance. By the fundamental property described above there must be such a resolvent. In this fashion a clause is attached to each node, of which the clause already at that node is an instance. The clause attached to the terminal node must therefore be □, since the clause already there is □ and since instantiation cannot produce □ from a nonempty clause. It is easy then to see that the tree together with the *attached* clauses is a deduction of □ from C by the resolution of *latent* clashes.

Now if we say that C is *latently* truth-functionally unsatisfiable when there is a θ such that $C\theta$ is truth-functionally unsatisfiable, and if we broaden the notion of a deduction so that the resolution of *latent* clashes is the operation connecting a clause with its immediate predecessors, we can in view of the above construction generalise the Clash Theorem to the following *Latent Clash Theorem*:

C is latently truth-functionally unsatisfiable

(6.9)   ⇔

there is a deduction of □ from C

which holds for every finite set C of clauses which have no variables in common. For if C is such a set, and if $C\theta$ is truth-functionally unsatisfiable, there is by the Clash Theorem a deduction of □ from $C\theta$ from which we can construct the required deduction of □ from C. On the other hand, if there is a deduction of □ from C, it is easy to see that $C\sigma$ is truth-functionally unsatisfiable, where σ is the simultaneous substitution obtained from the several most general unifiers used in the resolution of the latent clashes in C in the "first layer" of the given deduction. Indeed σ is simply the union of those substitutions.

In view of (6.9), the process of adding to a set of clauses all the resolvents of latent clashes composed of variants of clauses in the set will, if iterated sufficiently often, eventually produce □ if and only if the initial set of clauses is unsatisfiable. Thus, given an S in the normal form mentioned at the start of this section, we can initiate this iterative process by first forming the set of clauses which occur in S.

Although the main part of the computing in this process is given over, as before, to the examination of partitions of sets of atoms with the unification algorithm, we now have the distinct advantage that the sets of atoms to be examined are now reasonably small. The number of clauses in a clash cannot exceed $n + 1$, where n is the number of literals in the "nuclear" clause in the clash; and in most problems the number of literals in any one clause does not get very large. Moreover it is possible to consider only clashes containing *two* clauses, and in this case the number of atoms in the set to be examined is usually quite small.

7. **Discussion of the resolution methods.** Clearly, in the overall process sketched above, there is plenty of leeway in the selection of which latent clashes to resolve. One can, for example, confine one's choices to *minimal* clashes (as was done in [13]) and even, within this constraint, select only those clashes which correspond to some particular choice of A-literals (e.g., the unnegated literals; this gives the P_1-resolution method of [14]). Meltzer, in [9], has suggested that other useful systems of A-literals can be easily found just by systematically exchanging one or more relation symbols with the complements of those symbols, and taking the A-literals to be the new set of unnegated literals thus obtained.

As we remarked in the previous section, the smaller the size of the latent clash, the less computational effort is needed to detect that it is one and to compute all of its resolvents, with minimal latent clashes being the simplest of all to manage. Thus an obvious thing to think of is to resolve only minimal latent clashes. But one pays rather a heavy price for this, since there is much duplication and redundancy in resolving, for instance, all of the "subclashes" of some maximal clash, when one could in one single operation resolve the maximal clash itself. An example will illustrate this. The following system C of clauses has been frequently used as an example [12, 13, 14]:

$$\{\overline{P}(x,y,u), \overline{P}(y,z,v), \overline{P}(x,v,w), P(u,z,w)\} = \{\overline{L}_1, \overline{L}_2, \overline{L}_3, L_4\},$$

$$\{P(g(x_1,y_1), x_1, y_1)\} = \{L_5\},$$

$$\{P(x_2, h(x_2,y_2), y_2)\} = \{L_6\},$$

$$\{\overline{P}(k(x_3), x_3, k(x_3))\} = \{\overline{L}_7\},$$

Now this set of clauses is unsatisfiable, and in fact is itself a (maximal) latent clash. Using the abbreviated notation given on the right above, the partition P, where:

$$P = \{\{L_1, L_3, L_5\}, \{L_2, L_6\}, \{L_4, L_7\}\}$$

is unifiable (as may be easily verified by using the unification algorithm with P as input), and hence the set C has $\square$ as a resolvent. However, if one tackles this example by resolving minimal clashes only, one runs into a very heavy computational load, and as far as is known at present this example has never been computed out by that method.

Considerable advantages would seem to lie in confining oneself to the resolution of maximal clashes only. However these take rather more computational effort to detect. The task of detecting them can be organized in a great many ways, but most of these ways will surely make use of the fact that resolvents $[A_1, \cdots, A_n, B]$ satisfy the equation

(7.1) $$[A_1, \cdots, A_n, B] = [A_{i_1}, [A_{i_2}, \cdots, [A_{i_n}, B] \cdots]]$$

where $i_1, i_2, \cdots, i_n$ is any permutation of $1, 2, \cdots, n$.

Thus, each maximal clash is in this sense decomposable (in $n!$ different ways) into a maximal chain of minimal clashes, and its resolvent can therefore be computed by means of (7.1), taking due precautions not to traverse more than one of the $n!$ paths to the identical destination.

One possible way of exploiting (7.1) would be to record, with each minimal resolvent $[A_{i_p}, [A_{i_{p+1}}, \cdots, [A_{i_n}, B] \cdots]]$ as one computes it, both the clause B and the literals $L_{i_p}, L_{i_{p+1}}, \cdots, L_{i_n}$ which have already been "removed from B." Then the choice of $A_{i_{p-1}}$ can be restricted to those clauses, if any, which do not contain any of the literals $L_{i_p}, \cdots, L_{i_n}$ or their complements, and which contain the complement of exactly one of the literals in the set $B - \{L_{i_p}, \cdots, L_{i_n}\}$. If there are no clauses satisfying these restrictions, then the clash $\{A_{i_p}, \cdots, A_{i_n}, B\}$ is maximal and we already have its resolvent.

Having computed, in this way, a maximal resolvent with some clause B as "nucleus" of the clash it resolves, we may repeat the process, (supposing ourselves to be dealing with a set K of clauses that is truth-functionally unsatisfiable) for each of the other clauses in K as "nucleus" in turn, henceforth imposing the extra restriction that the successive A's contain no complements of any of the literals occurring in any of the previously chosen A's, not only in the chain involving the current nucleus, but also for all previous chains.

This will provide us with a collection of resolvents of maximal clashes in K satisfying the following conditions: there is a set A, as described in the proof of the Lemma (6.6), which contains every clause A_i which was involved in any of the computations (and possibly others); A is determined by the property that a clause is in A if and only if each of its literals can be found in some such A_i; the nuclei, $B_1, \cdots, B_r$, of the maximal clashes are thus all in $K - A$; and, for any clause in $K - A$ for which there *exists* a maximal clash having it as nucleus and all the remaining clauses in A, we can be sure that it is among $B_1, \cdots, B_r$. But the proof of (6.6) guarantees that none of the maximal resolvents whose nuclei among $B_1, \cdots, B_r$ contain *fewest* complements of A-literals, are in K. The overall process we have just described therefore produces at least one maximal resolvent which is not in K.

By appropriate application of the unification theory this process may be adapted to the resolution of latent clashes, but the details are tedious.

8. **Set of support method. Heuristic devices.** Wos et al., [19] describe and justify a way of restricting the selection of minimal latent clashes in the resolution of an unsatisfiable set K of clauses, which they call the *set of support strategy*. This method goes as follows: let T be any subset of K such that $K - T$ is *satisfiable*; then it suffices to compute only those minimal resolvents $[A, B]$ which meet the condition that not both A and B are in $K - T$. T is said to be a *set of support* for K.

The same authors have made extensive experiments on the computer (see [19, 20]) with additional, more "heuristic" selection principles guiding the choice of minimal clashes for resolution. These normally involve one or more *heuristic control parameters* whose settings are chosen by the human user of the theorem-proving procedure either before or during the execution of it. Similar ideas are put forward by Chinlund et al., [1]. These parameters restrict, for example, the *depth* of the tree deductions considered (i.e., the length of the longest branch therein); the *complexity* of the literals which may be generated, (as measured, e.g., by the number of symbols they contain, or by the depth of syntactical nesting needed to construct them from their constituent symbols); the number of literals in a clause; and so on.

Once the fundamental structure of the "search space" is well established, there is every reason to seek good devices of this sort to improve the likelihood of successful outcomes for searches, and there is room for much ingenuity in contriving them. Here, however, the issues shade over into the more general area of heuristic problem solving, into which we cannot, on this occasion, go.

9. **Summary. Future prospects.** The present situation in the theory of automatic theorem-proving, when compared with that of four or five years ago, shows that some progress has been made, in more or less the directions which were at that time beginning to suggest themselves. The appropriate structures and concepts have become a little clearer, and problems can now be handled on the machine with comparative ease, which five years ago seemed entirely unfeasible (see, especially, Wos et al., [19, 20]).

No one has yet proposed a really good way to exploit computationally the special properties of the *equality* relation. At present, as has been much stressed by Wang [18], Chinlund et al., [1] and others, we are sorely handicapped by having to treat equality as simply one more binary relation symbol, with a special collection of extra axioms, in each problem, being required to make it behave as it should. This, it seems to me, is the next large problem which must be solved before we get off the present plateau.

Beyond that, and much more difficult still, is the problem of handling the *membership* relation in an efficient way, so that theorem-proving problems involving set-theoretic notions can be treated. The only available way at present is to use a finite system of axioms for set theory, say, those given in Gödel [6] or in Mendelson [10], and to formulate all our other theorem-proving problems *within* that theory. While in principle this approach is capable of handling any mathematical problem which can be formulated in any meaningful way that is known at present, it is of purely academic and theoretical interest unless the efficiency of the basic first-order theorem-proving procedures is improved by further orders of magnitude.

As to whether such improvements are possible, one can only say that nothing is known at the present time which conclusively establishes that they are not.

BIBLIOGRAPHY

1. T. J. Chinlund, M. Davis, P. G. Hinman and M. D. McIlroy, *Theorem-proving by matching*, Comm. Assoc. Comput. Mach. (to appear).

2. M. Davis and H. Putnam, *A computing procedure for quantification theory*, J. Assoc. Comput. Mach. 7 (1960), 201-215.

3. M. Davis, *Eliminating the irrelevant from mechanical proofs*, Proc. Sympos. Appl. Math., Vol. 18, Amer. Math. Soc., Providence, R.I., 1963, pp. 15-30.

4. _____, *The undecidable*, Raven Press, New York, 1965.

5. K. Gödel, *Die Vollständigkeit der Axiome des logischen Functionenkalküls*, Monatsh. Math. Phys. 37 (1930), 349-360.

6. _____, *The consistency of the continuum hypothesis*, Annals of Mathematics Studies, No. 3, Princeton Univ. Press, Princeton, N.J., 1940.

7. J. Herbrand, *Recherches sur la theorie de la demonstration*, Travaux de la Société des Sciences et des Lettres de Varsovie, Classe III sciences mathematiques et physiques, No. 33, 1930.

8. D. W. Loveland, *Mechanical theorem-proving by model elimination*, J. Assoc. Comput. Mach. (to appear).

9. B. Meltzer, *Theorem-proving for computers: some results on resolution and renaming*, Comput. J. 8 (1966), 341-343.

10. E. Mendelson, *Introduction to mathematical logic*, Van Nostrand, Princeton, N.J., 1964.

11. D. Prawitz, *An improved proof procedure*. Theoria 26 (1960), 102-139.

12. J. A. Robinson, *Theorem proving on the computer*, J. Assoc. Comput. Mach. 10 (1963), 163-174.

13. _____, *A machine-oriented logic based on the resolution principle*, J. Assoc. Comput. Mach. 12 (1965), 23-41.

14. _____, *Automatic deduction with hyper-resolution*, Internat. J. Assoc. Comput. Math. 1 (1965), 227-234.

15. T. Skolem, *Über die mathematische Logik*, Norsk Mat. Tidskr. 10 (1928), 125-142.

16. _____, *Über einige Grundlagenfragen der Mathematik*, Skrifter utgitt av Det Norske Videnskaps-Academi i Oslo. I, Mat.-Natur. Klasse, no. 4, 1929.

17. H. Wang, *Towards mechanical mathematics*, IBM J. Res. Develop. 4 (1960), 2-22.

18. _____, *Formalization and automatic theorem-proving*, Proc. IFIP Congr. Vol. 1, Spartan Books, Washington, D.C., 1965.

19. L. Wos, G. A. Robinson and D. Carson, *Efficiency and completeness of the set of support strategy in theorem-proving*, J. Assoc. Comput. Mach. 12 (1965), 536-541.

20. L. Wos., D. Carson and G. A. Robinson, *The unit preference strategy in theorem-proving*, AFIPS Conf. Proc. no. 26, Spartan Books, Washington, D.C., 1964, pp. 615-621.

RICE UNIVERSITY
HOUSTON, TEXAS

Robert W. Floyd

ASSIGNING MEANINGS TO PROGRAMS[1]

Introduction. This paper attempts to provide an adequate basis for formal definitions of the meanings of programs in appropriately defined programming languages, in such a way that a rigorous standard is established for proofs about computer programs, including proofs of correctness, equivalence, and termination. The basis of our approach is the notion of an interpretation of a program: that is, an association of a proposition with each connection in the flow of control through a program, where the proposition is asserted to hold whenever that connection is taken. To prevent an interpretation from being chosen arbitrarily, a condition is imposed on each command of the program. This condition guarantees that whenever a command is reached by way of a connection whose associated proposition is then true, it will be left (if at all) by a connection whose associated proposition will be true at that time. Then by induction on the number of commands executed, one sees that if a program is entered by a connection whose associated proposition is then true, it will be left (if at all) by a connection whose associated proposition will be true at that time. By this means, we may prove certain properties of programs, particularly properties of the form: "If the initial values of the program variables satisfy the relation R_1, the final values on completion will satisfy the relation R_2." Proofs of termination are dealt with by showing that each step of a program decreases some entity which cannot decrease indefinitely.

These modes of proof of correctness and termination are not original; they are based on ideas of Perlis and Gorn, and may have made their earliest appearance in an unpublished paper by Gorn. The establishment of formal standards for proofs about programs in languages which admit assignments, transfer of control, etc., and the proposal that the semantics of a programming language may be defined independently of all processors for that language, by establishing standards of rigor for proofs about

---

[1] This work was supported by the Advanced Research Projects Agency of the Office of the Secretary of Defense (SD-146).

programs in the language, appear to be novel, although McCarthy [1, 2] has done similar work for programming languages based on evaluation of recursive functions.

A semantic definition of a programming language, in our approach, is founded on a syntactic definition. It must specify which of the phrases in a syntactically correct program represent commands, and what conditions must be imposed on an interpretation in the neighborhood of each command.

We will demonstrate these notions, first on a flowchart language, then on fragments of ALGOL.

DEFINITIONS. A *flowchart* will be loosely defined as a directed graph with a command at each vertex, connected by *edges* (arrows) representing the possible passages of control between the commands. An edge is said to be an *entrance* to (or an *exit* from) the command c at vertex v if its destination (or origin) is v. An *interpretation* I of a flowchart is a mapping of its edges on propositions. Some, but not necessarily all, of the free variables of these propositions may be variables manipulated by the

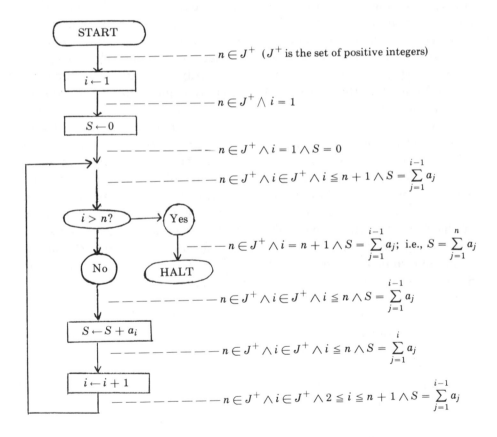

FIGURE 1. Flowchart of program to compute $S = \sum_{j=1}^{n} a_j \ (n \geq 0)$

program. Figure 1 gives an example of an interpretation. For any edge e, the associated proposition $I(e)$ will be called the *tag* of e. If e is an entrance (or an exit) of a command c, $I(e)$ is said to be an *antecedent* (or a *consequent*) of c.

For any command c with k entrances and l exits, we will designate the entrances to c by $a_1, a_2, \cdots, a_k$, and the exits by $b_1, b_2, \cdots, b_l$. We will designate the tag of a_i by P_i $(1 \leq i \leq k)$, and that of b_i by Q_i $(1 \leq i \leq l)$. Boldface letters will designate vectors formed in the natural way from the entities designated by the corresponding nonboldface letters: for example, **P** represents $(P_1, P_2, \cdots, P_k)$.

A *verification* of an interpretation of a flowchart is a proof that for every command c of the flowchart, if control should enter the command by an entrance a_i with P_i true, then control must leave the command, if at all, by an exit b_j with Q_j true. A *semantic definition* of a particular set of command types, then, is a rule for constructing, for any command c of one of these types, a *verification condition* $V_c(\mathbf{P}; \mathbf{Q})$ on the antecedents and consequents of c. This verification condition must be so constructed that a proof that the verification condition is satisfied for the antecedents and consequents of each command in a flowchart is a verification of the interpreted flowchart. That is, if the verification condition is satisfied, and if the tag of the entrance is true when the statement is entered, the tag of the exit selected will be true after execution of the statement.

A *counterexample* to a particular interpretation of a single command is an assignment of values (e.g., numbers in most programming languages) to the free variables of the interpretation, and a choice of entrance, such that on entry to the command, the tag of the entrance is true, but on exit, the tag of the exit is false for the (possibly altered) values of the free variables. A semantic definition is *consistent* if there is no counterexample to any interpretation of any command which satisfies its verification condition. A semantic definition is *complete* if there is a counterexample to any interpretation of any command which does not satisfy its verification condition. A semantic definition clearly must be consistent. Preferably, it should also be complete; this, however, is not always possible.

In what follows, we shall have in mind some particular deductive system D, which includes the axioms and rules of inference of the first-order predicate calculus, with equality. We shall write $\Phi_1, \Phi_2, \cdots, \Phi_n \vdash \Psi$ to mean that Ψ is a proposition deducible from $\Phi_1, \Phi_2, \cdots, \Phi_n$ and the axioms of D by the rules of inference of D. We shall designate by

$$S_{f_1, f_2, \cdots, f_n}^{x_1, x_2, \cdots, x_n}(\Phi) \quad \text{or, more briefly,} \quad S_f^x(\Phi),$$

the result of simultaneously substituting f_i for each occurrence of x_i in Φ, after first systematically changing bound variables of Φ to avoid conflict with free variables of any f_i.

Connectives will be assumed to distribute over the components of vectors; for instance, $\mathbf{X} \wedge \mathbf{Y}$ means $(X_1 \wedge Y_1, X_2 \wedge Y_2, \cdots, X_n \wedge Y_n)$, and $\mathbf{X} \vdash \mathbf{Y}$ means $(X_1 \vdash Y_1) \wedge (X_2 \vdash Y_2) \wedge \cdots \wedge (X_n \vdash Y_n)$.

General axioms. In order for a semantic definition to be satisfactory, it must meet several requirements. These will be presented as axioms, although they may also be deduced from the assumptions of completeness and consistency, where these hold.

If $V_c(\mathbf{P}; \mathbf{Q})$ and $V_c(\mathbf{P}'; \mathbf{Q}')$, then:

AXIOM 1. $V_c(\mathbf{P} \wedge \mathbf{P}'; \mathbf{Q} \wedge \mathbf{Q}')$;

AXIOM 2. $V_c(\mathbf{P} \vee \mathbf{P}'; \mathbf{Q} \vee \mathbf{Q}')$;

AXIOM 3. $V_c((\exists x)(\mathbf{P}); (\exists x)(\mathbf{Q}))$.

Also,

AXIOM 4. If $V_c(\mathbf{P}; \mathbf{Q})$ and $\mathbf{R} \vdash \mathbf{P}$, $\mathbf{Q} \vdash \mathbf{S}$, then $V_c(\mathbf{R}; \mathbf{S})$.

COROLLARY 1. *If* $V_c(\mathbf{P}; \mathbf{Q})$ *and* $\vdash (\mathbf{P} \equiv \mathbf{R})$, $\vdash (\mathbf{Q} \equiv \mathbf{S})$, *then* $V_c(\mathbf{R}; \mathbf{S})$.

Axiom 1, for example, essentially asserts that if whenever P is true on entering command c, Q is true on exit, and whenever P' is true on entry, Q' is true on exit, then whenever both P and P' are true on entrance, both Q and Q' are true on exit. Thus Axiom 1 shows that if separate proofs exist that a program has certain properties, then these proofs may be combined into one by forming the conjunction of the several tags for each edge. Axiom 2 is useful for combining the results of a case analysis, for instance, treating several ranges of initial values of certain variables. Axiom 3 asserts that if knowing that the value of the variable x has property P before executing a command assures that the (possibly altered) value will have property Q after executing the command, then knowing that a value exists having property P before execution assures that a value exists having property Q after execution. Axiom 4 asserts that if P and Q are verifiable as antecedent and consequent for a command, then so are any stronger antecedent and weaker consequent.

To indicate how these axioms are deducible from the hypotheses of completeness and consistency for V_c, consider Axiom 1 as an example. Suppose $V_c(\mathbf{P}; \mathbf{Q})$ and $V_c(\mathbf{P}'; \mathbf{Q}')$. Consider any assignment of initial values $\mathbf{V}$ to the free variables $\mathbf{X}$ of the interpretation such that P_i is true (that is, $\vdash S_{\mathbf{V}}^{\mathbf{X}}(P_i)$) and P_i' is true. Then, if the statement is entered by a_i, the exit chosen will be some b_j such that Q_j is true at that time (that is, $\vdash S_{\mathbf{W}}^{\mathbf{X}}(Q_j)$, where $\mathbf{W}$ is the vector of final values of $\mathbf{X}$ after execution of c), and Q_j' is also true, by the assumption of consistency. Thus, there can be no counterexample to the interpretation $I(\mathbf{a}) = (\mathbf{P} \wedge \mathbf{P}')$, $I(\mathbf{b}) = (\mathbf{Q} \wedge \mathbf{Q}')$, and by the assumption of completeness, $V_c(\mathbf{P} \wedge \mathbf{P}'; \mathbf{Q} \wedge \mathbf{Q}')$.

A flowchart language. To make these notions more specific, consider a particular flowchart language with five statement types, represented pictorially as in Figure 2, having the usual interpretations as an assignment operation, a conditional branch, a join of control, a starting point for the program, and a halt for the program.

Take specifically the assignment operator $x \leftarrow f(x, \mathbf{y})$, where x is a variable and f is an expression which may contain occurrences of x and of the vector $\mathbf{y}$ of other program variables. Considering the effect of the command, it is clearly desirable that if P_1 is $(x = x_0 \wedge R)$, and Q_1 is $(x = f(x_0, \mathbf{y}) \wedge R)$, where R contains no free occurrences of x, then $V_c(P_1; Q_1)$. Applying the axioms, we shall establish a definition of $V_{x \leftarrow f(x,y)}$ which is complete and consistent if the underlying deductive system is, and which is, in that sense, the most general semantic definition of the assignment operator.

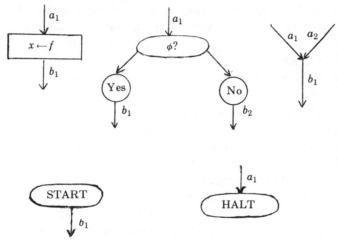

FIGURE 2

Designating the command $x \leftarrow f(x, \mathbf{y})$ by c, we apply Axiom 3 to $V_c(P_1, Q_1)$, to obtain

$$V_c((\exists x_0) P_1; (\exists x_0) Q_1).$$

Because $[(\exists x)(x = e \wedge P(x))] \equiv P(e)$, provided x does not occur free in e, we apply Corollary 1, to get $V_c(R(x, \mathbf{y}); (\exists x_0)(x = f(x_0, \mathbf{y}) \wedge R(x_0, \mathbf{y})))$. Finally, by Corollary 1, we have

The verification condition for assignment operators.

(1)   If P_1 has the form $R(x, \mathbf{y})$ and if $(\exists x_0)(x = f(x_0, \mathbf{y}) \wedge R(x_0, \mathbf{y})) \vdash Q_1$, then $V_{x \leftarrow f(x,y)}(P_1, Q_1)$.

Taking this as the semantic definition of $x \leftarrow f(x, \mathbf{y})$, and assuming the completeness and consistency of the deductive system D, we show that the semantic definition is complete and consistent.

To show consistency, assume that x_1 and $\mathbf{y}_1$ are initial values of x and $\mathbf{y}$ such that $\vdash R(x_1, \mathbf{y}_1)$. Then after execution of $x \leftarrow f(x, \mathbf{y})$, the values x_2 and $\mathbf{y}_2$ are such that $x = x_2 = f(x_1, \mathbf{y}_1)$, $\mathbf{y} = \mathbf{y}_2 = \mathbf{y}_1$; thus $x_2 = f(x_1, \mathbf{y}_2) \wedge R(x_1, \mathbf{y}_2)$, or $(\exists x_0)(x_2 = f(x_0, \mathbf{y}_2) \wedge R(x_0, \mathbf{y}_2))$. Designating $(\exists x_0)(x = f(x_0, \mathbf{y}) \wedge R(x_0, \mathbf{y}))$ as $T_c(R(x, \mathbf{y}))$, we have shown that upon exit from c, $S^{xy}_{x_2 y_2}(T_c(R(x, \mathbf{y})))$ is true. Now since $T_c(R(x, \mathbf{y})) \vdash Q$, we find $\vdash S^{xy}_{x_2 y_2}(Q)$, by the assumption of the consistency of D, so that V_c is consistent.

To show completeness, assume it false that $T_c(R(x, \mathbf{y})) \vdash Q$. Then, by the completeness of D, there is a set of values x_2 and $\mathbf{y}_2$ for x and $\mathbf{y}$ such that $S^{xy}_{x_2 y_2}(T_c(R(x, \mathbf{y})))$ is true, but $S^{xy}_{x_2 y_2}(Q)$ is false. Thus, $(\exists x_0)(x_2 = f(x_0, \mathbf{y}_2) \wedge R(x_0, \mathbf{y}_2))$. Let x_1 be a particular value of x_0 for which $x_2 = f(x_1, \mathbf{y}_2) \wedge R(x_1, \mathbf{y}_2)$. Now using x_1 and $\mathbf{y}_2$ as initial values for x and $\mathbf{y}$, we may generate a counterexample to the interpretation $I(a_1) = R(x, \mathbf{y})$, $I(b_1) = Q$.

Thus we have shown that V_c is complete (consistent) if D is complete (consistent). By consideration of vacuous statements such as $x \leftarrow x$, we could change each "if" to "if and only if." Thus, the semantic definition (1) we have given is the natural generalization of the original sufficient condition for verification; V_c is both necessary and sufficient.

The other command types of Figure 2 are more easily dealt with. For the branch command, $V_c(P_1; Q_1, Q_2)$ is $(P_1 \wedge \Phi \vdash Q_1) \wedge (P_1 \wedge \neg \Phi \vdash Q_2)$. For the join command, $V_c(P_1, P_2; Q_1)$ is $(P_1 \vee P_2 \vdash Q_1)$. For the start command the condition $V_c(Q_1)$, and for the halt command the condition $V_c(P_1)$ are identically true. All of these semantic definitions accord with the usual understanding of the meanings of these commands, and in each case V_c is complete and consistent if D is.

Using these semantic definitions, it is not hard to show that Figure 1 is a verifiable interpretation of its flowchart provided D contains a suitable set of axioms for the real numbers, summation, the integers, inequalities, and so forth. Thus, if the flowchart is entered with n a positive integer, the value of i on completion will be $n + 1$ (assuming that the program terminates) and the value of S will be $\sum_{j=1}^{n} a_j$. Presumably, the final value of i is of no interest, but the value of S is the desired result of the program, and the verification proves that the program does in fact compute the desired result if it terminates at all. Another section of this paper deals with proofs of termination.

Each of the given semantic definitions of the flowchart commands takes the form that $V_c(\mathbf{P}, \mathbf{Q})$ if and only if $(T_1(\mathbf{P}) \vdash Q_1) \wedge \cdots \wedge (T_l(\mathbf{P}) \vdash Q_l)$, where T_j is of the form $T_{j1}(P_1) \vee T_{j2}(P_2) \vee \cdots \vee T_{jk}(P_k)$. In particular there is the following:

(1) For an assignment operator $x \leftarrow f$

$$T_1(P_1) \quad \text{is} \quad (\exists x_0)(x = S^x_{x_0}(f) \wedge S^x_{x_0}(P_1)).$$

(2) For a branch command

$$T_1(P_1) \quad \text{is} \quad P_1 \wedge \Phi,$$
$$T_2(P_1) \quad \text{is} \quad P_1 \wedge \neg \Phi.$$

(3) For a join command

$$T_1(P_1, P_2) \quad \text{is} \quad P_1 \vee P_2; \quad \text{that is,}$$
$$T_{11}(P_1) \quad \text{is} \quad P_1, \qquad T_{12}(P_2) \quad \text{is} \quad P_2.$$

(4) For a start command, $T_1(\ )$ is **false**.
   Thus, $V_c(Q_1)$ is identically true.
(5) For a halt command, the set of T_j's and Q_j's is empty.
   Thus $V_c(P_1)$ is identically true.

For any set of semantic definitions such that

$$V_c(\mathbf{P}, \mathbf{Q}) \equiv (T_1(\mathbf{P}) \vdash Q_1) \wedge \cdots \wedge T_l(\mathbf{P}) \vdash Q_l),$$

in any verifiable interpretation, it is possible to substitute $T_j(\mathbf{P})$ for Q_j as a tag for any particular exit of a command without loss of verifiability. It is obvious that this substitution satisfies the semantic definition of the command whose exit is b_j; since $\vdash (T_j(\mathbf{P}) \supset Q_j)$, by Axiom 4 the substitution satisfies the semantic definition of the command whose entrance is b_j, and there are no other commands whose verification condition involves $I(b_j)$.

It is, therefore, possible to extend a partially specified interpretation to a complete interpretation, without loss of verifiability, provided that initially there is no closed loop in the flowchart all of whose edges are not tagged and that there is no entrance which is not tagged. This fact offers the possibility of automatic verification of programs, the programmer merely tagging entrances and one edge in each innermost loop; the verifying program would extend the interpretation and verify it, if possible, by mechanical theorem-proving techniques.

We shall refer to $T_c(\mathbf{P})$ as the *strongest verifiable consequent* of the command c, given an antecedent $\mathbf{P}$. It seems likely that most semantic definitions in programming languages can be cast into the form $V_c(\mathbf{P}, \mathbf{Q}) \equiv (T_c(\mathbf{P}) \vdash \mathbf{Q})$, where T_c has several obvious properties:

(1) If $\mathbf{P} \supset P_1$, $T_c(\mathbf{P}) \supset T_c(P_1)$.

(2) If upon entry by entrance a_i with initial values $\mathbf{V}$, a command is executed and left by exit b_j with final values $\mathbf{W}$, then $T_c(\mathbf{P}) \equiv \mathbf{Q}$, where P_α is defined as **false** for $\alpha \neq i$, $\mathbf{X} = \mathbf{V}$ for $\alpha = i$, and Q_β is defined as **false** for $\beta \neq j$, $\mathbf{X} = \mathbf{W}$ if $\beta = j$.

(3) If $P = P_1 \wedge P_2$, $T_c(P) \equiv T_c(P_1) \wedge T_c(P_2)$.

If $P = P_1 \vee P_2$, $T_c(P) \equiv T_c(P_1) \vee T_c(P_2)$.

If $P = (\exists x)(P_1)$, $T_c(P) \equiv (\exists x)(T_c(P_1))$.

That is, the transformation T_c distributes over conjunction, disjunction, and existential quantification. A semantic definition having these properties satisfies Axioms 1-4.

An ALGOL subset. To apply the same notions to a conventional programming language on the order of ALGOL, one might adopt a formal syntax for the language, such as the existing syntactic definition of ALGOL; designate certain phrase types as semantic units, such as the statements in ALGOL; and provide semantic definitions for these semantic units. Let us say that each statement Σ in an ALGOLic language is tagged with an antecedent and a consequent proposition (P_Σ and Q_Σ respectively), said to hold whenever control enters and leaves the statement in the normal sequential mode of control.

Now we may readily set up a verification condition for each common statement type.

(1) If Σ is an assignment statement, $x := f$, then

$$V_\Sigma(P_\Sigma; Q_\Sigma) \quad \text{is} \quad (\exists x_0)(S_{x_0}^x(P_\Sigma) \wedge x = S_{x_0}^x(f)) \vdash Q_\Sigma.$$

This assumes for simplicity that f is a true function of its free variables and has no side effects.

(2) If Σ is a conditional statement of the form **if** Φ **then** Σ_1 **else** Σ_2,

$$V_\Sigma(P_\Sigma, Q_{\Sigma 1}, Q_{\Sigma 2}; P_{\Sigma 1}, P_{\Sigma 2}, Q_\Sigma) \quad \text{is} \quad (P_\Sigma \wedge \Phi \vdash P_{\Sigma 1})$$

$$\wedge (P_\Sigma \wedge \neg \Phi \vdash P_{\Sigma 2}) \wedge (Q_{\Sigma 1} \vee Q_{\Sigma 2} \vdash Q_\Sigma).$$

Observe that here the exits of Σ_1 and Σ_2 become entrances to Σ, and so on.

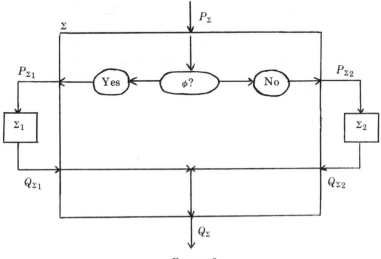

FIGURE 3

Consideration of the equivalent flowchart (Figure 3) indicates why this is true.

(3) If Σ_1 is a go-to statement of the form **go to** l, then $V_\Sigma(P_\Sigma; Q_\Sigma)$ is the identically true condition (**false**$\vdash Q_\Sigma$), because the sequential exit is never taken.

(4) If Σ is a labeled statement of the form $l: \Sigma_1$), then

$$V_\Sigma(P_\Sigma, P_l, Q_{\Sigma 1}; Q_\Sigma, P_{\Sigma 1})$$

is $(P_\Sigma \vee P_l \vdash P_{\Sigma 1}) \wedge (Q_{\Sigma 1} \vdash Q_\Sigma)$, where P_l is the disjunction of the antecedents of all statements of the form **go to** l.

(5) If Σ is a for-statement of the form **for** $x := a$ **step** b **until** c **do** Σ_1, where x is a variable and a, b, c are expressions, the verification rule is most easily seen by constructing the equivalent flowchart (Figure 4).

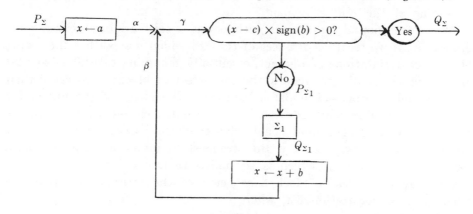

FIGURE 4

The strongest verifiable proposition P_α on edge α is

$$(\exists x_0)\,(S_{x_0}^x(P_\Sigma) \wedge x = S_{x_0}^x(a)).$$

The strongest verifiable proposition P_β on edge β is

$$(\exists x_0)\,(S_{x_0}^x(Q_{\Sigma 1}) \wedge x = x_0 + (S_{x_0}^x(b)),$$

which, if b contains no free occurrences of x, can be simplified to $S_{x-b}^x(Q_{\Sigma 1})$. The strongest verifiable proposition P_γ on edge γ is $P_\alpha \vee P_\beta$. Now the condition of verification is

$$(P_\gamma \wedge (x - c) \times \operatorname{sign}(b) > 0 \vdash Q_\Sigma) \wedge (P_\gamma \wedge (x - c) \times \operatorname{sign}(b) \leq 0 \vdash P_{\Sigma 1}).$$

More precisely, since the definition of ALGOL 60 states that x is undefined after exhaustion of the for statement, the first half of the verification condition should be $(\exists x)(P_\gamma \wedge (x - c) \times \operatorname{sign}(b) > 0) \vdash Q_\Sigma$. In typical cases, these conditions may be greatly simplified, since normally a, b, and c do not contain x, Σ_1 does not alter x, $\operatorname{sign}(b)$ is a constant, etc.

(6) Compound statements. A compound statement Σ is of the form **begin** Σ_1 **end**, where Σ_1 is a statement list. Then $V_\Sigma(P_\Sigma, Q_{\Sigma 1}; P_{\Sigma 1}, Q_\Sigma)$ $\equiv (P_\Sigma \vdash P_{\Sigma 1}) \wedge (Q_{\Sigma 1} \vdash Q_\Sigma)$. Alternatively, one might identify P_Σ with $P_{\Sigma 1}$ and Q_Σ with $Q_{\Sigma 1}$. A statement list Σ is either a statement, or is of the form $\Sigma_1; \Sigma_2$ where Σ_1 is a statement list and Σ_2 is a statement. In the latter case,

$$V_\Sigma(P_\Sigma, Q_{\Sigma 1}, Q_{\Sigma 2}; P_{\Sigma 1}, P_{\Sigma 2}, Q_\Sigma) \quad \text{is} \quad (P_\Sigma \vdash P_{\Sigma 1}) \wedge (Q_{\Sigma 1} \vdash P_{\Sigma 2}) \wedge (Q_{\Sigma 2} \vdash Q_\Sigma).$$

Alternately, identify P_Σ with $P_{\Sigma 1}$, $Q_{\Sigma 1}$ with $P_{\Sigma 2}$, and $Q_{\Sigma 2}$ with Q_Σ.

(7) A null statement Σ is represented by the empty string. $V_\Sigma(P_\Sigma; Q_\Sigma)$ is $P_\Sigma \vdash Q_\Sigma$. Verification conditions are very similar to relations of deducibility, and in this case the verification condition reduces to precisely a relation of deducibility. One might say facetiously that the subject matter of formal logic is the study of the verifiable interpretations of the program consisting of the null statement.

Blocks (compound statements with bound local variables) cause some difficulties. If we treat occurrences of the same identifier within the scopes of distinct declarations as distinct, essentially renaming identifiers so that all variables have distinct names, the only effect of blocks is to cause their local variables to become undefined on exit. The effect of the undefining of a variable can be achieved by existential quantification of that variable. For instance, if a statement could have the form "**undefine** x," and the antecedent were $w < x \wedge x < y$, the strongest verifiable consequent would be $(\exists x)(w < x \wedge x < y)$, which is simplified to $w < y$.

One may then treat a block Σ as being of the form **begin** $\Sigma_1; \Sigma_2$ **end** where Σ_1 is a declaration list, where

$$V_\Sigma(P_\Sigma, Q_{\Sigma 1}, Q_{\Sigma 2}; P_{\Sigma 1}, P_{\Sigma 2}, Q_\Sigma) \quad \text{is} \quad (P_\Sigma \vdash P_{\Sigma 2}) \wedge (Q_{\Sigma 2} \vdash P_{\Sigma 1}) \wedge (Q_{\Sigma 1} \vdash Q_\Sigma).$$

A declaration Σ of the form (say) **real** x is treated as undefining x when executed at the end of the execution of a block. Thus $V_\Sigma(P_\Sigma; Q_\Sigma)$ is $(\exists x) P_\Sigma \vdash Q_\Sigma$.

A declaration list Σ is either a declaration, or is of the form $\Sigma_1; \Sigma_2$ where Σ_1 is a declaration list and Σ_2 is a declaration;

$$V_\Sigma(P_\Sigma, Q_{\Sigma 1}, Q_{\Sigma 2}; P_{\Sigma 1}, P_{\Sigma 2}, Q_\Sigma) \quad \text{is} \quad (P_\Sigma \vdash P_{\Sigma 1}) \wedge (Q_{\Sigma 1} \vdash P_{\Sigma 2}) \wedge (Q_{\Sigma 2} \vdash Q_\Sigma).$$

The above is a poor approximation to the actual complexities of ALGOL block structure; for example, it does not reflect the fact that transfers out of a block by go-to statements cause local variables of the block to become undefined. It may serve, however, to indicate how a complete treatment could be carried out. Note that it does not say that local variables lose their values upon leaving a block, but that preservation of their values may not be assumed in proofs of programs.

The ALGOL procedure statement offers even more complexities, with its several types of parameters, the dynamic-**own** feature, the possibility of recursive call, side effects, etc. We will not consider procedure statements in detail, but will illustrate the treatment of side effects by analyzing extended assignment statements allowing embedded assignments as subexpressions. For example, consider the statement $a := c + (c := c + 1) + c$, which has the effect of assigning $3c_0 + 2$ to a, where c_0 is the initial value of c, and assigning $c_0 + 1$ to c. Such a treatment requires saving the value of the leftmost c before executing the embedded assignment. Let us reluctantly postulate a processor, with a pushdown accumulator stack S. Introducing appropriate stacking and unstacking operators, we say that S_h (the *head* of S) is the contents of the top cell of S; that S_t (the *tail* of S) is the remainder of S, the value S would have if the stack were popped; and $x : S$ is the value S would have if x were stacked on S. These three operators are recognizable as the CAR, CDR, and CONS operators of LISP. The axioms governing them are $(x : S)_h = x$ and $(x : S)_t = S$. Now we may say that if an assignment statement has the form $x := f$, the processor should perform **begin** STACK (f); UNSTACK (x) **end**. If f is of the form $g + h$, STACK (f) is **begin** STACK (g); STACK (h); ADD **end**, where ADD pops the two top stack cells, adds their contents, and stacks the result; ADD is $S := (S_h + (S_t)_h) : ((S_t)_t)$. If x is a variable, STACK (x) is $S := x : S$. If f is of the form $x := g$, STACK (f) is **begin** STACK (g); STORE (x) **end**, where STORE (x) is $x := S_h$. UNSTACK (x) is **begin** $x := S_h$; $S := S_t$ **end**.

On this basis, any assignment statement is equivalent to a sequence of simple assignments without side effects; for instance,

$$a := c + (c := c + 1) + c$$

is equivalent to

begin $S := c : S$; $\quad S := c : S$; $\quad S := 1 : S$; $\quad S := ((S_t)_h + S_h) : ((S_t)_t)$;

$c := S_h$; $\quad S := ((S_t)_h + S_h) : ((S_t)_t)$; $\quad S := c : S$; $\quad S := ((S_t)_h + S_h) : ((S_t)_t)$;

$a := S_h$; $\quad S := S_t$ **end**.

If the antecedent of the original statement is $P(a, c, S)$, the strongest verifiable consequents of the successive statements in the equivalent compound statement are:

(1) $(S := c : S) : (\exists S')(S = c : S' \wedge P(a, c, S'))$.

(2) $(S := c : S) : (\exists S'')(\exists S')(S = c : S'' \wedge S'' = c : S' \wedge P(a, c, S'))$, or $(\exists S')(S = c : (c : S') \wedge P(a, c, S'))$.

(3) $(S := 1 : S) : (\exists S')(S = 1 : (c : (c : S')) \wedge P(a, c, S'))$.

(4) $(S := ((S_t)_h + S_h) : ((S_t)_t)) : (\exists S'')(\exists S')(S = ((S''_t)_h + S''_h) :$
$$((S''_t)_t) \wedge S'' = 1 : (c : (c : S')) \wedge P(a, c, S'))$$

which simplifies, by application of the equation $S'' = 1 : (c : (c : S'))$, to
$(\exists S')(S = (c + 1) : (c : S') \wedge P(a, c, S'))$.

(5) $(c := S_h) : (\exists c')(\exists S')(c = S_h \wedge S = (c' + 1) : (c' : S') \wedge P(a, c', S'))$.

Noting that $S_h = c' + 1$, or $c' = S_h - 1 = c - 1$, this becomes
$(\exists S')(S = c : (c - 1 : S') \wedge P(a, c - 1, S'))$.

(6) $(S := ((S_t)_h + S_h) : ((S_t)_t)) : (\exists S')(S = 2c - 1 : S' \wedge P(a, c - 1, S'))$.

(7) $(S := c : S) : (\exists S')(S = c : (2c - 1 : S') \wedge P(a, c - 1, S'))$.

(8) $(S := ((S_t)_h + S_h) : ((S_t)_t)) : (\exists S')(S = 3c - 1 : S' \wedge P(a, c - 1, S'))$.

(9) $(a := S_h) : (\exists a')(\exists S')(a = S_h \wedge S = 3c - 1 : S' \wedge P(a', c - 1, S'))$, or
$$(\exists a')(\exists S')(a = 3c - 1 \wedge S = 3c - 1 : S' \wedge P(a', c - 1, S'))$$

(10) $(S \leftarrow S_t) : (\exists S'')(\exists a')(\exists S')(S = S''_t \wedge a = 3c - 1 \wedge S'' = 3c - 1 : S'$
$$\wedge P(a', c - 1, S')), \text{ or}$$
$$(\exists a')(\exists S')(S = S' \wedge a = 3c - 1 \wedge P(a', c - 1, S')), \text{ or}$$
$$(\exists a')(a = 3c - 1 \wedge P(a, c - 1, S)).$$

For this statement, then, the condition of verification $V_\Sigma(P(a, c, S); Q)$
is $((\exists a')(a = 3c - 1 \wedge P(a', c - 1, S))) \vdash Q$, which is exactly the verification
condition for either of

$$\textbf{Begin}\, c := c + 1; \quad a := 3c - 1\ \textbf{end}$$

and

$$\textbf{Begin}\, a := 3c + 2; \quad c := c + 1\ \textbf{end}.$$

Thus, the three statements are shown to be precisely equivalent, at least
under the axioms (of exact arithmetic, etc.) used in the proof.

Proofs of termination. If a verified program is entered by a path whose
tag is then true, then at every subsequent time that a path in the program
is traversed, the corresponding proposition will be true, and in particular
if the program ever halts, the proposition on the path leading to the selected
exit will be true. Thus, we have a basis for proofs of relations between
input and output in a program. The attentive reader, however, will have
observed that we have not proved that an exit will ever be reached; the
methods so far described offer no security against nonterminating loops.
To some extent, this is intrinsic; such a program as, for example, a mechanical proof procedure, designed to recognize the elements of a recursively
enumerable but not recursive set, cannot be guaranteed to terminate without
a fundamental loss of power. Most correct programs, however, can be
proved to terminate. The most general method appears to use the properties
of well-ordered sets. A well-ordered set W is an ordered set in which each

nonempty subset has a least member; equivalently, in which there are no infinite decreasing sequences.

Suppose, for example, that an interpretation of a flowchart is supplemented by associating with each edge in the flowchart an expression for a function, which we shall call a W-function, of the free variables of the interpretation, taking its values in a well-ordered set W. If we can show that after each execution of a command the current value of the W-function associated with the exit is less than the prior value of the W-function associated with the entrance, the value of the function must steadily decrease. Because no infinite decreasing sequence is possible in a well-ordered set, the program must sooner or later terminate. Thus, we prove termination, a global property of a flowchart, by local arguments, just as we prove the correctness of an algorithm.

To set more precisely the standard for proofs of termination, let us introduce a new variable δ, not used otherwise in an interpreted program. Letting W designate the well-ordered set in which the W-functions are to be shown decreasing, and letting $\bigcirc\!\!\!<$ be the ordering relation of W, it is necessary to prove for a command c whose entrance is tagged with proposition P and W-function ϕ, and whose exit is tagged with proposition Q and W-function ψ that

$$V_c(P \wedge \delta = \phi \wedge \phi \in W; Q \wedge \psi \bigcirc\!\!\!< \delta \wedge \psi \in W).$$

Carrying out this proof for each command in the program, with obvious generalizations for commands having multiple entrances and exits, suffices not only to verify the interpretation, but also to show that the program must terminate, if entered with initial values satisfying the tag of the entrance.

The best-known well-ordered set is the set of positive integers, and the most obvious application of well-orderings to proofs of termination is to use as the W-function on each edge a formula for the number of program steps until termination, or some well-chosen upper bound on this number. Experience suggests, however, that it is sometimes much more convenient to use other well-orderings, and it may even be necessary in some cases. Frequently, an appropriate well-ordered set is the set of n-tuples of positive (or nonnegative) integers, for some fixed n, ordered by the assumption that $(i_1, i_2, \cdots, i_n) \bigcirc\!\!\!< (j_1, j_2, \cdots, j_n)$ if, for some k, $i_1 = j_1$, $i_2 = j_2$, $\cdots$, $i_{k-1} = j_{k-1}$, $i_k < j_k$, $1 \leq k \leq n$. The flowchart of Figure 5 shows an interpretation using this well-ordering, for $n = 2$, to prove termination. It is assumed in the interpretation that the variables range over the integers; that is, the deductive system used in verifying the interpretation must include a set of axioms for the integers.

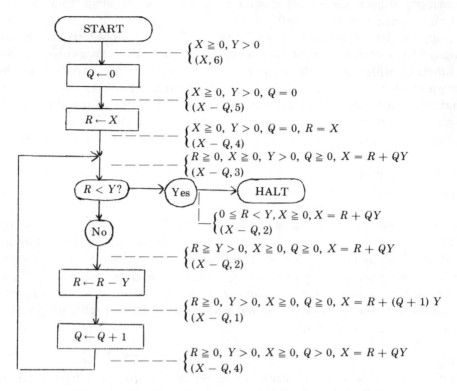

FIGURE 5. Algorithm to compute quotient Q and remainder R of
$X \div Y$, for integers $X \geq 0, Y > 0$

REFERENCES

1. J. McCarthy, "A basis for a mathematical theory of computation" in *Computer programming and formal systems*, North-Holland, Amsterdam, 1963, pp. 33-70.

2. _____, *Towards a mathematical science of computation*, Proc. IFIP Congr. 62, North-Holland, Amsterdam, 1962, pp. 21-28.

CARNEGIE INSTITUTE OF TECHNOLOGY
PITTSBURGH, PENNSYLVANIA

John McCarthy
James Painter[1]

CORRECTNESS OF A COMPILER
FOR ARITHMETIC EXPRESSIONS[2]

1. **Introduction.** This paper contains a proof of the correctness of a simple compiling algorithm for compiling arithmetic expressions into machine language.

The definition of correctness, the formalism used to express the description of source language, object language and compiler, and the methods of proof are all intended to serve as prototypes for the more complicated task of proving the correctness of usable compilers. The ultimate goal, as outlined in references [1], [2], [3] and [4] is to make it possible to use a computer to check proofs that compilers are correct.

The concepts of abstract syntax, state vector, the use of an interpreter for defining the semantics of a programming language, and the definition of correctness of a compiler are all the same as in [3]. The present paper, however, is the first in which the correctness of a compiler is proved.

The expressions dealt with in this paper are formed from constants and variables. The only operation allowed is a binary $+$ although no change in method would be required to include any other binary operations. An example of an expression that can be compiled is

$$(x + 3) + (x + (y + 2))$$

although, because we use abstract syntax, no commitment to a particular form is made.

The computer language into which these expressions are compiled is a single address computer with an accumulator, called ac, and four instructions: li (load immediate), load, sto (store) and add. Note that there are no jump instructions. Needless to say, this is a severe restriction on the generality of our results which we shall overcome in future work.

---

[1] IBM Resident Graduate Student, IBM Corporation.
[2] The research reported here was supported in part by the Advanced Research Projects Agency of the Office of the Secretary of Defense (SD 183).

The compiler produces code that computes the value of the expression being compiled and leaves this value in the accumulator. The above expression is compiled into code which in assembly language might look as follows:

$$
\begin{array}{ll}
\text{load} & x \\
\text{sto} & t \\
\text{li} & 3 \\
\text{add} & t \\
\text{sto} & t \\
\text{load} & x \\
\text{sto} & t+1 \\
\text{load} & y \\
\text{sto} & t+2 \\
\text{li} & 2 \\
\text{add} & t+2 \\
\text{add} & t+1 \\
\text{add} & t
\end{array}
$$

Again because we are using abstract syntax there is no commitment to a precise form for the object code.

2. **The source language.** The abstract analytic syntax of the source expressions is given by the table:

predicate	associated functions	
isconst(e)		
isvar(e)		
issum(e)	$s1(e)$	$s2(e)$

which asserts that the expressions comprise constants, variables and binary sums, that the predicates isconst, isvar, and issum enable one to classify each expression and that each sum e has summands $s1(e)$ and $s2(e)$.

The semantics is given by the formula

(2.1)
$$
\text{value}(e, \xi) = \textbf{if } \text{isconst}(e) \textbf{ then } \text{val}(e) \textbf{ else if } \text{isvar}(e) \textbf{ then } c(e, \xi)
$$
$$
\textbf{else if } \text{issum}(e) \textbf{ then } \text{value}(s1(e), \xi) + \text{value}(s2(e), \xi)
$$

where val(e) gives the numerical value of an expression e representing a constant, $c(e, \xi)$ gives the value of the variable e in the state vector ξ and $+$ is some binary operation. (Naturally, usually $+$ will be interpreted as an operation that resembles addition of real numbers, but our results do not depend on this.)

For our present purposes we do not have to give a synthetic syntax for the source language expressions since both the interpreter and the compiler use only the analytic syntax. However, we shall need the following induction principle for expressions:

Suppose Φ is a predicate applicable to expressions, and suppose that for all expressions e we have

$$\text{isconst}(e) \supset \Phi(e) \quad \text{and}$$
$$\text{isvar}(e) \supset \Phi(e) \quad \text{and}$$
$$\text{issum}(e) \wedge \Phi(s1(e)) \wedge \Phi(s2(e)) \supset \Phi(e).$$

Then we may conclude that $\Phi(e)$ is true for all expressions e.

3. **The object language.** We must give both the analytic and synthetic syntaxes for the object language because the interpreter defining its semantics uses the analytic syntax and the compiler uses the synthetic syntax. We may write the analytic and synthetic syntaxes for instructions in the following table.

operation	predicate	analytic operation	synthetic operation
li α	isli(s)	arg(s)	mkli(α)
load x	isload(s)	adr(s)	mkload(x)
sto x	issto(s)	adr(s)	mksto(x)
add x	isadd(s)	adr(s)	mkadd(x)

A program is a list of instructions and null(p) asserts that p is the null list. If the program p is not null then first(p) gives the first instruction and rest(p) gives the list of remaining instructions. We shall use the operation $p1 * p2$ to denote the program obtained by appending $p2$ onto the end of $p1$. Since we have only one level of list we can identify a single instruction with a program that has just one instruction.

The synthetic and analytic syntaxes of instructions are related by the following:

(3.1)
$$\text{isli}(\text{mkli}(\alpha))$$
$$\alpha = \text{arg}(\text{mkli}(\alpha))$$
$$\text{isli}(s) \supset s = \text{mkli}(\text{arg}(s))$$
$$\text{null}(\text{rest}(\text{mkli}(\alpha)))$$
$$\text{isli}(s) \supset \text{first}(s) = s$$

(3.2)
$$\text{isload}(\text{mkload}(x))$$
$$x = \text{adr}(\text{mkload}(x))$$
$$\text{isload}(x) \supset x = \text{mkload}(\text{adr}(x))$$
$$\text{null}(\text{rest}(\text{mkload}(x)))$$
$$\text{isload}(s) \supset \text{first}(s) = s$$

$$\text{issto}(\text{mksto}(x))$$

$$x = \text{adr}(\text{mksto}(x))$$

(3.3) $\quad\text{issto}(x) \supset x = \text{mksto}(\text{adr}(x))$

$$\text{null}(\text{rest}(\text{mksto}(x)))$$

$$\text{issto}(s) \supset \text{first}(s) = s$$

$$\text{isadd}(\text{mkadd}(x))$$

$$x = \text{adr}(\text{mkadd}(x))$$

(3.4) $\quad\text{isadd}(x) \supset x = \text{mkadd}(\text{adr}(x))$

$$\text{null}(\text{rest}(\text{mkadd}(x)))$$

$$\text{isadd}(x) \supset \text{first}(s) = s$$

(3.5) $\qquad\qquad \neg\,\text{null}(p) \supset p = \text{first}(p) * \text{rest}(p),$

(3.6) $\qquad \neg\,\text{null}(p1) \wedge \text{null}(\text{rest}(p1)) \supset p1 = \text{first}(p1 * p2)$

(3.7) $\qquad\qquad \text{null}(p1 * p2) \equiv \text{null}(p1) \wedge \text{null}(p2).$

The $*$ operation is associative. (The somewhat awkward form of these relations comes from having a general concatenation operation rather than just an operation that prefixes a single instruction onto a program.)

A state vector for a machine gives, for each register in the machine, its contents. We include the accumulator denoted by ac as a register. There are two functions of state vectors as introduced in [3], namely

1. $c(x, \eta)$ denotes the value of the contents of register x in machine state η.

2. $a(x, \alpha, \eta)$ denotes the state vector that is obtained from the state vector η by changing the contents of register x to α leaving the other registers unaffected.

These functions satisfy the following relations:

(3.8) $\qquad\qquad c(x, a(y, \alpha, \eta)) = \textbf{if } x = y \textbf{ then } \alpha \textbf{ else } c(x, \eta),$

(3.9) $\quad a(x, \alpha, a(y, \beta, \eta)) = \textbf{if } x = y \textbf{ then } a(x, \alpha, \eta) \textbf{ else } a(y, \beta, a(x, \alpha, \eta)),$

(3.10) $\qquad\qquad\qquad a(x, c(x, \eta), \eta) = \eta.$

Now we can define the semantics of the object language by

$$\text{step}(s, \eta) = \textbf{if } \text{isli}(s) \textbf{ then } a(\text{ac}, \text{arg}(s), \eta) \textbf{ else if}$$

$$\text{isload}(s) \textbf{ then } a(\text{ac}, c(\text{adr}(s), \eta), \eta) \textbf{ else if}$$

(3.11)

$$\text{issto}(s) \textbf{ then } a(\text{adr}(s), c(\text{ac}, \eta), \eta) \textbf{ else if}$$

$$\text{isadd}(s) \textbf{ then } a(\text{ac}, c(\text{adr}(s), \eta) + c(\text{ac}, \eta), \eta)$$

which gives the state vector that results from executing an instruction and

(3.12)
$$\text{outcome}(p, \eta)$$
$$= \mathbf{if}\,\text{null}(p)\,\mathbf{then}\,\eta\,\mathbf{else}\,\text{outcome}\,(\text{rest}\,(p), \text{step}\,(\text{first}(p), \eta))$$

which gives the state vector that results from executing the program p with state vector η.

The following lemma is easily proved.

(3.13) $\qquad \text{outcome}(p1 * p2, \eta) = \text{outcome}\,(p2, \text{outcome}(p1, \eta))$

4. **The compiler.** We shall assume that there is a map giving for each variable in the expression a location in the main memory of the machine. $\text{loc}(v, \text{map})$ gives this location and we shall assume

(4.1) $\qquad\qquad c(\text{loc}(v, \text{map}), \eta) = c(v, \xi)$

as a relation between the state vector η before the compiled program starts to act and the initial state vector ξ of the source program.

Now we can write the compiler. It is

$$\text{compile}(e, t) = \mathbf{if}\,\text{isconst}(e)\,\mathbf{then}\,\text{mkli}(\text{val}(e))\,\mathbf{else\ if}$$

(4.2) $\qquad\qquad\qquad \text{isvar}(e)\,\mathbf{then}\,\text{mkload}(\text{loc}(e, \text{map}))\,\mathbf{else\ if}$

$\text{issum}(e)\,\mathbf{then}\,\text{compile}(s1(e), t) * \text{mksto}(t) * \text{compile}(s2(e), t + 1) * \text{mkadd}(t)$

Here t is the number of a register such that all variables are stored in registers numbered less than t, so that registers t and above are available for temporary storage.

Before we can state our definition of correctness of the compiler, we need a notion of partial equality for state vectors

$$\varsigma_1 =_A \varsigma_2$$

where ς_1 and ς_2 are state vectors and A is a set of variables means that corresponding components of ς_1 and ς_2 are equal except possibly for values of variables in A. Symbolically, $x \notin A \supset c(x, \varsigma_1) = c(x, \varsigma_2)$. Partial equality satisfies the following relations:

(4.3) $\quad \varsigma_1 = \varsigma_2$ is equivalent to $\varsigma_1 =_{\{\ \}} \varsigma_2$ where $\{\ \}$ denotes the empty set,

(4.4) $\qquad\qquad$ if $A \subset B$ and $\varsigma_1 =_A \varsigma_2$ then $\varsigma_1 =_B \varsigma_2$,

(4.5) $\qquad\qquad$ if $\varsigma_1 =_A \varsigma_2$ then $a(x, \alpha, \varsigma_1) =_{A-\{x\}} a(x, \alpha, \varsigma_2)$,

(4.6) $\qquad\qquad$ if $x \in A$ then $a(x, \alpha, \varsigma) =_A \varsigma$,

(4.7) $\qquad\qquad$ if $\varsigma_1 =_A \varsigma_2$ and $\varsigma_2 =_B \varsigma_3$ then $\varsigma_1 =_{A \cup B} \varsigma_3$.

In our case we need a specialization of this notation and will use

$$\varsigma_1 =_t \varsigma_2 \text{ to denote } \varsigma_1 =_{\{x \mid x \geq t\}} \varsigma_2$$

and

$$\zeta_1 = {}_{ac} \zeta_2 \text{ to denote } \zeta_1 = {}_{\{ac\}} \zeta_2$$

and

$$\zeta_1 = {}_{t,ac} \zeta_2 \text{ to denote } \zeta_1 = {}_{\{x \mid x = ac \lor x \geq t\}} \zeta_2.$$

The correctness of the compiler is stated in

THEOREM 1. *If η and ξ are machine and source language state vectors respectively such that*

(4.8) $c(\text{loc}(v, \text{map}), \eta) = c(v, \xi)$, *then*

$$outcome(compile(e, t), \eta) = {}_t a(\text{ac}, \text{value}(e, \xi), \eta).$$

It states that the result of running the compiled program is to put the value of the expression compiled into the accumulator. No registers except the accumulator and those with addresses $\geq t$ are affected.

5. **Proof of Theorem 1.** The proof is accomplished by an induction on the expression e being compiled. We prove it first for constants, then for variables, and then for sums on the induction hypothesis that it is true for the summands. Thus we have three cases.

I.   isconst(e). We have   Justification

$$
\begin{aligned}
outcome(compile(e, t), \eta) &= outcome(\text{mkli}(\text{val}(e)), \eta) & &4.2 \\
&= \text{step}(\text{mkli}(\text{val}(e)), \eta) & &3.12, 3.1 \\
&= a(\text{ac}, \arg(\text{mkli}(\text{val}(e))), \eta) & &3.1, 3.11 \\
&= a(\text{ac}, \text{val}(e), \eta) & &3.1 \\
&= a(\text{ac}, \text{value}(e, \xi), \eta) & &2.1 \\
&= {}_t a(\text{ac}, \text{value}(e, \xi), \eta). & &4.3, 4.4
\end{aligned}
$$

II.   isvar(e). We have

$outcome(compile(e, t), \eta)$

$$
\begin{aligned}
&= outcome(\text{mkload}(\text{loc}(e, \text{map})), \eta) & &4.2 \\
&= a(\text{ac}, c(\text{adr}(\text{mkload}(\text{loc}(e, \text{map}))), \eta), \eta) & &3.12, 3.2, 3.11 \\
&= a(\text{ac}, c(\text{loc}(e, \text{map}), \eta), \eta) & &3.2 \\
&= a(\text{ac}, c(e, \xi), \eta) & &4.1 \\
&= a(\text{ac}, \text{value}(e, \xi), \eta) & &2.1 \\
&= {}_t a(\text{ac}, \text{value}(e, \xi), \eta). & &4.3, 4.4
\end{aligned}
$$

III.   issum(e). In this case we first write

outcome$(\text{compile}(e, t), \eta)$

$= \text{outcome}(\text{compile}(s1(e), t) * \text{mksto}(t)$

$\qquad\qquad * \text{compile}(s2(e), t + 1) * \text{mkadd}(t), \eta)$ 4.2

$= \text{outcome}(\text{mkadd}(t), \text{outcome}(\text{compile}(s2(e), t + 1),$

$\qquad\qquad \text{outcome}(\text{mksto}(t), \text{outcome}(\text{compile}(s1(e), t), \eta))))$ 3.13

using the relation between concatenating programs and composing the functions they represent. Now we introduce some notation. Let

$$v = \text{value}(e, \xi),$$
$$v_1 = \text{value}(s1(e), \xi),$$
$$v_2 = \text{value}(s2(e), \xi),$$

so that $v = v_1 + v_2$. Further let

$$\zeta_1 = \text{outcome}(\text{compile}(s1(e), t), \eta),$$
$$\zeta_2 = \text{outcome}(\text{mksto}(t), \zeta_1),$$
$$\zeta_3 = \text{outcome}(\text{compile}(s2(e), t + 1), \zeta_2),$$
$$\zeta_4 = \text{outcome}(\text{mkadd}(t), \zeta_3)$$

so that $\zeta_4 = \text{outcome}(\text{compile}(e, t), \eta)$ and we want to prove that

$$\zeta_4 = {}_t a(\text{ac}, v, \eta).$$

We have

$\quad \zeta_1 = \text{outcome}(\text{compile}(s1(e), t), \eta)$

$\qquad = {}_t a(\text{ac}, v_1, \eta)$ and   Induction Hypothesis

$\quad c(\text{ac}, \zeta_1) = v_1.$ 3.8

Now

$\quad \zeta_2 = \text{outcome}(\text{mksto}(t), \zeta_1)$

$\qquad = a(t, c(\text{ac}, \zeta_1), \zeta_1)$ 3.12, 3.3, 3.11

$\qquad = a(t, v_1, \zeta_1)$ Substitution

$\qquad = {}_{t+1} a(t, v_1, a(\text{ac}, v_1, \eta))$ 4.5

$\qquad = {}_{t+1, \text{ac}} a(t, v_1, \eta)$ 4.6, 3.9

and

$\quad c(t, \zeta_2) = v_1.$ 3.8

Next

$$\zeta_3 = \text{outcome}(\text{compile}(s2(e), t+1), \zeta_2)$$

$$=_{t+1} a(\text{ac}, v_2, \zeta_2).$$

Here we again use the induction hypothesis that $s2(e)$ is compiled correctly. In order to apply it we need $c(\text{loc}(v, \text{map}), \zeta_2) = c(v, \xi)$ for each variable v which is proved as follows:

$$c(\text{loc}(v, \text{map}), \zeta_2) = c(\text{loc}(v, \text{map}), a(t, v_1, \eta)) \text{ since } \text{loc}(v, \text{map}) < t$$

$$= c(\text{loc}(v, \text{map}), \eta) \text{ for the same reason}$$

$$= c(v, \xi) \text{ by the hypothesis of the theorem.}$$

Now we can continue with

$$\zeta_3 =_{t+1} a(\text{ac}, v_2, a(t, v_1, \eta)) \qquad\qquad 3.9, 4.5$$

and

$$c(\text{ac}, \zeta_3) = v_2 \text{ and } c(t, \zeta_3) = v_1. \qquad\qquad 3.8$$

Finally,

$$\zeta_4 = \text{outcome}(\text{mkadd}(t), \zeta_3)$$

$$= a(\text{ac}, c(t, \zeta_3) + c(\text{ac}, \zeta_3), \zeta_3) \qquad\qquad 3.12, 3.4, 3.11$$

$$= a(\text{ac}, v, \zeta_3) \qquad\qquad \text{Definition of } v, \text{ substitution}$$

$$=_{t+1} a(\text{ac}, v, a(\text{ac}, v_2, a(t, v_1, \eta))) \qquad\qquad 4.5$$

$$=_{t+1} a(\text{ac}, v, a(t, v_1, \eta)) \qquad\qquad 3.9$$

$$=_{t} a(\text{ac}, v, \eta). \qquad\qquad 3.9, 4.6, 4.7$$

This concludes the proof.

6. REMARKS. The problem of the relations between source language and object language arithmetic is dealt with here by assuming that the $+$ signs in formulas (2.1) and (3.11) which define the semantics of the source and object languages represent the same operation. Theorem 1 does not depend on any properties of this operation, not even commutativity or associativity.

The proof is entirely straightforward once the necessary machinery has been created. Additional operations such as subtraction, multiplication and division could be added without essential change in the proof.

For example, to put multiplication into the system the following changes would be required.

1. Add $\text{isprod}(e)$, and $p1(e)$, and $p2(e)$ to the abstract syntax of the source language.

2. Add a term

$$\textbf{if } \text{isprod}(e) \textbf{ then } \text{value}(p1(e), \xi) \times \text{value}(p2(e), \xi)$$

to Equation (2.1).

3. Add

$$\text{isprod}(e) \bigwedge \Phi(p1(e)) \bigwedge \Phi(p2(e)) \supset \Phi(e)$$

to the hypotheses of the source language induction principle.

4. Add an instruction mul x and the three syntactical functions ismul(s), adr(s), mkmul(x) to the abstract syntax of the object language together with the necessary relations among them.

5. Add to the definition (3.11) of step a term

$$\textbf{else if } \text{ismul}(s) \textbf{ then } a(\text{ac}, c(\text{adr}(s), \eta) \times c(\text{ac}, \eta), \eta).$$

6. Add to the compiler a term

$$\textbf{if } \text{isprod}(e) \textbf{ then } \text{compile}(p1(e), t) * \text{mksto}(t)$$

$$* \text{compile}(p2(e), t+1) * \text{mkmul}(t).$$

7. Add to the proof a case isprod(e) which parallels the case issum(e) exactly.

The following other extensions are contemplated.

1. Variable length sums.

2. Sequences of assignment statements.

3. Conditional expressions.

4. *go to* statements in the source language.

In order to make these extensions a complete revision of the formalism will be required.

REFERENCES

1. J. McCarthy, *Computer programs for checking mathematical proofs*, Proc. Sympos. Pure Math. Vol. 5, Amer. Math. Soc., Providence, R. I., 1962, pp. 219-227.

2. ———, "A basis for a mathematical theory of computation" in *Computer programming and formal systems*, edited by P. Braffort and D. Hershberg, North-Holland, Amsterdam, 1963.

3. ———, *Towards a mathematical theory of computation*, Proc. Internat. Congr. on Information Processing, 1962.

4. ———, *A formal description of a subset of Algol*, Proc. Conf. on Formal Language Description Languages, Vienna, 1964.

STANFORD UNIVERSITY
  STANFORD, CALIFORNIA

J. Hartmanis

CONTEXT-FREE LANGUAGES
AND TURING MACHINE COMPUTATIONS

Abstract. The purpose of this paper is to derive a result which establishes a very close link between complements or intersections of context-free languages and Turing machine computations. This result is then used to derive directly from the undecidability of the stopping rule for Turing machines several known and some new results about context-free languages, their complements, intersections and quotients.

Introduction. During the recent years there has been considerable interest in abstract languages and especially in context-free languages about which many interesting results have been obtained. Much of this work has been motivated by the growing interest in computer languages and the formal aspects of natural languages. In both areas of study context-free languages have supplied unifying concepts and several results have found direct applications.

Also, through the characterization of context-free languages as sets of sequences recognized by push-down automata, they have become a part of automata theory [1]. Automata theory is the study of abstract computing devices and the mechanical aspects of computation and information processing. In this study, context-free languages fit naturally in the overall classification of computations by their inherent complexity and the computational power of the automata which perform them [2, 3].

Among the many results about context-free languages there is a set of results which show that many questions about the properties of context-free languages, their complements and intersections are recursively undecidable. All these undecidable results so far have been obtained by reducing problems about languages to problems about the solution of Post's correspondence problem. Since the correspondence problem is recursively undecidable, the original problems about languages are also undecidable [4, 5]. Though the reduction of these problems to Post's correspondence problem is not difficult, the proof that Post's problem itself is undecidable is not simple [6]. Particularly, for people working in automata and computer

42

theory the more natural approach is through Turing machines and the undecidability of the stopping rule for Turing machines.

The purpose of this paper is to show that a very close relationship exists between context-free languages and Turing machine computations. We will show that for every Turing machine $\mathcal{T}$ we can construct a context-free language whose complement is a complete description of all the terminating computations which are performed by $\mathcal{T}$. We will then exploit this result to give very simple proofs of some new and some known results about context-free languages, their complements and intersections. This approach derives the undecidable results about context-free languages directly from the undecidability of the stopping rule for Turing machines, thus avoiding the use of Post's correspondence problem.

A closely related approach to the derivation of undecidable results for context-free languages has been used by R. W. Floyd in [7].

Preliminaries. In this section we summarize the basic definitions and some elementary results which are used later.

A *context-free grammar* is defined as a four-tuple

$$G = \langle T, N, S, P \rangle,$$

where

> T is the finite set of *terminal symbols;*
>
> N is the finite set of *nonterminal symbols* and N is disjoint from T;
>
> S is a designated symbol in N, referred to as the *initial symbol*;
>
> P is a finite set of *rewriting rules* or *productions* all of the form
> $X \to x$ with X in N and x in $(T \cup N)^*$.

The set $(T \cup N)^*$ contains all finite strings including the null string formed from the alphabet $T \cup N$.

The sequence w_1 *directly generates* w_2 in grammar G, $w_1 \Rightarrow w_2$, if and only if there exist strings u and v in $(T \cup N)^*$ such that $w_1 = uXv$, $w_2 = uxv$ and $X \to x$ is in P.

The sequence w_1 *generates* w_2 in grammar G, $w_1 \overset{*}{\Rightarrow} w_2$, if and only if there exist strings $x_0, x_1, x_2, \cdots, x_n$ such that

$$w_1 = x_0 \Rightarrow x_1 \Rightarrow x_2 \Rightarrow \cdots \Rightarrow x_n = w_2.$$

The *language* generated by grammar G is the set of sequence in terminal symbols which are generated from the initial symbol S:

$$L(G) = \{w \mid w \in T^* \quad \text{and} \quad S \overset{*}{\Rightarrow} w\}.$$

The *complement* of $L(G)$ is given by

$$\overline{L(G)} = T^* - L(G).$$

We now state some well-known results about languages, which are used later [1, 4 or 5].

LEMMA 1. *The set union of two context-free languages is a context-free language.*

The next result is not needed to derive our main theorem, but it makes its proof intuitively very clear and we will indicate later how it can be used.

LEMMA 2. *The set of sequences accepted by a push-down automaton is a context-free language.*

LEMMA 3. *For every context-free grammar G there is an algorithm to decide (for all w) whether L(G) contains a string starting with w.*

Next we introduce some notation about Turing machine computations which is used in the next section.

We are considering one tape Turing machines which can print a zero or one on the tape but can also read a blank (designated by a dash, —). These machines are used as sequence recognizers and are started in the starting state s_0, with the reading head scanning the left most symbol of the binary input string on its tape. We further assume that the Turing machine can stop only by entering the stopping state s_s and that this can happen only after an even number of operations. One operation of the Turing machine consists of reading the tape symbol under the reading head, overprinting this symbol, changing the internal state of the machine and moving the reading head one square left, right or remaining stationary on the tape.

Before each operation the Turing machine can be described by listing the zero-one sequence written on its tape and inserting the symbol of the state the machine is in to the left of the symbol the reading head is scanning. We refer to this sequence as the *instantaneous description* of the Turing machine. For example, the instantaneous description

$$w = -10110s_j11-$$

shows that the Turing machine is in state s_j and that the reading head is scanning the second one from the right. The dashes at both ends stand for the two blank squares of the tape which the machine could be scanning and they are always added to both ends of the sequence.

For a Turing machine $\mathscr{T}$ we write

$$w_i \overset{\mathscr{T}}{\rightarrow} w_j$$

if and only if in one operation the machine $\mathscr{T}$ goes from the configuration given by the instantaneous description w_i to the configuration given by w_j.

Thus a machine $\mathscr{T}$ started with input sequence w on its tape can stop with the sequence

$$a_1 a_2 \cdots a_j \cdots a_n$$

on its tape and the reading head scanning a_j, if and only if there exists a sequence of instantaneous descriptions

$$w_1, w_2, \cdots, w_{2k}$$

such that

$$-s_0 w- = w_1 \overset{\mathcal{T}}{\to} w_2 \overset{\mathcal{T}}{\to} w_3 \overset{\mathcal{T}}{\to} \cdots \overset{\mathcal{T}}{\to} w_{2k-1} \overset{\mathcal{T}}{\to} w_{2k} = -a_1 a_2 \cdots s_s a_j \cdots a_n-.$$

If we introduce a new symbol m (for marker) then we can rewrite this description of the computation by $\mathcal{T}$ as follows

$$w_1\, m\, w_2\, m\, w_3\, m \cdots m\, w_{2k}\, m\, m.$$

To link these descriptions of the computations of $\mathcal{T}$ to context-free languages we transpose (reverse) every second instantaneous description in this sequence,

$$w_1\, m\, w_2^T\, m\, w_3\, m\, w_4^T\, m \cdots m\, w_{2k-1}\, m\, w_{2k}^T\, m\, m,$$

and refer to it as the *alternating description* of a computation by $\mathcal{T}$. The *transposition* is defined as follows:

If $w = a_1 a_2 \cdots a_n$, then $w^T = a_n a_{n-1} \cdots a_1$.

Context-free languages and Turing machines. We now state and prove the result which links the complements and intersections of context-free languages to Turing machine computations. To do this we construct by an effective procedure for every Turing machine $\mathcal{T}$ a context-free grammar $G_{\mathcal{T}}$ such that the complement of $L(G_{\mathcal{T}})$ consists of exactly those strings which are alternating descriptions of the terminating computations performed by $\mathcal{T}$.

THEOREM. *There is an effective procedure to construct for every Turing machine $\mathcal{T}$ a context-free grammar $G_{\mathcal{T}}$, such that*

$$L(G_{\mathcal{T}}) = \overline{W}$$

and

$$W = \{z \mid z = w_1\, m\, w_2^T\, m\, w_3\, m \cdots m\, w_{2k}^T\, m\, m,$$
$$w_1 = -s_0 w- \overset{\mathcal{T}}{\to} w_2 \overset{\mathcal{T}}{\to} w_3 \overset{\mathcal{T}}{\to} \cdots \overset{\mathcal{T}}{\to} w_{2k} = x s_s y \}.$$

PROOF. Our strategy is to construct effectively for any given Turing machine $\mathcal{T}$ two auxiliary context-free languages, L_1 and L_2, whose complements, $\overline{L_1}$ and $\overline{L_2}$, are also context-free languages and such that

$$L_1 \cap L_2 = W.$$

Since the complements of these auxiliary languages are also context-free their union is a context-free language. Thus there exists a context-free grammar $G_{\mathcal{F}}$ such that

$$L(G_{\mathcal{F}}) = \overline{L_1} \cup \overline{L_2} = \overline{L_1 \cap L_2}.$$

We now carry out the construction of L_1 and L_2. Let

$$L_1 = \{ w_i m w_j^T m \mid w_i \overset{\mathcal{F}}{\rightarrow} w_j \} *m,$$

where the star again indicates that we take all finite strings made up from members of this set. Thus L_1 consists of the string m and all strings which can be made up from pairs of consecutive instantaneous descriptions of $\mathcal{F}$, in which the second member is reversed and placed between m markers.

It is easily seen that this is a context-free language since it is generated by a context-free grammar G. We can avoid the explicit construction of the grammar for L_1 by showing that L_1 is recognized by a deterministic push-down automaton and then use Lemma 2 to conclude that it is a context-free language. To do this we now sketch how the push-down recognizer for L_1 operates.

The automaton pushes down in its stack (push-down store) the input string until it encounters a state symbol at which time it determines what $\mathcal{F}$ would have done in one operation with this instantaneous description and pushes down the new head position, overprinted symbol and new state of $\mathcal{F}$. After this the automaton pushes down the remaining input sequence until an m marker is encountered. At this point, the automaton pops up the stack and compares symbol for symbol the stack content with the input string after the m marker. (We now see the reason for writing the second instantaneous description backwards.) If all symbols match and the input sequence terminates with $m\,m$ the sequence is accepted. If only one m marker is encountered the process is repeated until an inconsistent string is found and the input is rejected; or else a pair of m markers is found after a sequence of proper matches of instantaneous description of $\mathcal{F}$ and the input sequence is accepted.

Note that the push-down automaton which accepts L_1 is a deterministic device which stops for each input sequence and either accepts it or rejects it. Therefore we can reverse the meaning of accepting and rejecting and obtain a push-down recognizer for $\overline{L_1}$ and thus we know that this complement is also a context-free language.

The language L_2 is given by

$$L_2 = w_I m \{ w_i^T m w_j m \mid w_i \overset{\mathcal{F}}{\rightarrow} w_j \} *w_s^T m\,m,$$

where w_I is an instantaneous description of a starting configuration and w_s is an instantaneous description of a stopping configuration. In some applications we will consider only the blank tape as a starting configuration, $w_I = -s_0-$, which we will indicate by writing L_2' and correspondingly

$$\overline{L_1 \cap L_2'} = L'(G_{\mathcal{F}}).$$

By a push-down automaton argument or explicitly writing out the grammars for L_2 and $\bar{L}_2$ we can show that they are again context-free languages.

Now observe that a sequence

$$w_1 \, m \, w_2^T \, m \, w_3 \, m \, w_4^T \, m \, \cdots \, m \, w_{2k}^T \, m \, m$$

is in L_1 if and only if

$$w_1 \stackrel{\mathscr{T}}{\to} w_2, w_3 \stackrel{\mathscr{T}}{\to} w_4, \cdots, w_{2k-1} \stackrel{\mathscr{T}}{\to} w_{2k},$$

and that this sequence is in L_2 if and only if

$$w_1 = w_I, w_2 \stackrel{\mathscr{T}}{\to} w_3, w_4 \stackrel{\mathscr{T}}{\to} w_5, \cdots, w_{2k-2} \stackrel{\mathscr{T}}{\to} w_{2k-1}, w_{2k} = w_s.$$

Therefore this sequence is in

$$L_1 \cap L_2$$

if and only if it is an alternating description of a computation of $\mathscr{T}$. Thus

$$W = L_1 \cap L_2.$$

To show that for some context-free grammar $G_{\mathscr{T}}$ we have

$$L(G_{\mathscr{T}}) = \bar{W}$$

we recall that

$$\bar{W} = \overline{L_1 \cap L_2} = \bar{L}_1 \cup \bar{L}_2.$$

Since $\bar{L}_1$ and $\bar{L}_2$ are context-free languages, we have by Lemma 1 our desired result. This completes the proof.

Some applications. We now proceed to derive several applications from our main result. First of all we show that the complements of context-free languages are more complicated than the languages themselves.

We recall that there is an effective procedure to decide for every given context-free grammar G and string w whether

$$w \text{ is in } L(G).$$

Thus the context-free languages are recursive sets and therefore also their complements are recursive sets. At the same time the prefixes of the languages behave quite differently from the prefixes of their complements. From Lemma 3 we know that the set of prefixes of L also forms a recursive set. On the other hand this is not the case for some complements and intersections of context-free languages.

COROLLARY. *There exists a context-free grammar G such that there is no algorithm to decide (for all w) whether there is a sequence in $\overline{L(G)}$ which starts with w.*

PROOF. We know that there is a Turing machine $\mathcal{T}$ for which the stopping rule is undecidable. Construct $L(G_{\mathcal{T}})$. Then there is a sequence in $\overline{L(G_{\mathcal{T}})}$ which starts with $-s_0 w-$ if and only if $\mathcal{T}$ stops for input w. Since the stopping of $\mathcal{T}$ is an undecidable problem the prefix problem for $\overline{L(G_{\mathcal{T}})}$ is also undecidable, as was to be shown.

From this corollary we see that there exist complements and intersections (since $\overline{L(G_{\mathcal{T}})} = L_1 \cap L_2$) of context-free languages which are not context-free. Thus we have a new proof of a well-known result about languages:

COROLLARY. *The set of context-free languages is not closed under complementation and intersection.*

The first corollary can be restated to emphasize the properties of its prefixes.

COROLLARY. *There exists a context-free language L such that the set of prefixes of $\overline{L}$,*

$$\mathcal{P} = \{w \mid \exists x \ni wx \text{ in } \overline{L}\},$$

is recursively enumerable but not recursive.

Next we derive from our theorem a number of other known results about context-free languages.

COROLLARY. *There is no algorithm for the following problems about context-free language:*
(1) *Is $\overline{L}_1$ (or $L \cap L'$) empty?*
(2) *Is $L = L'$?*
(3) *Is $L \subseteq L'$?*
(4) *Is $\overline{L}$ (or $L \cap L'$) finite?*
(5) *Is $\overline{L}$ (or $L \cap L'$) regular?*
(6) *Is $\overline{L}$ (or $L \cap L'$) a context-free language?*
(7) *Is the set of prefixes of $\overline{L}$ (or $L \cap L'$) recursive?*

PROOF. (1) We first recall that L_2' admits only the blank tape as a starting configuration and therefore

$$L_1 \cap L_2' = \overline{L'(G_{\mathcal{T}})}$$

is empty if and only if $\mathcal{T}$ does not stop when started on the blank tape. Since the stopping rule is an undecidable problem we conclude that (1) is undecidable.

(2) To show that (2) is undecidable let

$$L' = T^*$$

and

$$L = L'(G_{\mathcal{T}}).$$

Then

$$L = L'$$

if and only if $\mathcal{T}$ does not stop. Thus (2) is again an undecidable problem.

(3) The undecidability of (3) follows from (2).

(4) The set

$$\overline{L(G_{\mathcal{T}})} = L_1 \cap L_2$$

is finite if and only if $\mathcal{T}$ stops only for a finite number of input sequences. This is again an undecidable problem and therefore (4) is undecidable.

(5) We show that it is undecidable whether $L \cap L'$ is a regular set. We recall that

$$Q = \{a^n b^n \,|\, n = 1, 2, \cdots \}$$

is a nonregular context-free language. Choose

$$L = QL_1 \quad \text{and} \quad L' = QL_2'.$$

Then

$$L \cap L' = Q(L_1 \cap L_2') = \emptyset$$

if and only if $\mathcal{T}$ does not stop. Otherwise

$$L \cap L' = Qw,$$

where w is a finite string. Since $\emptyset$ is regular and Qw is not (5) is an undecidable problem.

(6) This problem can again be reduced to the undecidability of the stopping problem.

(7) Since it is undecidable whether $\mathcal{T}$ stops for a recursive set of sequences we conclude that (7) is an undecidable problem.

Next, we show that the problem of ambiguity for grammars is also undecidable. We recall that a grammar G is *ambiguous* if and only if there exists a w in $L(G)$ which has two different *derivations* or *structural descriptions* (i.e., there are two different derivation trees for w).

COROLLARY. *There is no algorithm for deciding if a context-free grammar is ambiguous.*

PROOF. Consider L_1 and L_2 (constructed in the proof of our theorem). Since these languages are recognized by deterministic push-down machines they each have unambiguous grammars [8]. Let these grammars be

$$G_1 = \langle T, N_1, S_1, P_1 \rangle \quad \text{and} \quad G_2 = \langle T, N_2, S_2, P_2 \rangle,$$

and choose $N_1 \cap N_2 = \emptyset$. A grammar G for the language $L_1 \cup L_2$ is given by

$$G = \langle T, N_1 \cup N_2 \cup \{S\}, S, P_1 \cup P_2 \cup \{S \to S_1, S \to S_2\} \rangle.$$

Then some w in $L(G)$ has two different derivations if and only if $L_1 \cap L_2$ is not empty, but this is an undecidable problem. Thus the ambiguity of grammars cannot be recursively decided.

This result can be easily extended to show, for example, that there is no algorithm to decide whether the set of ambiguous strings in $L(G)$ is finite, regular or context-free.

Quotients of context-free languages. In this section we show that with a slight modification of our languages we can show that every recursively enumerable set can be represented as a quotient of two context-free languages. (This result has been obtained independently by D. Knuth of the California Institute of Technology.)

The *quotient* of two sets of sequences X and Y is given by

$$X/Y = \{z| \exists y \ \text{in} \ Y \ni zy \ \text{in} \ X\}.$$

THEOREM. *For every recursively enumerable set E there exist two context-free languages L_E and L'_E such that*

$$E = L_E/L'_E.$$

PROOF. First we recall that E can be represented as a set of sequences for which some Turing machine $\mathscr{T}$ stops.

To construct L_E and L'_E let $\#$ be a new symbol and let

$$L_E = x \ \# \ (-s_0 x-)^T m \ \{w_i \, m \, w_j^T m| \ w_i \xrightarrow{\mathscr{T}} w_j\}^*$$

and

$$L'_E = \# \ \{w_p^T m \, w_q \, m| \ w_p \xrightarrow{\mathscr{T}} w_q\}^* w_s^T.$$

Then clearly

$$L_E/L'_E = \{x| \ \mathscr{T} \ \text{stops for input} \ x\} = E,$$

as was to be shown.

This result can be used to show that "nothing" can be algorithmically decided about quotients of context-free languages.

COROLLARY. *Let $\mathscr{P}$ be a property which is possessed by some but not all recursively enumerable sets. Then there is no algorithm to decide whether the quotient of two context-free languages has property $\mathscr{P}$.*

PROOF. This is just a restatement of the corresponding (and easily proven) result for recursively enumerable sets.

REFERENCES

1. N. Chomsky, "Formal properties of grammars" in *Handbook of mathematical psychology*, Vol. II, Chapter 12, Wiley, New York, 1963.

2. J. Hartmanis, P. M. Lewis and R. E. Stearns, *Classification of computations by time and memory requirements*, Proc. IFIP Congr. Vol. I, Spartan Books, Washington, D.C., 1965.

3. P. M. Lewis, R. E. Stearns and J. Hartmanis, *Memory bounds for recognition of context-free and context-sensitive languages*, Proc. Sixth Annual Sympos. on Switching Circuit Theory and Logical Design, IEEE, New York, 1965, pp. 191-202.

4. Y. Bar-Hillel, M. Perles and E. Shamir, *On formal properties of simple phrase structure grammars*, Z. Phonetik Sprachwiss. Kommunikat. **14** (1961), 143-172.

5. S. Ginsburg, *The mathematical theory of context-free languages*, McGraw-Hill, New York, 1966.

6. E. Post, *A variant of a recursively unsolvable problem*, Bull. Amer. Math. Soc. **52** (1946), 262-268.

7. R. W. Floyd, *New proofs of old theorems in logic and formal linguistics*, Research Paper C.A.-6505-1411, Computer Associates, Inc., 1965.

8. S. Ginsburg and S. Greibach, *Deterministic context-free languages*, Proc. Sixth Annual Sympos. on Switching Circuit Theory and Logical Design, IEEE, New York, 1965, pp. 203-220.

CORNELL UNIVERSITY
ITHACA, NEW YORK

Susumu Kuno

COMPUTER ANALYSIS
OF NATURAL LANGUAGES[1]

Computational linguistics encompasses a study of linguistic problems using computers, and the application of linguistics to computer problems (Oettinger [40]). This paper is intended as a survey of certain aspects of the field.

1. **Study of linguistic problems using computers.** The aspects of languages which have been studied with the use of computers can be classified into two major categories according to the types of mathematics used: statistics versus logic or discrete mathematics. Statistical studies are concerned with such problems as compilation of concordances of natural language corpora, frequency distribution of phonemes, words, etc., statistics of style and the identification of authorship, quantitative study of generic relationships of languages, and "time-depth" computations of lexico-statistics. Surveys and bibliographies concentrating on these areas are found in Guiraud [23], Plath [43], and Oettinger [38]. More recent work in the field of literary data processing is found in Bessinger et al. [3].

Nonstatistical studies, which are by far the more prevalent and interesting of the two categories, are concerned with the syntax and semantics of natural languages. Syntactic descriptions of languages have been heavily dependent upon models of grammar which are called *rewriting systems*, and upon new grammatical models called *transformational grammars*. Semantic analysis is still in its infancy, and awaits future theoretical investigations.

1.1. *Rewriting Systems.* A rewriting system consists of a finite vocabulary V and a finite set P of rewriting rules (or productions). The vocabulary V

---

[1] This work has been supported in part by the National Science Foundation under grant GN-329, and by the Division of Engineering and Applied Physics and the Department of Linguistics, Harvard University. The author is greatly indebted to several of his colleagues and students, especially S. Nathanson, G. Carden, G. Lakoff, and S. Greibach, who have read draft versions of the paper and contributed to the accuracy and clarity of the exposition.

is divided into the terminal vocabulary V_T and nonterminal vocabulary V_N ($V_T \cup V_N = V$, $V_T \cap V_N = \emptyset$). Rewriting rules are of the form

$$\alpha \gamma \beta \rightarrow \alpha \omega \beta$$

where α, β, γ, ω are strings on V, possibly null, except for γ, which cannot be null. Rewriting systems of this type are known to have the same generative power as Turing machines. It is also known that the question of whether or not a given string can be generated by an arbitrary rewriting system is undecidable.

Figure 1 shows the restricted rewriting systems in order of decreasing generality:

Name	Restrictions	Equivalent Machine
Context-Sensitive Grammar with Erasing	$\alpha A \beta \rightarrow \alpha \omega \beta$, $A \in V_N$; α, β, ω are strings on V, possibly null	Turing Machine
Context-Sensitive Grammar without Erasing	$\alpha A \beta \rightarrow \alpha \omega \beta$, ω cannot be null	Linear Bounded Automaton
Context-Free Grammar	$A \rightarrow \omega$	Pushdown Store Machine
Finite-State Grammar	$A \rightarrow a$, $a \in V_T$, $B \in V_N$ $A \rightarrow aB$	Finite State Machine

FIGURE 1. Restricted Rewriting Systems

Finite state grammars are the most restricted grammars in the hierarchy of rewriting systems so far studied that are capable of generating an infinite number of strings by a finite set of rewriting rules.[2] However, they cannot account for an infinite depth of embeddings, and are quite inadequate for the description of natural languages, which display unbounded depth of embedded structures. Context-free grammars and context-sensitive grammars are called *phrase structure grammars*, and

---

[2] One could define a more restricted rewriting system whose rules are all of the form $A \rightarrow a$. Such a grammar is essentially a list (or dictionary) of all terminal strings allowable in the language. Since natural languages are infinite sets of terminal strings, consideration of such a grammar is immediately eliminated.

have been the underlying model for linguistic description predominant in American descriptive linguistics in the 1940's and 1950's.

Several technical terms relevant to phrase structure grammars should be introduced at this point. When a rewriting rule $\alpha A\beta \rightarrow \alpha\gamma\beta$ is applied to a given string $\omega_1\alpha A\beta\omega_2$, a new string $\omega_1\alpha\gamma\beta\omega_2$ is obtained. We use the notational convention $\omega_1\alpha A\beta\omega_2 \Rightarrow \omega_1\alpha\gamma\beta\omega_2$ to represent this relation that holds between the two strings. We use the notation $\phi \overset{*}{\Rightarrow} \psi$ if, given a phrase structure grammar, there is a sequence of strings $\phi_0, \phi_1, \cdots, \phi_n$ such that $\phi = \phi_0$, $\phi_0 \Rightarrow \phi_1$, $\phi_1 \Rightarrow \phi_2, \cdots, \phi_{n-1} \Rightarrow \phi_n$, $\phi_n \Rightarrow \psi$. In such a case, we say that $\phi_0, \phi_1, \cdots, \phi_n$ is a ϕ-*derivation* of ψ. Where ψ is a string of terminal symbols, we say that a ϕ-derivation of ψ is *terminated*. We say that ψ is a *terminal string* (*sentence*) if there is a terminated X-derivation of ψ where X is the designated initial symbol of the grammar. Assume that we have a context-free grammar $G1$ which contains the following set of rewriting rules:

(1) $X \rightarrow a$
(2) $X \rightarrow YX$
(3) $Y \rightarrow YZ$
(4) $Y \rightarrow b$
(5) $Z \rightarrow c$

"*bca*" is a terminal string with respect to $G1$ since we have a terminated X-derivation of "*bca*":

X
YX
YZX
bZX
bcX
bca

The derivation of a terminal string in a given grammar can be represented by a tree called a *phrase-marker* or *structural description*. The phrase-marker of Figure 2 represents the X-derivation of "*bca*" in $G1$ shown above.

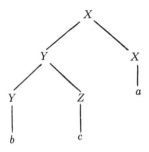

FIGURE 2. Phrase-Marker

Given a grammar, *recognition* of a string is a problem of assigning a phrase-marker to the string if there is an X-derivation of the string in the grammar.

A variety of recognition procedures have been proposed and programmed for the recognition of sentences of context-free languages. Most of the presently operating systems of automatic syntactic analysis for natural languages are based on context-free models. Grammars for most of the current syntax-directed compilers are also context-free. No efficient recognition procedures have been proposed thus far for context-sensitive grammars (Griffiths [19]). Surveys and bibliographies on rewriting systems are found in Chomsky and Miller [12], Chomsky [10], and Oettinger [41]. A survey of various phrase structure models for linguistic description is found in Postal [44].

1.2. *Automatic Syntactic Analysis of Context-Free Languages.* Surveys of phrase structure models for automatic syntactic analysis of natural languages by computer are given by Bobrow [5] and Gross [22]. Relative efficiency of context-free grammar recognizers is discussed in Griffiths and Petrick [20]. In fact, the field is flooded with context-free grammar recognizers of various kinds, each of which has its own advantages and drawbacks. Three such algorithms are described below for comparison.

The Predictive Analyzer (PA) and the Immediate Constituent Analyzer (ICA) have been chosen because they are the types of automatic syntactic analyzer which have actually been used for natural languages. The Selective Top-to-Bottom Algorithm (STBA), familiar from syntax directed compilers, is presented for comparison purposes.

1.2.1. *The Predictive Analyzer (PA).* A predictive analyzer (Kuno and Oettinger [32], [33], Kuno [29]) produces, for a given sentence, all possible syntactic interpretations compatible with its standard-form grammar G_s. The rules of a standard-form grammar are of the form:

$$Z \rightarrow c\,Y_1 \cdots Y_m, \quad m \geqq 0$$

where Z, Y_i are nonterminal symbols, and c is a terminal symbol. Analysis of an input string $c_1 \cdots c_n$ $(c_i \in V_T)$ is initiated with a pushdown store (PDS) containing the initial symbol X $(X \in V_N)$. At c_k in the course of the analysis of the string, assume Z_k is the nonterminal symbol topmost in the PDS. If a rule $Z_k \rightarrow c_k W_1 \cdots W_m$ $(m \geqq 0)$ is found in the grammar, we say that Z_k has been fulfilled by c_k. The Z_k in the PDS then is replaced by the sequence of new nonterminal symbols $W_1 \cdots W_m$ (possibly null) with W_m at the bottom. The input string is well-formed if processing the last terminal symbol yields an empty PDS. On the other hand, if a rule with the current nonterminal symbol Z_k and the current terminal symbol

c_k is not found in the grammar, the analysis path backs up to the immediately preceding branching point at c_{k-1}: the PDS configuration at c_{k-1} is reconstructed, and the next alternative path is traversed. The cycling mechanism which controls the exhaustive processing of all analysis paths for a given input string is explained in detail in Kuno [29].

Figure 3 shows the analysis paths followed for the processing of a terminal string "*bca*" with the standard-form grammar $G1_s$.[3] ☐ is a PDS. Quotation marks enclose a string of terminal symbols remaining to be processed. The number of each rule used for the processing of the topmost symbol A of $\boxed{A\,|\,\gamma}$ with the leftmost symbol c of "*cβ*" is shown next to the appropriate branch from $\boxed{A\,|\,\gamma}$ "*cβ*". * indicates a path which has come to an impasse because of the absence of a rule in the grammar of the form $A \rightarrow cB_1 \cdots B_m$. "Λ" is the null string. A path starting at $\boxed{X}$ "*ω*" and terminating at $\boxed{\Lambda}$ "Λ" shows an analysis of the input string "*ω*".

$G1_s$: (1) $X \rightarrow a$
       (2) $X \rightarrow bX$
       (3) $X \rightarrow bWX$
       (4) $W \rightarrow c$
       (5) $W \rightarrow cW$

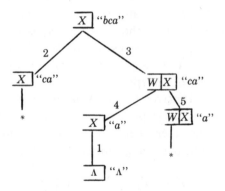

FIGURE 3. Analysis Paths of the Predictive Analyzer

Several additional techniques increase the efficiency of the working model. For example, the "Shaper" test rejects at once any path where the number of nonterminal symbols in the PDS is greater than the number of terminal symbols remaining to be processed. Such a path cannot lead to a successful analysis because the grammar on which the Predictive Analyzer is based does not allow erasing. The "well-formed string identifier" records

---

[3] This grammar $G1_s$, and the grammar $G1$ which generates the same language, will be used throughout this paper as examples.

well-formed substrings as they are identified in the course of analysis, and prevents the analyzer from processing these substrings twice.

The current version of the Predictive Analyzer, operational at Harvard on an IBM 7094, consists of an English grammar with approximately 3,500 standard-form rules and a dictionary with approximately 25,000 inflected word forms; and can process an ordinary 70-word sentence within a minute. There are many structures which it cannot analyze at the moment, or to which it assigns structural descriptions, correct with respect to the grammar used, but incorrect with respect to what we know about English. This is due to the inadequacy of phrase structure grammars for linguistic analysis which will be discussed in §1.3. One example of its inadequacy is the following. The current version of the analyzer produces four analyses for "Time flies like an arrow.": (1) time passes as quickly as an arrow flies; (2) you should time (the) flies as quickly as an arrow times the flies; (3) you should time (the) flies which are similar to an arrow; (4) there is a species of flies called "time flies" which are fond of an arrow. However, the Predictive Analyzer is adequate for certain limited purposes when no sophisticated analysis is required. It is a practical tool since it can process a large corpus very efficiently and since no system which provides us with more sophisticated analysis is now in operation.

One area in the real world where context-free analysis can be of some use is in the *detection* of certain types of ambiguities, rather than the complete analysis of sentences.

Langevin and Owens [35], [36] have used the Predictive Analyzer to detect ambiguities in sentences of the U.S. Constitution and the Nuclear Test Ban Treaty. In such an experiment, a syntactic analyzer assigns to a given sentence all possible syntactic analyses compatible with the grammar, out of which a user has to choose those which are semantically plausible. It is too much to expect the analyzer to explain such concepts as the objective of a law or the sovereignity of a federal power. However, ambiguities such as whether "The Congress shall have Power to lay and collect Taxes, Duties, Imposts and Excises, to pay the Debts and provide for the common Defense and general Welfare to the United States."[4] means "The Congress shall have power to provide for the common defense ⋯," "The Congress shall have power to lay and collect taxes, duties, ⋯, in order to pay the debts and in order to provide for the common defense, ⋯" or "The Congress shall provide for the common defense ⋯" could be detected by a syntactic analyzer. This technique could be refined to provide legislators with a practical detector for sentence structure ambiguities.

---

[4] Section 8, Article 1, The U.S. Constitution.

Recent research on the nature of the Predictive Analyzer has shown that it could, with some modifications, be turned into a general recognition system for arbitrary context-free languages. Two problems prevented us from making this claim earlier. First, although Greibach [16], [17], [18] had shown by construction that, for any given context-free grammar, there is a standard-form grammar which accepts the same language, her algorithm, which depends upon the use of finite-state graphs and regular expressions, could not be programmed. Secondly, the structural descriptions $SD(G_s, \omega)$ assigned to an accepted sentence ω by a standard-form grammar G_s are almost without exception radically different from the structural descriptions $SD(G, \omega)$ assigned to the same sentence by the original context-free grammar G. Compare, for example, the structural descriptions shown in Figure 4.

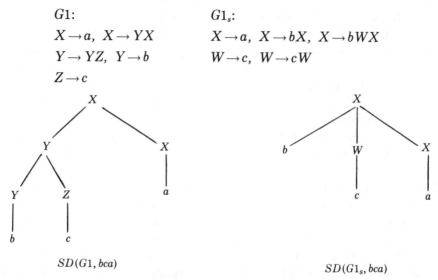

$G1$:

$X \rightarrow a, \; X \rightarrow YX$

$Y \rightarrow YZ, \; Y \rightarrow b$

$Z \rightarrow c$

$G1_s$:

$X \rightarrow a, \; X \rightarrow bX, \; X \rightarrow bWX$

$W \rightarrow c, \; W \rightarrow cW$

$SD(G1, bca)$

$SD(G1_s, bca)$

FIGURE 4. Comparison of Structural Descriptions

Both problems have been solved quite recently: details of the standardization algorithm and the structural description transformation algorithm are given in Abbott and Kuno [1] and Kuno [31]. Experimental programs for both algorithms have been written; and so we now have a system (Figure 5) for recognizing arbitrary context-free languages.

1.2.2. *The Selective Top-to-Bottom Algorithm* (*STBA*). This context-free recognition algorithm is described by Griffiths and Petrick [20] using a Turing-machine model. On the basis of the given grammar ($G1$, for example) a matrix $m(p)$ (Figure 6) is constructed: $P(x_i, y_i) = 1$ if the grammar can generate from the symbol x_i, some string whose leftmost symbol is the terminal symbol y_i; otherwise $P(x_i, y_i) = 0$. There is an algorithm for constructing the matrix for a given context-free grammar.

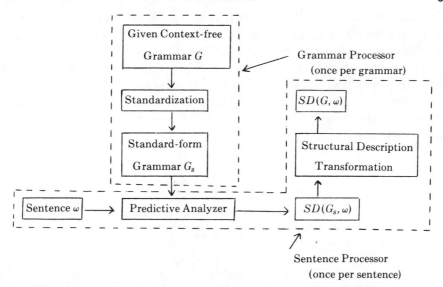

FIGURE 5. System for Recognizing Arbitrary Context-free Languages

Analysis of an input string starts with a PDS holding the initial symbol X. At a given point in the analysis of a string, the topmost symbol A_k of the PDS is checked to see whether it is terminal or nonterminal. If A_k is terminal, then it is compared with the current terminal symbol c_k of the input string. If they are equal, A_k is dropped from the PDS and the analysis proceeds to c_{k+1}. If c_k is not equal to A_k, the analysis backs up to c_{k-1} and a new path is tested.

x_i \ y_i	a	b	c
X	1	1	0
Y	0	1	0
Z	0	0	1
a	1	0	0
b	0	1	0
c	0	0	1

FIGURE 6. $P(x_i, y_i)$ for $G1$

If A_k is not terminal, the grammar is searched for a rule of the form $A_k \rightarrow W_1\gamma$. If such a rule is found, the matrix is checked to see if $P(W_1, c_k) = 1$. If so, $W_1\gamma$ of the rule replaces A_k in the PDS. The new topmost symbol of the PDS is then tested with the "current" input symbol c_k. If $P(W_1, c_k) = 0$, the grammar is searched for the next rule with generatrix A_k.[5]

If such a rule is not found, the analysis backs up to c_{k-1} as before. An analysis of the input string is complete if the PDS is empty after the last input symbol has been processed.

$$G1: \quad (1) \ X \rightarrow a$$
$$(2) \ X \rightarrow YX$$
$$(3) \ Y \rightarrow YZ$$
$$(4) \ Y \rightarrow b$$
$$(5) \ Z \rightarrow c$$

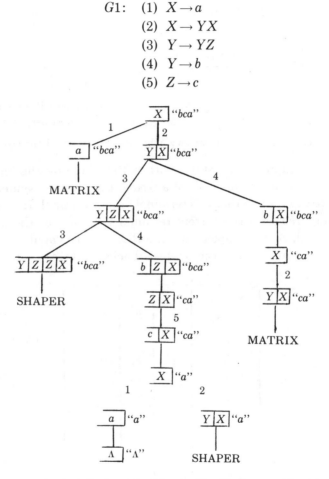

FIGURE 7. Analysis Paths of the Selective Top-To-Bottom Algorithm

---

[5] In a rule of the form $Z \rightarrow Y_1 \cdots Y_m$, where $Z \in V_N$, $Y_i \in V$, $m \geq 1$, Z is called the *generatrix*, and Y_1 the *handle* of the rule.

Figure 7 shows the paths for the analysis of "*bca*" with grammar $G1$. MATRIX and SHAPER mark those analysis paths which come to an impasse by $P(W_1, c_k) = 0$ and the Shaper test (comparison of the number of nonterminal symbols in the PDS with the number of remaining terminal symbols to be processed) respectively. The set of rules corresponding to the branches which lead to $\boxed{\Lambda}$ "Λ" configuration gives a structural description of the input terminal string. The Selective Top-to-Bottom Algorithm is essentially the one described by Irons [25]. The top-to-bottom algorithm described in Cheatham and Sattley [8] is similar to the above algorithm, but does not use the $P(x_i, y_i)$ matrix.

Note the similarity between the PA as adapted for arbitrary context-free grammars and the STBA. Compare the path in Figure 3 from $\boxed{X}$ "*bca*" to $\boxed{W|X}$ "*ca*" with the path in Figure 7 from $\boxed{X|}$ "*bca*" to $\boxed{Z|X}$ "*ca*". In the latter, three rules are applied successively to topmost symbols in the PDS in order to obtain the terminal symbol "*b*" as the topmost symbol. This process, however, is exactly what is followed in the standardization of a given context-free grammar to a corresponding standard-form grammar. In the PA, the standardization is made only once for each grammar. In the STBA, it is performed locally; that is, each time a given input string is analyzed, the standardization of the grammar is performed for each analysis path: therefore, the PA is more efficient than the STBA in processing time. Note, however, that the PA requires more mechanisms: the standardization algorithm (part of which should be in the STBA) and the structural description transformation.

1.2.3. *The Immediate Constituent Analyzer* (*ICA*). The Immediate Constituent Analyzer is a parsing algorithm of arbitrary context-free languages (developed at Harvard), which differs from the systems described before in that it does not use a pushdown store. The algorithm is an extension of Sakai's [49] parsing algorithm for normal grammars.[6] The Cocke-Robinson English analyzer for normal grammars (Hays [24], Robinson [46], [47]) and the Kay system [28] for arbitrary context-free grammars are based on a similar principle.

The basic flow of logic is as follows. First, the kth terminal symbol ($k = 1$ initially) of the input string is stored in d_j, where $j = 1$ initially (see Figure 8). a_j and b_j are set to k, indicating that the leftmost and the rightmost word positions of d_j are both k. c_j is set to 0, indicating that d_j is a

---

[6] A normal grammar is a context-free grammar whose rules are all of the forms: (a) $Y \rightarrow c$, or (b) $Y \rightarrow Z_1 Z_2$, where Y, Z_1, Z_2 are intermediate symbols and c a terminal symbol. See Chomsky [10], pp. 369-370.

terminal symbol and does not contain any constituents.[7] Both k and j are incremented by 1. Next, lines $m_1, m_2, \cdots, m_r$ ($0 < m_1 < m_2 < \cdots < m_r = i$; $m_1, m_2, \cdots$ do not have to be consecutive; $r > 0$, $i = 1$ initially) are checked to see if the following two conditions are satisfied:

(a)
$$b_{m_1} + 1 = a_{m_2}$$

$$\cdot$$
$$\cdot$$
$$\cdot$$

$$b_{m_{r-1}} + 1 = a_{m_r};$$

(b) there is some symbol Y such that
$$Y \rightarrow d_{m_1} d_{m_2} \cdots d_{m_r} \in P.$$

Analysis of String "bca" according to grammar $G1$

$G1$: (1) $X \rightarrow a$
       (2) $X \rightarrow YX$
       (3) $Y \rightarrow YZ$
       (4) $Y \rightarrow b$
       (5) $Z \rightarrow c$

Line Number	Constitute		Constitute Comes from Line Numbers	Rule Used	Name of Constitute
	Start at Word	End at Word			
j	a_j	b_j	c_j		d_j
1	i	i	0	–	b
2	i	i	1	4	Y
3	ii	ii	0	–	c
4	ii	ii	3	5	Z
5	i	ii	2, 4	3	Y
6	iii	iii	0	–	a
7	iii	iii	6	1	X
8	i	iii	5, 7	2	X

FIGURE 8. Work Area Layout of the Immediate Constituent Analyzer

If both conditions are satisfied, Y is stored in d_j. Also, $m_1, m_2, \cdots, m_r$ are stored in c_j; a_{m_1} and b_{m_r} in a_j and b_j respectively. j is incremented by 1,

---

[7] If $Y \rightarrow Z_1 \cdots Z_m$, then Y is a "constitute" and each Z_i is a "constituent" of Y.

and some other set of lines ending with i is checked for conditions (a) and (b). If it is found that there is no further set satisfying the conditions, i is incremented by 1. If the new value i is smaller than j, the same test on conditions (a) and (b) is repeated. On the other hand, if $i = j$, all the symbols which have previously been obtained have been exhaustively tested. Therefore k is incremented by 1, and a new terminal symbol is processed. The process terminates when k is greater than n, the number of terminal symbols in the input string. A sequence of lines which have led to line number q where $a_q = 1$, $b_q = n$, and $d_q = X$ (X is the initial symbol of the grammar) shows an analysis of the input string. In Figure 8, line number 8 satisfies this condition. The initial symbol X ($= d_8$) comes from Y ($= d_5$) and X ($= d_7$) as is indicated by c_8. Y ($= d_5$), in turn, comes from Y ($= d_2$) and Z ($= d_4$), etc. Thus we obtain the structural description of "bca" as shown in Figure 9.

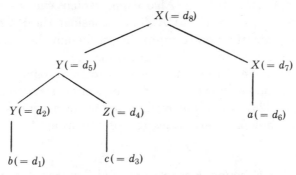

FIGURE 9. Structural Description of "bca" in $G1$

1.2.4. *Criteria for "Efficiency" of Parsing Algorithms.* After having described three recognition procedures, it is natural to raise the question: Which is the most efficient of these procedures? However, at least three factors determine the relative efficiency of parsing algorithms:

(i) core storage requirement (for grammar and work area),
(ii) complexities of the program,
(iii) processing time for sentence structure recognition.

What weight one should assign to each of these factors depends as much on the intended applications of a parsing algorithm as on the computer for which it is designed. If a parsing algorithm is to be used over and over again, with many grammars and input strings, the complexities of the algorithm and the cost of programming for it may be negligible. If an algorithm is to be used with grammars of a fairly small size, as will be the case in most syntax-directed compilers, the expansion of the size of grammars due to standardization for the predictive analyzer may be of negligible importance. On the other hand, the expansion may be crucial, as when a given grammar fits the core of a given computer while its corresponding standard-form grammar does not. Again, in the case of syntax-directed compilers, the time needed for the parsing of a given statement may be of negligible importance if the emphasis is on obtaining optimal machine code from structural description; or it may be crucial if the compiler is to be used for compiling a large number of rather short programs for students in a programming course, where the compilation time is a decisive factor and the compiled programs may be used only once to test them.

Griffiths and Petrick [20] have made a comparison of processing-time efficiencies of various context-free recognition procedures each modeled on a Turing machine. For a few test grammars, the number of instructions required in the analysis of test sentences by each recognition procedure was compared with the number required for the others. They empirically found their STBA described in this paper to be much less efficient than their Selective Bottom-to-Top Algorithm, which can be likened to a Turing-machine version of the ICA. They consider the PA with the well-formed substring identifier quite promising, although they did not program a Turing-machine version of this algorithm.

Another way of measuring the efficiency of a recognition procedure is to find upper bounds of processing time for sentence recognition. A recent study by Kasami [26] shows that recognition of an n-word sentence with a standard-form grammar whose rules are of the form

$$Z \rightarrow c Y_1 \cdots Y_m$$

where $0 \leq m \leq 2$ is n^3 bound. Kasami's recognition procedure is considerably different from that of the PA. Younger [55] has independently shown that, for a normal grammar (see §1.2.3) whose rules are of the form $Y \rightarrow c$ or $Y \rightarrow Z_1 Z_2 (c \in V_T; Y, Z_1, Z_2 \in V_N)$, the processing time also increases at worst as n^3 with the recognition algorithm very similar to our ICA. These two results are significant because both our PA in its present form, and the models of context-free recognition described in Griffiths and Petrick have the feature that the processing time can increase exponentially with n in the worst cases.[8] Our latest study shows that, with the use of a standard-m form grammar, where m is the maximum number of nonterminal symbols to the right of the arrow in a rule, and with the use of a right-to-left analysis procedure instead of the left-to-right procedure of the current PA, the processing time is bounded by n^{m+1} (if $m = 2$, the upperbound is n^3, and thus agrees with Kasami's result).

1.3. *Transformational Grammars.* The past ten years have seen a rapid development of a new theory of grammar called transformational grammar.

---

[8] I am indebted to Kasami, Petrick and Griffiths for drawing my attention to the above-mentioned results on the upperbound of recognition time.

Its prototype model, described by Chomsky [9], has undergone constant revisions. I shall attempt below to describe the mechanisms[9] of the current version of transformational grammar characterized by Chomsky's *Aspects of the theory of syntax* [11]. References to literature in the field and detailed discussions on the linguistic motivations for utilizing the proposed mechanisms are found in Chomsky [11]. This model is by no means the final one. Some revisions to it have already been proposed: for example, see Lakoff [34].

1.3.1. *The Organization of a Generative Grammar.* The central role of a transformational grammar is to assign two structures to each sentence it generates: one a *deep structure*, the other a *surface structure*. The deep structure of a sentence determines the semantic interpretation, and the surface structure the phonetic representation of the sentence. For example, the grammar should assign to "John is easy to please" a deep structure which explicitly indicates that "John" is the object of the verb "please," that the subject of "please" is an unspecified person "someone," and that the subject of "is easy" is not "John," but "for someone to please John." The deep structure of the sentence is shown informally in Figure 10. The same deep structure will be assigned to "It is easy to please John," and "To please John is easy," which should receive the same semantic interpretation as "John is easy to please."

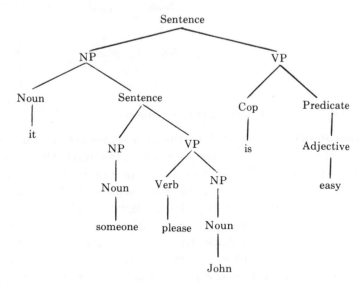

FIGURE 10. Deep Structure (1)

─────────────

[9] Chomsky [11] gives alternative proposals at various places through his discussions of the mechanisms for transformational grammars. I have chosen a model which is slightly different from any of Chomsky's for simplicity of exposition.

The grammar should assign to "John is eager to please" the deep structure, shown in Figure 11, which indicates that "John" is the subject of "please," that the object of "please" is an unspecified person "someone," and that "John" is also the subject of "is eager."

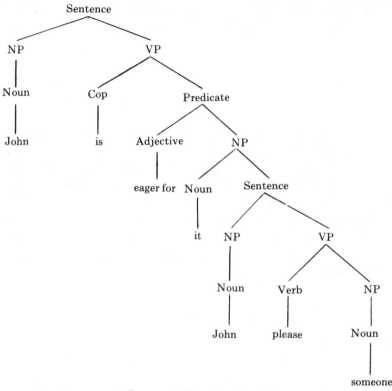

FIGURE 11. Deep Structure (2)

The surface structures assigned to the two sentences by the grammar should be similar: phonetically, the two sentences have the same stress and intonation patterns. The phrase-marker of Figure 12, in fact, is of the type which a phrase structure grammar discussed in §1.2 would assign to the two sentences under discussion. In the light of this observation, one can characterize a phrase structure grammar of a natural language as a grammar which assigns only surface structures to sentences of the language. Drawbacks of a phrase structure grammar for linguistic description should be obvious upon inspection of the phrase-marker of Figure 12. The fact that "John" is the "subject" of "is easy" in the surface structure is totally irrelevant to the semantic interpretation of the sentences.[10]

---

[10] See §2.1 for the need of deep structures in applications such as question-answering.

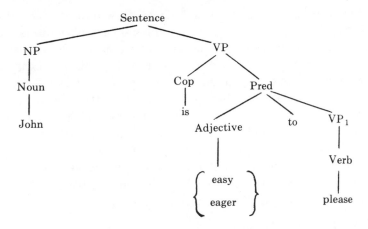

FIGURE 12. Surface Structure

A transformational grammar consists of three components: a *base component*, a *transformational component*, and a *phonological component*. The base component generates a set of *terminal strings*, each with an associated structural description called a *generalized phrase-marker* of the type shown in Figures 10 and 11. The transformational component is a set of rules which map phrase-markers into phrase-markers. It accepts as input the generalized phrase-marker of Figure 10, for example, and outputs the *derived* phrase-marker of Figure 12 by successive applications of transformations. The phonological component accepts as input a derived phrase-marker, and produces a phonetic representation of the sentence.[11] Mechanisms used in the first two components of the transformational grammar are described below.

1.3.2. *The Base Component.* The base component of a transformational grammar consists of two subcomponents: a set of rules and rule schemata and a lexicon. I shall borrow from Chomsky's *Aspects* an illustrative fragment of the base component of a transformational grammar for English (Chomsky [**11**], pp. 106-107)[12] with some modifications (see Figures 13(a) and 13(b)).

Three types of symbols are used in Figure 13(a): *categorial symbols, complex symbols CS,* and *syntactic features.* Categorial symbols are non-

---

[11] Since the present paper is concerned mainly with problems of syntax and semantics, I shall not discuss the mechanisms utilized in the phonological component, which opens a wide area of studies that canno' e surveyed here.

[12] Parentheses are used for optional symbols, and braces for alternative rewriting of symbols. For example, $A \to B(C)$ stands for two rules: $A \to B$ and $A \to BC$; $A \to \{{B \atop C}\}$ for two rules: $A \to B$, $A \to C$. $[+A] \to [\pm B]$ stands for $[+A] \to [+B]$ and $[+A] \to [-B]$.

terminal symbols of rewriting rules such as S (sentence), NP, Predicate-Phrase. Categorial symbols such as V, N, which, in ordinary phrase structure grammar, would be replaced by lexical forms as in $N \rightarrow sincerity$, boy, $V \rightarrow frighten$ are called *lexical symbols*. A lexical symbol is expanded into a complex symbol which is an unordered set of positively or negatively specified syntactic features that subcategorizes the lexical symbol. A complex symbol is replaced by an entry in the lexicon. For example, if the complex symbol corresponding to an N has the features [+ Count] and [+ Animate], only Countable Animate Nouns (such as "boy," "dog") can replace the N. On the other hand, if the complex symbol has the features [− Count] and [+ Abstract], only Noncountable Abstract Nouns (such as "sincerity," "democracy") can replace the N.

1. $S \rightarrow$ (Q) NP Predicate-Phrase
2. Predicate-Phrase $\rightarrow$ Aux VP (Place) (Time)
3.

$$VP \rightarrow \left\{ \begin{array}{l} \text{Copula Predicate} \\ V \left\{ \begin{array}{l} \text{(NP) (Prep-Phrase) (Prep-Phrase) (Manner)} \\ \# \text{ S } \# \\ \text{Predicate} \end{array} \right\} \end{array} \right\}$$

4. Predicate $\rightarrow \left\{ \begin{array}{l} \text{Adjective} \\ (like) \text{ NP} \end{array} \right\}$

5. Prep-Phrase $\rightarrow$ Direction, Duration, Place, Frequency, etc.
5a. Manner $\rightarrow$ by passive
6. $V \rightarrow CS$
7. $NP \rightarrow$ (Det) N (# S #)
8. $N \rightarrow CS$
9.   [+ Det−] $\rightarrow$ [± Count]
10. [+ Count] $\rightarrow$ [± Animate]
11. [+ N, +−] $\rightarrow$ [± Animate]
12. [+ Animate] $\rightarrow$ [± Human]
13. [− Count] $\rightarrow$ [± Abstract]
14. [+ V] $\rightarrow CS/$[+ N] $\cdots - (\cdots$ [+ N])
15. Adjective $\rightarrow CS/$[+ N] $\cdots -$
16. Aux $\rightarrow$ Tense (M) (Aspect)
16a. M $\rightarrow CS$
16b. Tense $\rightarrow$ present, past
16c. Aspect $\rightarrow$ (have en) (be ing)
17. Det $\rightarrow$ (pre-Article of) Article (post-Article)
18. Article $\rightarrow$ [± Definite]

FIGURE 13(a). Rules and Rule Schemata
(An Illustrative Fragment of the Base Component)

(*sincerity*, [+ N, + Det−, − Count, + Abstract, ⋯])
(*boy*, [+ N, + Det−, + Count, + Animate, + Human, ⋯])
(*frighten*, [+ V, +−NP, + [+ Abstract]−[+ Animate], + Object-deletion, ⋯])
(*may*, [+ M, ⋯])

FIGURE 13(b). Lexicon (An Illustrative Fragment of the Base Component)

There are two types of rules and rule schemata in Figure 13: *branching rules*, such as Rules 1-5, 7, 16, 17 and *subcategorization rules*, such as Rules 6, 8-15, 16a, 18. A branching rule replaces a categorial symbol by a sequence of categorial symbols. A subcategorization rule either replaces a lexical symbol by a complex symbol, or adds one or more specified new syntactic features to a complex symbol.

1.3.2.1. *Branching Rules in the Base Component.* Branching rules in the base component are phrase structure rules. Notice that all the branching rules in Figure 13 are context-free.

1.3.2.2. *Subcategorization Rules in the Base Component.* There are two types of subcategorization rules: context-free and context-sensitive. The former type (Rules 9-13, 18) adds a new syntactic feature to a complex symbol of a lexical symbol. For example, if the lexical symbol N has associated with it a complex symbol which contains $[-\text{Count}]$, the application of Rule 13 to this complex symbol yields a new complex symbol which has an additional syntactic feature $[+\text{Abstract}]$ or $[-\text{Abstract}]$.

There are two types of context-sensitive subcategorization rules: the first type (called *strict subcategorization rules*, e.g., Rules 6, 8) subcategorizes a lexical symbol in terms of the frame of categorial symbols in which it appears, e.g., $[+\text{Det}—]$, $[+—\text{NP}]$; the second type (called *selectional rules,* e.g., Rules 14, 15) subcategorizes the complex symbol of a lexical symbol in terms of syntactic features that appear in specified positions in the sentence, e.g., $[+[+\text{Count}]—[+\text{Abstract}]]$.

Now, assume that we have obtained a phrase-marker[13] shown in Figure 14 by the application of Rules 1, 2 and 3 to the initial string $\# S \#$. Next,

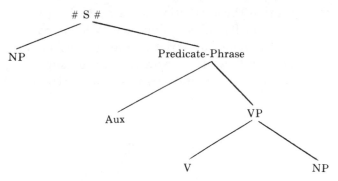

FIGURE 14. Branching Rules (1).

Rule schema 6 ($V \rightarrow CS$) is applied to V of Figure 14. $A \rightarrow CS$ is the nota-

---

[13] In the following discussions on the base component, I shall show how the phrase-marker underlying the sentence "Sincerity may frighten John" is generated. This is why Rule 4 is used as VP → V̂ NP, and not in any other possible form (for example, VP → Copula Predicate).

tion for an abbreviation of

$$A \rightarrow [+A, +Z-Y]/Z-Y$$

where A is a lexical symbol, and ZAY is immediately dominated by some categorial symbol B (i.e., the base component has a branching rule $B \rightarrow ZAY$ which has been applied to yield the current phrase-marker). Since $Z = \Lambda$ and $Y = NP$ in Figure 14, the application of Rule schema 6 to V yields the phrase-marker shown in Figure 15.

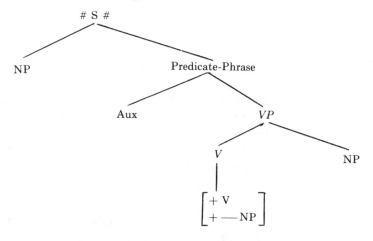

FIGURE 15. Strict Subcategorization Rule (1).

Note that $[+V]$, $[+-NP]$ for V indicates that a lexical entry which eventually replaces the complex symbol must have syntactic features $[+V]$ and $[+-NP]$. Note that the syntactic feature $[+-NP]$ represents a sub-category of verbs traditionally called "Transitive Verbs." Syntactic features of the form $[+X-Y]$ assigned by strict subcategorization rules are called *strict subcategorization features*. In contrast, features such as $[+\text{Count}]$, $[-\text{Animate}]$ introduced by context-free subcategorization rules, and

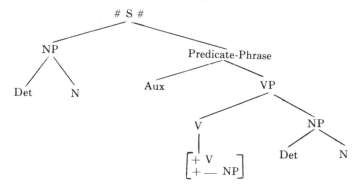

FIGURE 16. Branching Rule (2).

features $[+ \text{V}]$, $[+ \text{N}]$, etc. due to lexical symbols, are called *inherent features*.

Rule 7 is now applied to two *NP*'s in Figure 15, yielding the tree of Figure 16.

Rule schema 8 (strict subcategorization rule) is applied to *N*'s in Figure 16. $Z = \text{Det}$, and $Y = \Lambda$ for both *N*'s; therefore, the phrase-marker of Figure 17 is obtained. Note that the syntactic feature $[+ \text{Det}-]$ represents a subcategory of nouns traditionally called "Common Nouns," that is, nouns like *boy* which may have determiners (*the, a*) and unlike *John*, which may not (**a John*).

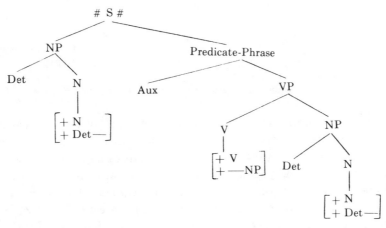

FIGURE 17. Strict Subcategorization Rule (2).

Now, context-free subcategorization rules (Rules 9-13) are applied to the two complex symbols for the *N*'s. For example, Rule 9 applied to $[+ \text{N}, + \text{Det}-]$ yields $[+ \text{N}, + \text{Det}-, + \text{Count}]$ or $[+ \text{N}, + \text{Det}-, - \text{Count}]$. Assume that, by application of Rules 9-13, we have obtained the phrase-marker shown in Figure 18. Notice that Figure 18 already indicates that the complex symbol corresponding to the left *N* will eventually have to be replaced by a lexical entry which is an Abstract, Noncountable, Common Noun (such as "sincerity," "democracy").

Now Rule schema 14, a context-sensitive selectional rule, is applied to the complex symbol containing $[+ \text{V}]$. Context-sensitive selectional rules are of the form

$$A \rightarrow CS/[\alpha] \cdots - \cdots [\beta]$$

where $[\alpha]$ and $[\beta]$ are specified features or a null (but either one or the other is nonnull). A rule of this form is applicable to any string

$$XWCUY$$

where (a) *C* is a complex symbol which contains *A*, (b) *X* and *Y* are complex

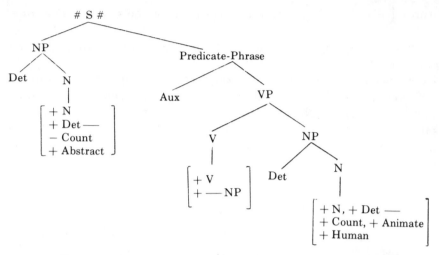

FIGURE 18. Subcategorization Rules Assigning Inherent Features

symbols which contain $[\alpha]$ and $[\beta]$ respectively, (c) W and U are null, or categorial symbols, or complex symbols which do not contain $[\alpha]$ and $[\beta]$ respectively. Moreover, $XWCUY$ must be analyzable as $Z_1, \cdots, Z_n$, where the expression "t is analyzable as $Z_1, \cdots, Z_n$" means that t, the sequence of bottom nodes of a phrase-marker, can be segmented into $t = t_1 \cdots t_n$ in such a way that t_i is dominated by Z_i in the phrase-marker.[14] Z_i is either a categorial symbol or a set of specified syntactic features. In the latter case, "t_i is dominated by Z_i" should mean that the complex symbol t_i includes the set of specified syntactic features represented by Z_i. The rule $A \rightarrow CS/[\alpha] \cdots - \cdots [\beta]$ applied to the string $XWCUY$ assigns to the complex symbol C a set of *selectional features* of the form $[+\gamma-\varsigma]$ where γ and ς are inherent features which belong to the complex symbols X and Y, respectively.

Now, Rule schema 14 ($[+V] \rightarrow CS/[+N] \cdots - (\cdots -[+N])$) is applied to the phrase-marker of Figure 18. The sequence of bottom nodes of the phrase-marker is:

$$
\text{Det} - \begin{bmatrix} +\,\text{N} \\ +\,\text{Det} - \\ -\,\text{Count} \\ +\,\text{Abstract} \end{bmatrix} - \text{Aux} - \begin{bmatrix} +\,\text{V} \\ +\,-\text{NP} \end{bmatrix} - \text{Det} - \begin{bmatrix} +\,\text{N} \\ +\,\text{Det} - \\ +\,\text{Count} \\ +\,\text{Animate} \\ +\,\text{Human} \end{bmatrix}
$$

---

[14] Selectional rules, in fact, are local transformational rules. See the definition of transformation in §1.3.3.

which is analyzable as

$$(\text{Det}\!-\!)\,[+\,N]\!-\!\cdots\!-\![+\,V]\!-\!\cdots\!-\![+\,N]$$

where the first $\cdots$ corresponds to the Aux, and the second $\cdots$ to the Det; $\gamma = [+\,N]$, $[-\,\text{Count}]$, $[+\,\text{Abstract}]$; and $\zeta = [+\,N]$, $[+\,\text{Count}]$, $[+\,\text{Animate}]$, $[+\,\text{Human}]$. After the application of the rule schema, we obtain a new complex symbol for V shown in Figure 19.

$$
\begin{bmatrix}
+\ V \\
+\ \text{---}\,NP \\
+\ [+\,N]\,\text{---}\,[+\,N] \\
+\ [+\,N]\,\text{---}\,[+\,\text{Count}] \\
+\ [+\,N]\,\text{---}\,[+\,\text{Animate}] \\
+\ [+\,N]\,\text{---}\,[+\,\text{Human}] \\
+\ [-\,\text{Count}]\,\text{---}\,[+\,N] \\
+\ [-\,\text{Count}]\,\text{---}\,[+\,\text{Count}] \\
+\ [-\,\text{Count}]\,\text{---}\,[+\,\text{Animate}] \\
+\ [-\,\text{Count}]\,\text{---}\,[+\,\text{Human}] \\
+\ [+\,\text{Abstract}]\,\text{---}\,[+\,N] \\
+\ [+\,\text{Abstract}]\,\text{---}\,[+\,\text{Count}] \\
+\ [+\,\text{Abstract}]\,\text{---}\,[+\,\text{Animate}] \\
+\ [+\,\text{Abstract}]\,\text{---}\,[+\,\text{Human}]
\end{bmatrix}
$$

FIGURE 19. Selectional Rule Assigning Selectional Features

Now, having applied Rules 16, 16a, 17 and 18, we obtain the phrase-marker shown in Figure 20.

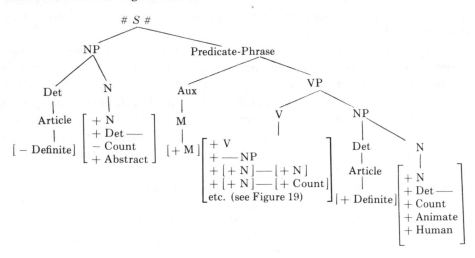

FIGURE 20. Phrase-Marker before Lexical Replacement

1.3.2.3. *The Lexicon.* The lexicon of the base component of a transformational grammar consists of *lexical entries* which are of the form (D, C), where D is a certain lexical formative[15] and C is a collection of specified syntactic features (a complex symbol).

The system of rules and rule schemata of the base component generates derivations terminating with strings that consists of grammatical formatives and complex symbols. Such a string is called a *preterminal string*. A *terminal string* is formed from a preterminal string by insertion of a lexical formative in accordance with the following *lexical rule* (Chomsky [11], p. 84).

> If Q is a complex symbol of a preterminal string and (D, C) is a lexical entry, where C is not *dinstinct from* Q, then Q can be replaced by (D, C).[16]

C is distinct from Q if for some syntactic feature which is *positively* or *negatively* specified in C, Q contains the same syntactic feature which is *negatively* or *positively* specified, respectively. For example, "sincerity" can replace the complex symbol corresponding to the left N of Figure 20, because $[+ \text{N}, + \text{Det}—, - \text{Count}, + \text{Abstract}, \cdots]$ for "sincerity" is not distinct from $[+ \text{N}, + \text{Det}—, - \text{Count}, + \text{Abstract}]$ for the N. On the other hand, "sincerity" cannot replace the complex symbol corresponding to the right N because the complex symbol of "sincerity" contains $[- \text{Count}]$ while the complex symbol for the right N in the phrase-marker contains $[+ \text{Count}]$.

The generalized phrase-marker that is obtained after the application of the lexical rule to complex symbols of Figure 20 will contain, with additional information given in the lexicon (represented by "$\cdots$"), everything necessary for the semantic interpretation of the sentence "Sincerity may frighten the boy."

1.3.2.4. *Ordering of Rules in the Base Component*. The rules and rule schemata of the base component are ordered: A derivation of a terminal string is initiated with an initial string $\# S \#$. Rules are applied in the order prescribed in the base component: after having applied Rule j to a symbol, only Rules j, j + 1, $\cdots$ can be used next. If the phrase-marker thus generated contains an S which has not been expanded, the cycle goes back to the first rule of the base component, and the sequential application of rules is initiated again.

One needs to order base component rules for the following reason: Assume that the rules are not ordered. Then, it would be allowable to apply Rule 14 $([+ \text{V}] \rightarrow CS/[+ \text{N}] \cdots — \cdots [+ \text{N}])$ prior to the application of Rules 9-13 (e.g., $[+ \text{Det}—] \rightarrow [+ \text{Count}]$). At this point, the complex symbols

---

[15] The lexical formative D in a lexical entry is not represented orthographically but by a phonological distinctive feature matrix. However, I shall not go into any details of phonological representation here.

[16] "$\cdots$ then Q can be replaced by D" in Chomsky [11]. Notice that the lexical rule is a rule of the theory of grammar, and not of any particular grammar.

for the two N's would contain only the features $[+N]$ and $[+Det—]$ (see Figure 17). Therefore, no selectional features would be assigned to the complex symbol of V except for $[+[+N]—[+N]]$.

1.3.3. *Transformational Component.* A transformational rule consists of two parts: a structural index and a structural change. A structural index specifies the condition that a phrase-marker has to fulfill in order for the rule to be applied to it, while a structural change defines the mapping of the phrase-marker into another.

Suppose that R is a phrase-marker of the terminal string t and t can be subdivided into successive segments $t_1, \cdots, t_n$ in such a way that each t_i is dominated in R by a node labeled A_i (see Figure 21). We say in such a case that t is analyzable as $(t_1, \cdots, t_n; A_1, \cdots, A_n)$ with respect to R. A string t with phrase-marker R is in the domain of a transformation T if it is analyzable as $(t_1, \cdots, t_n; A_1, \cdots, A_n)$ with respect to R, and $(A_1, \cdots, A_n)$ is the structural index of T. We say that $(t_1, \cdots, t_n)$ is a proper analysis of t (Chomsky and Miller [12], p. 301).

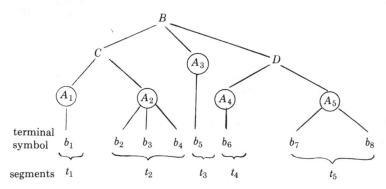

FIGURE 21. Analyzability

String $b_1 \cdots b_8$ is analyzable as $(b_1, \widehat{b_2 b_3 b_4}, b_5, b_6, \widehat{b_7 b_8}; A_1, A_2, A_3 A_4, A_5)$ with respect to the Phrase-marker R.

The structural change of a transformation T with structural index $A_1, \cdots, A_n$ is a sequence of elementary transformations. There are three types of elementary transformations: substitutions, deletions and adjunctions. Assume that the question transformation is defined as follows:

Structural Index: Q—NP—Tense—M—Aspect—X
$\qquad\qquad\qquad A_1 \ A_2 \quad\ A_3 \quad A_4 \quad A_5 \quad\ A_6$

Structural Change: (1) Adjoin $A_3 + A_4$ to the right of A_1
$\qquad\qquad\qquad\quad$ (2) Delete A_3
$\qquad\qquad\qquad\quad$ (3) Delete A_4
$\qquad\qquad\qquad\quad$ (4) Delete A_1

X in the structural index stands for an arbitrary sequence of symbols. *Adjunction* of C to the right of B has the effect of duplicating the node B over B and having that node dominate BC. *Deletion* of D causes the deletion of E if D is the only node immediately dominated by E.

Now, suppose we have the phrase-marker shown in Figure 22. The

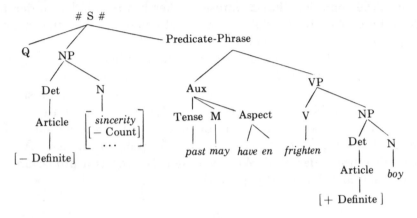

FIGURE 22. Generalized Phrase-Marker[17]

terminal string of Figure 22 is analyzable as $(Q, [-$ Definite$]$ *sincerity,* past, *may, have en, frighten* $[+$ Definite$]$ *boy;* Q, NP, Tense, M, Aspect, X) with respect to the phrase-marker. Therefore, the question transformation is applied to the phrase-marker, yielding the new phrase-marker shown in Figure 23.

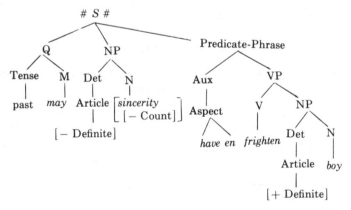

FIGURE 23. Question Transformation

If the phonological component of the grammar contains such rules as:

---

[17] Lexical formatives *boy, frighten,* etc. are used to represent complex symbols.

$$\text{past} + may \rightarrow might^{18}$$
$$[-\text{ Definite}] \rightarrow \emptyset / [-\text{ Count}]$$
$$[+\text{ Definite}] \rightarrow the$$
$$\text{en} + frighten \rightarrow frightened$$

we obtain "Might sincerity have frightened the boy?"

The definition of a transformation given above is applicable only to simple transformations. For example, it seems that a passive transformation must impose a special condition on the structural index:

Structural Index: $\text{NP}-\text{Aux}-\text{V}-\text{X}-\text{NP}-\text{Y}-\text{by}-passive^{19}-Z$

$\qquad\qquad\qquad A_1 \qquad A_2 \quad A_3 \ A_4 \quad A_5 \ A_6 \ A_7 \qquad A_8 \qquad A_9$

Condition: A_4 cannot contain an NP

Structural Change: (1) Substitute A_1 for A_8

(2) Substitute A_5 for A_1

(3) Delete A_5

(4) Adjoin $be +$ en to the right of A_2

where X, Y and Z are arbitrary sequences of symbols, possibly null. The condition prevents, for example, "the concert" of "John saw (Bill)$_{NP}$ during (the concert)$_{NP}$ by $passive$" from being analyzed as the NP (A_5) of the structural index of the passivization transformation ("The concert was seen Bill during by John" is ungrammatical), while making the transformation applicable to phrase-markers underlying "Everyone looks up to John by $passive$" ("John is looked up to by everyone"), "They agreed on the new course of action by $passive$" ("The new course of action was agreed on by them").[20]

Thus, the passive transformation has associated with its structural index the condition of dominance; that is, a certain term in the structural index must not contain a certain symbol. There are transformations which require that a sequence of symbols in their structural index be dominated by a certain symbol. There is yet a different type of restriction: some rules require that the subtree dominated by one term in the structural index be identical with the subtree dominated by another term in the structural

---

[18] Actually, the transformational component will have rules to reverse the order "past $+ may$" to "$may +$ past," etc., so that rules in the phonological component will be of the form $may +$ past $\rightarrow might$, etc.

[19] "By $passive$" is introduced by Rule 5a, Figure 13(a), in the base component as a dummy symbol which triggers passive transformation.

[20] The passive transformation, as stated above, would reject "The boy was taken care of by his relatives," while accepting ungrammatical sentences such as "The concert was slept during by John," etc. See Lakoff (Appendix F, 1965) for further discussion of passives.

index. For example, a relativization transformation requires that a noun phrase in an embedded sentence must be identical, with the exception of the determiner, to the noun phrase to which the embedded sentence is connected: for example, "A *man* # the *man* had resigned # returned to work" (see Figure 24) becomes "A man who had resigned returned to work"; but "A *man* # the *boy* had resigned # returned to work" does not satisfy the condition of identity and therefore cannot undergo the relativization transformation. At the moment, it is not clear what other types of restrictions are needed for transformational rules of natural languages.

Transformational rules are ordered. For example, the passive transformation must precede the number agreement transformation because the grammatical number of the predicate verb in a passive sentence agrees not with the *NP* after "by" but with the *NP* before the verb.

Transformational rules are cyclical or postcyclical. Cyclical transformational rules, which are ordered, are applied starting at the most deeply embedded subtree dominated by an *S*. After all the applicable rules are sequentially applied to the subtree, a new cycle is started with the next most deeply embedded subtree dominated by an *S*. The process terminates when the subtree corresponding to the whole phrase-marker is reached. Assume that we have a generalized phrase-marker informally represented in Figure 25 which underlies the sentence: "Were the men who were fired by the employer against whom they were on strike supported by the Union?"

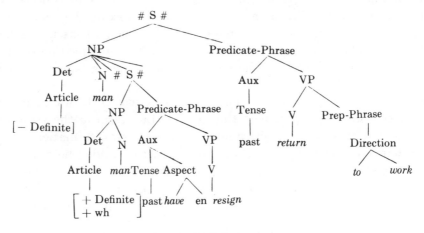

FIGURE 24. Relativization

The most deeply embedded subtree dominated by *S* in this generalized phrase-marker is the one at the bottom corresponding to "the men *past* be on strike against the employer." The first cycle operates on this subtree; the number agreement transformation is applied, yielding a new subtree corresponding to "the men *past plural* be on strike against the employer."

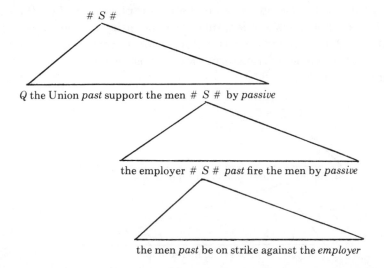

Q the Union *past* support the men # *S* # by *passive*

the employer # *S* # *past* fire the men by *passive*

the men *past* be on strike against the *employer*

FIGURE 25. Cyclical Applications of Transformational Rules (1)

Next, the second cycle operates on the subtree dominated by the next most deeply embedded *S*, which is the one corresponding to "the employer # the men *past plural* be on strike against the employer # *past* fire the men by *passive*." The relativization transformation applies, due to the identity of the noun phrases "employer" and "employer." The passivization transformation is then applied, triggered by the dummy symbol *passive* in the phrase-marker. Next, the number agreement transformation is applied, marking the verb as plural in agreement with the subject "the men." Thus, we obtain a new phrase-marker shown in Figure 26.

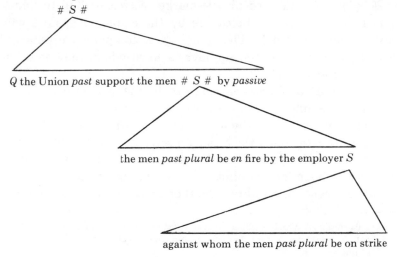

Q the Union *past* support the men # *S* # by *passive*

the men *past plural* be *en* fire by the employer *S*

against whom the men *past plural* be on strike

FIGURE 26. Cyclical Applications of Transformational Rules (2)

Next, the third cycle operates on the entire phrase-marker. The relativization transformation is applied, due to the identity of noun phrases "men" and "men." The passivization transformation is then applied, followed by the number agreement transformation. Thus, we obtain a new phrase-marker shown in Figure 27.

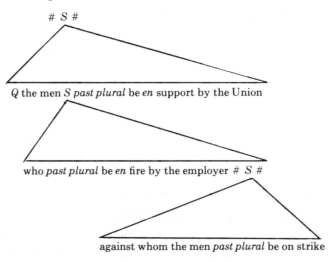

 # S #

Q the men *S past plural* be *en* support by the Union

who *past plural* be *en* fire by the employer *# S #*

against whom the men *past plural* be on strike

FIGURE 27. Cyclical Applications of Transformational Rules (3)

Next, post-cyclical transformations are applied to this phrase-marker. The question transformation, which can be applied only to the entire phrase-marker (cf. *He said that was it true.), is an example of a post-cyclical rule.[21] It inverts the order of "the men" and "*past plural* be" in Figure 27, yielding a derived phrase-marker corresponding to "*past plural* be the men who *past plural* be *en* fire by the employer against whom the men *past plural* be on strike." The phonological component produces: "Were the men who were fired by the employer against whom they were on strike supported by the Union?"

Not all generalized phrase-markers can be mapped into derived phrase-markers: for example, as was mentioned previously, the relativization transformation requires that the noun phrase of an embedded *S* be identical to the noun phrase to which the *S* is connected. If this condition is satisfied, a given phrase-marker undergoes the relativization transformation, which also deletes the boundary symbols # 's of the embedded *S*. Assume now that we have a generalized phrase-marker corresponding to "A man # the

---

[21] Another example of a post-cyclical transformation is the tag-question transformation: "He said that it was true, didn't he" is grammatical, but "*He said that it was true, wasn't it" is not.

boy *past* have *en* resign # *past* return to work" (compare this with the phrase-marker of Figure 24). Notice that the base component allows the generation of such a phrase-marker since it does not impose any contextual restrictions on the expansion of embedded S's. For such a phrase-marker, the identity condition is not fulfilled, and therefore, the relativization transformation is not applicable. After the application of cyclical and post-cyclical rules, we obtain a phrase-marker which still contains internal boundary symbols # 's.[22] At this point, the phrase-marker is rejected as being ill-formed. Thus, the transformational component acts as a filter between generalized and derived phrase-markers. A generalized phrase-marker which has been successfully mapped into a derived phrase-marker is called the deep structure of the sentence.

The theory of transformational grammar described above is still in the stage of development, and will be subject to constant future revision. Analysis of various features of natural languages in the framework of this theory has gone far deeper than was possible in the framework of traditional phrase structure grammars. Rules are now being found which govern some of the complex linguistic phenomena which traditional phrase structure grammarians have left untouched. However, it cannot be denied that linguists have scratched only the surface of the syntax of natural languages. More data on the analysis of natural languages has to be accumulated before the theory of transformational grammar can establish a stable characterization of its own mechanisms.

1.3.4. *Recognition Problems of Transformational Grammars.* Automatic recognition of sentences of a given transformational grammar is far more difficult than that of sentences of a phrase structure grammar simply because transformational grammars use more complex mechanisms than phrase structure grammars. In fact, a transformational grammar in its prototype model (Chomsky [9]) with no restriction on deletions of subtrees of a phrase-marker in the transformational component, has the same generative power as an unrestricted rewriting system, and therefore, the recognition of membership or nonmenbership of a given sentence in the language of a given transformational grammar is undecidable in general. In the past few years, linguists have been trying to impose more and more restrictions, from empirical linguistic motivations, on the forms of rules in both the base and transformational components. The only mathematical

---

[22] The presence of internal # 's is not the only condition for ill-formed derived phrase-markers. For example, a derived phrase-marker corresponding to "Even John loves even Mary" should be rejected as ill-formed since English allows only one occurrence of "even" in an S.

result (Ritchie and Peters [45]) so far obtained concerning the generative power of transformational grammars is that only primitive recursive (in fact elementary) languages can be generated by transformational grammars[23] which satisfy the following two conditions, both of which are linguistically well motivated.

(1) Deletion is allowed only when a copy of what is deleted is somewhere else in the phrase-marker *or* only when what is deleted is a member of a finite set of designated symbols such as *someone, something*.

(2) There is an upper bound on the number of subtrees dominated by *S* in the generalized phrase-marker underlying a sentence of a certain length.

Several recognition procedures have been proposed for transformational grammars. They are all based on earlier and simpler versions of grammar, and do not contain subcategorization rules in the base component. They are all experimental and far from achieving any reasonable efficiency in processing time.

A. *Analysis by Synthesis*. Walker and Bartlett [52] have proposed a system which parses the language of any given transformational grammar. Their system is essentially based on Matthews' proposal [37] for analysis by synthesis. Analysis of a sentence is performed by generation of all possible strings from the initial symbol "*S*" by means of a base component, a transformational component, and a phonological component. Each of the terminal strings thus generated is matched against the input sentence. When a match is found, the path which has led to the matched terminal string represents an analysis of the input sentence. Certain heuristics are used to distinguish transformations which could have been applied to generate the sentence under analysis from those which could not have. For example, if a sentence ends in a question mark, then it is certain that at some point the question transformation was used.

The Walker-Bartlett system, although drastically improved in efficiency compared to the prototype proposed by Matthews, seems to be still far from being practicable because of the number of sentences that will have to be generated before a match is found.

B. *The MITRE Syntactic Analysis Procedure* (Zwicky, Friedman, Hall and Walker, 1965). The MITRE transformational grammar has three components: the base component, the transformational component, and the lexicon. The lexicon bypasses the phonological component of the grammar. The base component consists of context-sensitive phrase structure rules which are ordered. A typical transformational rule is:

---

[23] The base component of their model of transformational grammars consists of only phrase structure rules, and does not contain subcategorization rules.

Structural Index: (#) (NP) ($SKIP NP $RES 2)

1   2   3

$RES 2: 3 dom *WH*

Structural Change: (3) ADLES 2

ERASE 3

$SKIP in segment 3 represents an arbitrary sequence of symbols, in the phrase-marker, between the *NP* of segment 2 and *NP* of segment 3. $RES indicates an extra restriction that the given phrase-marker has to satisfy in addition to the structural index of the rule. In the example above, $RES 2 states that the *NP* of segment 3 must dominate *WH*. There are two types of extra conditions: one of equality (one subtree must be identical to another) and one of dominance (the subtree must contain a certain node, or must have a certain structural index, or must be a terminal node). The structural change of the rule states (a) that a copy of the subtree corresponding to segment 3 should be *added as a left sister* of the subtree corresponding to segment 2, and (b) that segment 3 should be erased.

There are three types of instructions allowable in the structural change of a given transformational rule: the *adjunction* instructions, the *substitution* and the *erasure* instruction. The adjunction instructions are of the form (φ) AD n, where φ is a sequence containing numerals (referring to segment numbers) or particular grammatical symbols or both, where AD is one of the four adjunction operations:

ADLES   (add as left sister)[24]

ADRIS   (Add as right sister)

ADFID   (add as first daughter)

ADLAD (add as last daughter)

n is a numeral referring to the marked segment.

---

[24] A transformation defined as

Structural Index: (A) (B)

1   2

Structural Change: (a) ADLES 1

(1) ADFID 2

would map the phrase-marker (i) into (ii):

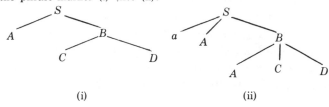

(i)   (ii)

The transformational rules are distinguished as being obligatory or optional, cyclical or noncyclical, and singular or embedding. A rule is cyclical if it can be applied more than once before the next rule is applied. Singular rules are distinguished from embedding rules by the conditions placed upon the search. In the case of a singular rule, the search cannot continue into a nested sentence—that is, beneath an instance of S within the sentence being examined. In the case of an embedding rule, the search continues into the first nested sentence, but not into a sentence nested in a nested sentence.

The approach of the MITRE procedure involves the construction of a surface grammar and reverse transformations. Consider the (infinite) set of derived phrase-markers obtainable from a given transformational grammar G_T of the type defined above. At the bottom of each derived phrase-marker is a string of symbols from which no branch emanates. Regard the set of all such strings corresponding to all derived phrase-markers as a language L_D. Given the original transformational grammar G_T, one can, by rules of thumb, construct a context-free grammar G_D (called a surface grammar) which accepts all the strings in L_D and assigns the corresponding derived phrase-markers to them. It is generally the case, however, that G_D accepts nonsentences in L_D as well as sentences in L_D, and also assigns some incorrect derived phrase-markers, as well as the correct one(s), to sentences in L_D. One can also construct, by rule of thumb, a reverse transformational component whose rules undo the transformations.

The analysis procedure works as follows (Figure 28). Given a sentence in the language of G_T, the lexicon lookup program, which essentially plays the role of the reverse phonological component, converts the sentence into a string in L_D. A context-free analyzer with grammar G_D assigns one (or more if the string is ambiguous in G_D) derived phrase-marker(s) to the string. Then, each such phrase-marker is transferred to the reverse transformational component. A test is made to see which of the transformational rules could have been applied to map some previous phrase-marker into the current phrase-marker in the course of generation of the given sentence. If a reverse transformational rule is found whose structural index matches the phrase-marker, the structural change specified by the rule is applied to the phrase-marker, and a new phrase-marker is obtained. If no more reverse transformational rules can be applied to the current phrase-marker, either the phrase-marker is a generalized phrase-marker, or the phrase-marker assigned by G_D was not a derived phrase-marker assigned to any sentence by G_T. The latter case is due to the condition that G_D accepts nonsentences as well as sentences in L_D and can give incorrect phrase-markers to sentences that are in L_D. In order to determine whether the phrase-marker under consideration is a real generalized phrase-marker or not, a test has to be made to see if the phrase-marker is obtainable by the base component of G_T. If not, the original derived phrase-marker, which initiated the reverse transformational analysis path, is abandoned. If it is obtainable, the forward application of the transformational rules which were reversely applied

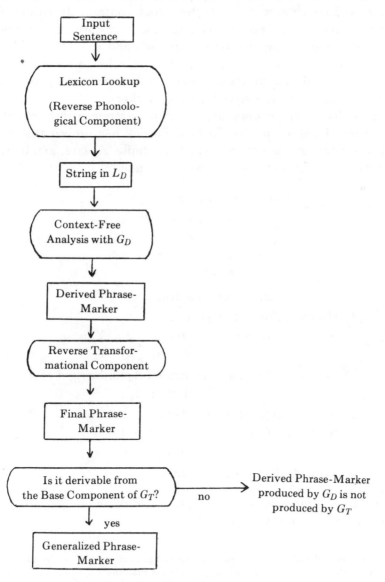

FIGURE 28. The MITRE Procedure

confirms that it is in fact the deep structure of the sentence under analysis. The deep structure, the set of reversely applied transformational rules, and phonological rules contained in the lexicon entries constitute the analysis of the input sentence.

C. *Petrick's Procedure.* Petrick [42] has proposed and programmed a recognition system of a transformational grammar which is similar to the MITRE procedure; however, his system does contain algorithms for producing the surface grammar G_D and reverse transformational rules. One of the main differences between his approach and the MITRE's is that he alternates the use of reverse transformational rules and surface grammar rules, while the MITRE procedure first applies surface grammar rules in order to obtain a set of derived phrase-markers.

Petrick's algorithm for obtaining a surface grammar does not work for all transformational grammars. In fact, Petrick has proved that there are transformational grammars[25] for which no finite surface grammar exists.

For example, consider the following grammar:

Phrase Structure Rules:

$$S \rightarrow A \# S \# B$$
$$S \rightarrow A \, B$$
$$A \rightarrow a$$
$$B \rightarrow b$$

Transformational Rules:

1. (Binary, Optional, Cyclical)

    Structural Index: $X - B - \# - B - Y$

                          $A_1 \; A_2 \; A_3 \; A_4 \; A_5$

    Structural Change: (1) Adjoin A_2 to the right of A_4

                              (2) Delete A_2

2. (Binary, Obligatory, Cyclical)

    Structural Index: $X - \# - A - \# - Y$

                          $A_1 \; A_2 \; A_3 \; A_4 \; A_5$

    Structural Change: Delete A_2, A_3, A_4

The phrase structure rules of this grammar produces, for example, the generalized phrase-marker of Figure 29.

---

[25] Forms of rules allowable in such transformational grammars may not be the linguistically correct ones, and such a proof may not be possible for grammars with the correct constraints on recoverability of deletion. Friedman [14] has also shown that there is no finite surface grammar for the MITRE transformational grammar.

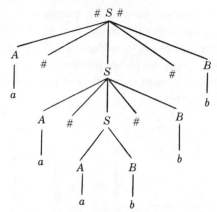

FIGURE 29. A Transformational Grammar for Which No Finite Surface Grammar Exists (1)

In the cyclical application of transformational rules to this generalized phrase-marker, the first cycle operates on the most embedded S, but neither of the two transformational rules is applicable. The second cycle, then, operates on the next S. Rule 1 applies, yielding the phrase-marker of Figure 30(a). Rule 2 operates on Figure 30(a), and eliminates #, A and #. The S which immediately dominates A is eliminated when A is eliminated due to the metarule that an intermediate node is deleted when its sole daughter is deleted by a transformation.

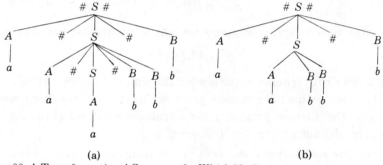

(a)   (b)

FIGURE 30. A Transformational Grammar for Which No Finite Surface Grammar Exists (2)

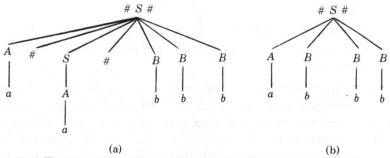

(a)   (b)

FIGURE 31. A Transformational Grammar for Which No Finite Surface Grammar Exists (3)

The third cycle operates on the entire phrase-marker of Figure 30(b). Rule 1 is applied twice, each time moving the B of the embedded S up to the right of the B of the highest S (see Figure 31(a)). Rule 2 is then applied to Figure 31(a), yielding the derived phrase-marker of Figure 31(b).

This transformational grammar is capable of generating surface structures of the type shown in Figure 32.

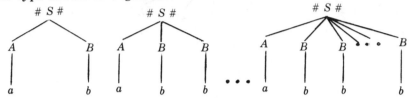

FIGURE 32. A Transformational Grammar for Which No Finite Surface Grammar Exists (4)

Since MITRE-Petrick recognition algorithms require that a surface grammar assign exactly the same surface structure to a given sentence as would have been assigned to the same sentence by the original transformational grammar, the surface grammar corresponding to our illustrative transformational grammar must consist of an infinite number of rules:

$$S \rightarrow AB$$
$$S \rightarrow ABB$$
$$S \rightarrow ABB \cdots B$$

and therefore is not finite. Suppose we use a notational convention

$$S \rightarrow AB(B)^*$$

which is a rewriting schema standing for the infinite number of rules shown above. If it is allowable for a surface grammar to contain rewriting schemata of this type, the surface grammar for a transformational grammar can be obtained algorithmically in the following way:

If all the nonterminal symbols of the transformational grammar are $A_1, \cdots, A_k$ and all the terminal symbols are $b_1, \cdots, b_m$, then the rule schemata:

$A_i \rightarrow (A_1)(A_2) \cdots (A_k)(b_1)(b_2) \cdots (b_m)((A_1) \cdots (A_k)(b_1) \cdots (b_m))^*$

for $i = 1, \cdots, k$ form a complete set of surface rules (Friedman [14], p. 4).

Such a surface grammar, however, would be inordinately impracticable because it would accept a vast number of strings which are not terminal strings of the original transformational grammar, and assign a large number of incorrect derived phrase-markers to well-formed terminal strings. Petrick's [42] and Friedman's [14] algorithms have attempted to form "minimum" surface grammars for given transformational grammars.

D. *Kuno's Procedure.* Kuno [30] has proposed a transformational analysis procedure which attempts to find the deep structure of a given sentence without explicitly using reverse transformations. The rules of a predictive grammar can have associated with them information pertaining to the transformational histories of their own derivation. When a phrase-structure analysis of the sentence is obtained, the set of surface grammar rules used for the analysis contains all the information necessary for the direct mapping of the surface phrase-marker into the corresponding generalized phrase-marker.

The difference in strategy between Kuno's procedure and the MITRE-Petrick procedures requires more explanation. After a derived phrase-marker, which should be exactly the same as the one which the original transformational grammar would assign to the sentence, is assigned to "He met a beautiful girl.," the MITRE procedure, for example, will compare the phrase-marker with the reverse transformational rules, and find that this derived phrase-marker is the result of a transformational rule which places an adjective in front of a noun. Therefore, by applying the corresponding reverse transformational rule, an intermediate phrase-marker corresponding to "He met a girl beautiful" is obtained. Next, it is found that this new phrase-marker is the result of the transformational rule which deletes a relative pronoun and a copula. Therefore, by applying the reverse rule, an intermediate phrase-marker corresponding to "He met a girl who was beautiful" is obtained. Next, this new intermediate phrase-marker is identified as being the result of a relativization rule. Therefore, the reverse relativization rule is applied, and a new phrase-marker corresponding to "He met a girl # the girl was beautiful # " is obtained. After comparing this phrase-marker with rules in the reverse transformational component, it is found that there are no more applicable rules. It is also found that the phrase-marker is derivable from the base component of the transformational grammar. Thus, the phrase-marker is identified as being a generalized phrase-marker, and forward application of the transformational rules confirms that it is in fact the deep structure of the sentence. Note that a surface phrase-marker assigned to an input sentence by the surface grammar must be identical to the derived phrase-marker that would have been assigned to the sentence when it is generated by the transformational grammar. Otherwise, the structural index of the reverse transformational rule to be applied first would not match the surface phrase-marker.

In Kuno's procedure, on the other hand, a derived phrase-marker assigned to a given sentence does not have to be exactly identical to the derived phrase-marker that the transformational grammar would have assigned to the sentence. A distorted derived phrase-marker, assigned to the sentence by a predictive analyzer, is mapped into the corresponding generalized phrase-marker in one step. The procedure takes advantage of the fact that the rule in the predictive grammar

$$NP \rightarrow Det\ A\ N$$

which is used for assigning a derived phrase-marker to the sentence "He met a beautiful girl" can include information indicating that an embedded sentence which constitutes a relative clause is involved here, that the subject of the embedded sentence is the same as a noun ("girl" in our example) which fulfills N of the rule, and that the adjective ("beautiful") which fulfills A is the predicate adjective of the embedded sentence. Each rule used for the surface analysis of the input sentence thus draws a subtree of the generalized phrase-marker. The combination of such subtrees drawn by all the rules yields the generalized phrase-marker of the sentence in its entirety.

In the absence of an algorithm for the construction of the surface grammar with transformational information for an arbitrary transformational grammar, Kuno's procedure must be considered limited to particular grammars. However, it seems to reflect, to some extent, the process of human perception of sentences, and deserves further studies, both from the mathematical and psychological point of view.

1.3.5. *Simulation of Sentence Generation of a Transformational Grammar.* Computer programs are now being developed at several places (Harvard; IBM's Thomas J. Watson Research Center; the MITRE Corporation) for the simulation of sentence generation by transformational grammars of varying complexity (Rosenbaum, Lochak, and Lieberman [48], L. Gross [21]). With proper man-machine communication phases interspersed in the program, such a system could serve two useful purposes. First, it can be used as a tool for a linguist to test his grammar. Due to ever-increasing complexities in the mechanisms used by various transformational grammars, it is now extremely difficult to check manually whether a given transformational grammar generates the language it is supposed to generate. Experiences at the MITRE Corporation and IBM's Thomas J. Watson Research Center show that testing whether all the rules in a transformational grammar of English really perform an intended role in sentence generation is not a simple task, even with grammars simple in their mechanisms and narrow in coverage of English sentences. If a linguist had a console and a display scope in his office as terminals to a central computer, with which he could check the generation of a sentence at every step on the spot, linguistic research would be greatly facilitated. Such a system should have capabilities for modifying grammar rules on line, and for keeping track of alternative formulations of rules for certain features under study. A sentence generation starts with the initial string $\#\ S\ \#$ displayed on the scope. Then, the system lists on the scope the set of rewriting rules for the expansion of S. The user specifies with a light pen which rule is to be used, and a phrase-marker is drawn on the scope up to that point. The same process is repeated for the application of other branching rules or subcategorization rules, and for the application of the lexical rule for the replacement of complex symbols by lexical entries. After a generalized phrase-marker is obtained, the system displays the transformational rules that have structural analyses which match the phrase-marker. Again, the user specifies which rule is to be used, and the new phrase-marker, produced by following the structural change of the rule, is displayed on the scope. Alternatively, the user may have in mind from the start the sequence of transformational rules to be applied; then, if the structural index of one of his rules does not match the phrase-marker to which it is supposed to be applied, the system will show that the user has made a mistake in rule specifications or that something is wrong with the grammar. More optimistically, if an efficient analysis procedure can be added to such a system, the user will be able to type on the console the sentence that he wants to follow the generation of. Again, the system displays on the scope the initial node, and thereafter, at the push of a key on the console, each step of the sentence generation will be displayed on the scope in succession.

Secondly, a system for the simulation of sentence generation will be of great use for teaching linguistics. It is difficult for a beginner to get the whole picture of a transformational grammar with its numerous components and highly involved rules. The teaching configuration of this system would have the additional property that the student would not be required to specify the rules to be applied, which could be specified in advance for a set of sample sentences. By typing one of the sentences on the console, a student can see how the sentence is generated—what sequence of nodes in a phrase-marker has been strung together to match the structural index of a given transformational rule, how phrase-marker configurations change by applications of transformational rules, and so on. Such a system may be able to suppress the operation of certain mechanisms: for example, by suppressing the selectional rules in the base component, the system can illustrate the deficiencies of transformational grammar lacking that mechanism. In fact, in the classroom, one could start with the simplest version of transformational grammar, suppressing complex mechanisms, and then proceed step by step to a more complex version.

The recent hardware development in the computer field has made such a system a practical one. A program now under development at Harvard aims at this goal.

1.4. *Semantic Theory.* In the previous sections, we have seen how a grammar generates sentences with their associated structural descriptions. We have also seen how a recognition procedure assigns one or more structural descriptions to a string of terminal symbols if the string is well formed with respect to a given grammar. Until quite recently, computational linguistics has been preoccupied with the latter problem of obtaining syntactic analyses of given sentences. However, even if we had a syntactic analyzer built around an ideal grammar which could assign to a given sentence all and only those structures that are regarded as well formed by the native speakers of the language, the task of assigning *readings* or semantic interpretations to each syntactic structure still remains to be solved. For example, assume that we have obtained a correct syntactic analysis of "The old man became a bachelor in 1966" and assume that the lexical item "bachelor" has four meanings shown in Figure 33. What mechanisms should the semantic component of a grammar have in order to accept the second meaning of "bachelor" and reject all the other three for "The old man became a bachelor in 1966"? How should the reading of this sentence be formally represented? How can the semantic component tell that "The old man obtained a bachelor's degree in 1966" does not add any new information to "The old man became a bachelor in 1966"? How can it tell that "My round table is square" is contradictory? These are some of the problems that semantic theory has to address itself to.

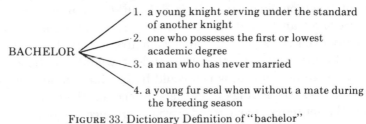

FIGURE 33. Dictionary Definition of "bachelor"

Computational semantics lags far behind computational syntax. "The literature of semantic studies to date consists mainly of philosophical analysis and fragmentary linguistic speculation, on the one hand, and of reports on limited experiments with very sharply-restricted semantic universes on the other hand" (Oettinger [40], p. 15).

Among various models of semantic analysis so far proposed, only those which are based on the transformational theory of grammar seem to promise any success. In fact, it is difficult to see how to assign the same reading to "John is easy to please" as to "it is easy for someone to please John" without assuming the same deep structure for the two sentences; and as was exemplified in §1.3, this is exactly what a transformational theory of grammar does.

Formalization of certain basic constraints that a semantic theory should meet in the framework of a transformational theory of grammar was first presented by Katz and Fodor [27]. Although few now believe that the proposed semantic theory is adequate, it has promoted serious research in an area which had previously lacked any formal theory or any serious discussion of goals. Katz and Fodor's formalization is outlined below.

Assume that a conventional dictionary assigns the meanings to the entry "bachelor," as was shown in Figure 33.

Katz and Fodor reject such definitions as unsystematic and propose the use of *semantic markers*—relational atomic concepts designed to exhibit the semantic structure in a dictionary and the semantic relations between dictionary entries. They claim "bachelor" should be represented by the diagram in Figure 34:

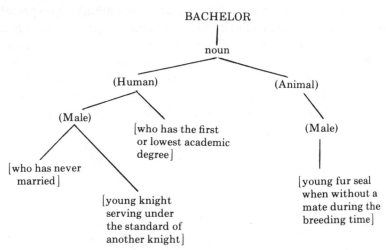

FIGURE 34. Katz and Fodor's Diagram for "bachelor"

The unenclosed elements in Figure 34 are *grammatical markers*, the elements enclosed in parentheses are *semantic markers*, and the expressions enclosed in brackets are *distinguishers*. Grammatical markers (Noun, Verb, Adjective, etc.) are the elements in terms of which syntactic relations are expressed, while semantic markers assigned to a lexical item are intended to reflect whatever systematic semantic relations hold between that item and the rest of the vocabulary of the language. On the other hand, the distinguisher assigned to a given meaning of a lexical item "distinguishes" the meaning from those meanings which have the same sequence of syntactic and semantic markers. A dualism between semantic markers and distinguishers is created by Katz and Fodor in order to have just enough information to do the job of disambiguation. However, the markers as given do not necessarily do the job. If the dictionary entry for "bachelor" is given as in Figure 34, it will not disambiguate such sentences as "the old bachelor finally died," which fluent speakers of English will not interpret as "The old *human male young knight serving under the standard of another knight* finally died." This disambiguation can be provided simply by taking the lexical information that a bachelor in the second sense is necessarily young, to be semantic marker information rather than distinguisher information. This is done by removing "young" from the distinguisher, and placing it as a semantic marker (Young) under (Male). Thus, we obtain a new path[26] noun → (Human) → (Male) → (Young) → [Knight serving under the standard of another knight] for the second definition of "bachelor."

A sentence and its grammatical description (base phrase-marker) provide the input to a semantic theory. Its output is a semantic interpretation of each input sentence. The semantic theory contains a projection rule component as well as a dictionary component. The projection rule component operates on the deep structure of a given sentence, and assigns a semantic interpretation to each node in the phrase-marker, effecting a series of amalgamations from bottom to top. For example, Katz and Fodor give the example: "The man hit the colorful ball" with the phrase-marker shown in Figure 35.

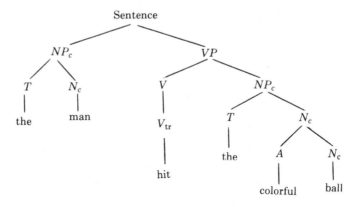

FIGURE 35. Phrase-Marker for "The man hit the colorful ball"

Assume that the dictionary component contains the following definitions of the meanings of "colorful" and "ball" which match the syntactic markers (N_c and N_c) of the two words in the phrase-marker of Figure 35.

1. Colorful → Adjective → (Color) → [Abounding in contrasts or variety of bright colors] ⟨(Physical Object)∨(Social Activity)⟩

---

[26] → is a branch in a tree diagram (see Figure 34, for example).

2. Colorful → Adjective → (Evaluative) → [Having distinctive character, vividness, or picturesqueness] ⟨(Aesthetic Object)∨(Social
Activity)⟩

1. Ball → Noun concrete → (Social Activity) → (Large) → (Assembly)
→ [For the purpose of social dancing]
2. Ball → Noun concrete → (Physical Object) → [Having globular shape]
3. Ball → Noun concrete → (Physical Object) → [Solid missile for projection by an engine of war]

⟨(Physical Object) ∨ (Social Activity)⟩ for the first definition of "colorful"
gives the contextual restriction of the word as (Color) → [Abounding in
contrast or variety of bright colors], i.e., an adjectival occurrence of "colorful" receives this interpretation just in case the element it modifies has
a path containing either the semantic marker (Physical Object) *or* (Social
Activity).

Now, the projection rules assign semantic interpretations to the node
N_c which dominates A ("colorful") and N_c ("ball") in Figure 35. The
following rule is used:

Given two paths of the form: (1) Lexical String$_1$ → syntactic markers
of head → (a_1) → (a_2) → $\cdots$ → (a_n) → [1] ⟨set of strings of markers
Ω_1⟩; (2) Lexical String$_2$ → syntactic markers of modifier → (b_1) → (b_2)
→ $\cdots$ → (b_m) → [2] ⟨set of strings of markers Ω_2⟩, such that Lexical
String$_1$ contains a sequence of syntactic or semantic markers that
satisfies the condition Ω_2.

Then, these two paths are replaced by:

Lexical String$_2$ + Lexical String$_1$ → dominating node marker → (a_1)
→ (a_2) → $\cdots$ → (a_n) → (b_1) → (b_2) → $\cdots$ → (b_m) → [[2] [1]] (Ω_1),
where any (b_i) is null when $(\exists a_i)$ $(b_i = a_i)$ and $[[2] [1]]$ is $[1]$
when $[2] = [1]$.

The amalgamation of "colorful" and "ball" is the set of derived paths
shown below:

1. Colorful + ball → Noun concrete → (Social Activity) → (Large)
→ (Assembly) → (Color) → [[Abounding in contrast or variety of
bright colors] [For the purpose of social dancing]]
2. Colorful + ball → Noun concrete → (Physical Object) → (Color)
→ [[Abounding in contrast or variety of bright colors] [Having
globular shape]]
3. Colorful + ball → Noun concrete → (Physical Object) → [[Abound-
ing in contrast or variety of bright colors] [Solid missile for projection by an engine of war]]
4. Colorful + ball → Noun concrete → (Social Activity) → (Large)
→ (Assembly) → (Evaluative) → [[Having distinctive character,
vividness, or picturesqueness] [For the purpose of social dancing]]

In his excellent review of Katz and Fodor's semantic theory, Bolinger [7] has raised the following objections among others: Bolinger rejects the marker-distinguisher dualism because: (a) It is unnecessary—the distinguisher could be a string of semantic markers; (b) Distinguishers contain redundant information. For example [knight serving ···] in the second definition of "bachelor" (Figure 33), contains the information that "bachelor is human and male" which has already been represented by the semantic markers (Human) and (Male); (c) The marker-distinguisher dualism does not seem to correspond to any clear division in natural language.[27] Bolinger demonstrates that the diagram of Figure 34 for "bachelor" can be converted into that of Figure 36 which does not require

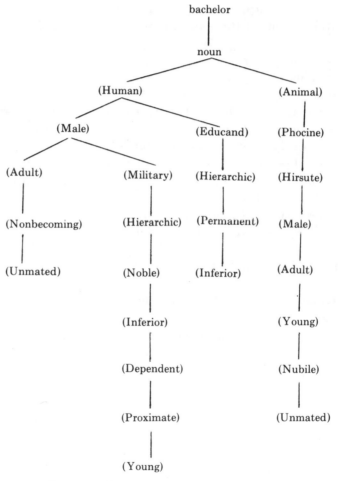

FIGURE 36. Bolinger's Diagram for "bachelor"

---

[27] Katz himself has abandoned the dualism recently.

any distinguishers. Notice that Figure 36 uses twenty distinct semantic markers while Figure 34 uses only 4. If 20 markers are needed for the single word "bachelor," how many markers will be needed for all the words? Will we arrive at a diminishing return after having coded, say, one thousand lexical items? These questions cannot be answered definitely since no one has yet tried to code more than a handful of lexical items.

It is also to be noted that, in the K-F theory, although semantic markers are given some hierarchical structure within the diagram for each lexical form, they are not ordered in general. The diagram of Figure 36 for "bachelor" clearly lacks the feature specification of "bachelor" as (Animate) and (Physical Object) in all of its four meanings. Including these features, on the other hand, in the lexical entry would cause too redundant feature specifications which would violate the criterion of simplicity for the grammar evaluation.

In view of these shortcomings, several modifications are necessary to the K-F semantic theory:

(1) A semantic theory should have a hierarchical structure imposed upon semantic markers which defines an "is a" relationship. Note that

"A bachelor ⟨in the sense of a man who has never married⟩ is a man."

"A bachelor is an adult."

"A bachelor is a human being."

"A bachelor is a higher-animal."

"A bachelor is a physical object."

are all grammatical sentences, whereas

"A bachelor is a nonhuman."

is ungrammatical. Similarly,

"A girl ⟨in the sense of a female who is not an adult⟩ is a child."

"A girl is a human being."

are grammatical, whereas

"A girl is a bachelor ⟨in the sense of a man who has never married⟩."

is not. These phenomena can be explained if we have a structure of semantic markers such as the one whose fragment is shown in Figure 37.

A meaning of a lexical entry can be defined by its position in the hierarchy: for example, the meaning of "human being" can be represented as $[+,+,+,+]$; that of "adult" as $[+,+,+,+,+]$; that of "child" as $[+,+,+,+,-]$; that of "boy" as $[+,+,+,+,-,+]$; etc. "An adult is a human being" is well-formed because the path leading to "adult" passes through the position for "human being."

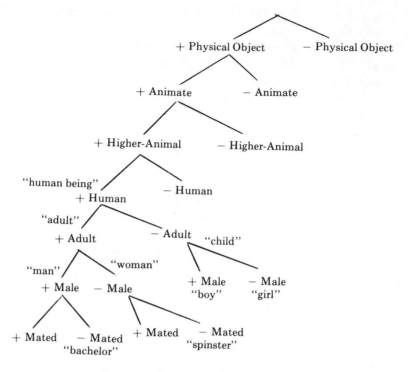

FIGURE 37. Structure of Semantic Markers

An adult $[+,+,+,+,+]$
is $|\ \ |\ \ |\ \ |$
a human being. $[+,+,+,+]$

On the other hand, "A child is an adult" is ungrammatical because the path leading to "child" does not pass through the position for "adult:"

A child $[+,+,+,+,-]$
is $|\ \ |\ \ |\ \ |\ \ |$ violation
an adult. $[+,+,+,+,+]$

It has been pointed out by Bever and Rosenbaum [4] that "X is Y" is grammatical if X *is dominated by* Y.

(2) A semantic theory should allow a given meaning of a lexical form to be representable by one or more paths in the semantic tree. The dictionary component of the K-F semantic theory allows only one string of semantic markers to be assigned to each meaning of a given lexical form. The lexical form "river," for example, requires at least three sets of semantic markers: One set defining it as a geographical stretch ("The river runs through the city," "The highway runs through the city," etc.); a second set defining the word as three-dimensional ("the bottom of the lake, river, etc."); and a third

set defining it as water which moves ("the river flows," but not "the lake flows"). However, if each such set is to constitute a distinct meaning of the word "river," the following *complex sentence* would be rejected as being anomalous:

> "The bottom of the river which flows gently running
> across the city is covered with mud."

The sentence contains the following three components: "The river flows gently," "The river runs across the city" and "The river has a bottom," in each of which the word "river" has a "different meaning." According to the proposed modification, the "river" is to be represented by a union of three paths in the semantic tree. Then, verbs such as "run" (in the sense of "stretch") is assigned a contextual restriction that its subject should be a noun whose semantic path contains [(Spatial) → (Stretch)]. Verbs such as "flows" require as its subject a noun with [(Spatial) → (Stretch)] and [(Water) → (Moving)]. In this way the three clauses contained in the above sentence are all accepted with the word "river" having the same meaning, but with each verb paying attention to a different aspect of "river."

(3) A semantic theory should have a hierarchical structure imposed upon lexical entries defining a "have" or "part of" relationship. Bever and Rosenbaum have shown that such a hierarchy should be a part of a semantic theory, and not a part of the encyclopaedic knowledge about the universe by pointing out that, in

(a) Most men have five toes.
(b) *Five toes have most men.
(c) Most men have forty-two toes.
(d) *Forty-two toes have most men.

(c) is a grammatical sentence although it contains information which is contradictory to what we know about this universe, while (b) and (d) are ungrammatical irrespective of whether the statement is contradictory or not to our knowledge of the universe. The tree defining a fragment of the "have" hierarchy may look as follows:

human being
|
body
|
leg
|
foot
|
toe
|
nail

Bever and Rosenbaum have noted an interesting characteristic of the "have" hierarchy that "*X has Y*" is grammatical if *X dominates Y*; notice, as was mentioned before, that "*X is Y*" is grammatical if *X is dominated by Y* in the "be" hierarchy.

The Katz and Fodor approach to semantic analysis, even with the proposed modifications, still cannot handle the following problems:

(1) Equivalence of meaning between (a) and (b), or between (c) and (d)[28]

    (a) John bought the book from Bill.

    (b) Bill sold the book to John.

    (c) John struck Bill.

    (d) Bill received a blow at the hands of John.

(2) That "John is taller than Bill and Bill is taller than Jack" implies that John is taller than Jack, but that "John likes Bill and Bill likes Jack" does not imply that John likes Jack.

(3) Conventions such as adulthood which starts at the age of 21 years for human beings but at the age of, say, 2 years for dogs.

(4) There are semantic features which are not only present or absent in a meaning of a lexical form, but also present in a certain degree. For example,

    (a) The semantic tree is not adequate for defining *petty* on a scale of pejorativeness: *petty* is more pejorative than *small-minded*, but less so than *mean* (Bolinger [7], p. 565).

    (b) A human being has two legs, while a dog has four legs.

    (c) We interpret "The toy is in the pen" (Bar-Hillel's example) as "The toy is in the crib," and not as "The toy is in the pen for writing" because we know the relative size of "toy" and "pen." The semantic tree is not adequate for representing such relations as "greater than," "smaller than," "superior to," etc.

To develop an integral theory of syntax and semantics which can handle these problems as well as K-F type semantic interpretations should be a major concern of computational semantics.

2. **Application of linguistics to computer problems.** Application of linguistics to computer problems includes such areas as mechanical translation, automatic fact retrieval, question-answering, automatic abstracting, automatic indexing and cataloguing, automatic content analysis, authorship identification, etc. Automatic question-answering and machine translation, the two most controversial areas of applied computational linguistics, are discussed in this section.

---

[28] These examples are borrowed from Chomsky [11].

2.1. *Question-Answering.* A *question-answering system* is an information retrieval system which is capable of answering specific questions posed in a subset of a natural language. For example, *Baseball* (Green et al. [**15**]) answers questions about the scores, teams, locations, and dates of baseball games. The input questions are limited to simple sentences. *Student* (Bobrow [**6**]) accepts algebra problems posed in a limited subset of English and transforms these into equations which it then solves. A recent survey by Simmons [**51**] describes and reviews fifteen experimental English language question-answering systems.

Most question-answering systems can be fitted into the diagram of Figure 38. Functions of the PARSER, TRANSLATOR, and RETRIEVER components will be described below using *Baseball* as an example.[29]

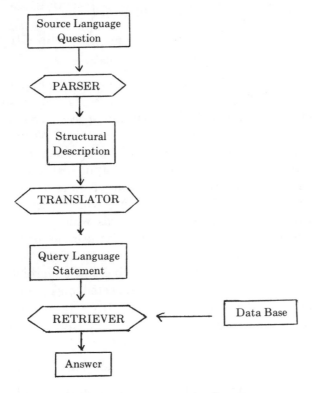

FIGURE 38. Question-Answering Systems

The data base of *Baseball* consists of the month, day, place, team, and score of 1959 American League baseball games stored in a list structure as shown in Figure 39. Note that all information in the data base is in terms

---

[29] The author is indebted to P. A. Shapiro [**50**] for this description of *Baseball.*

of Attribute-Value (A-V) pairs such as MONTH = April, GAME = 1, etc.

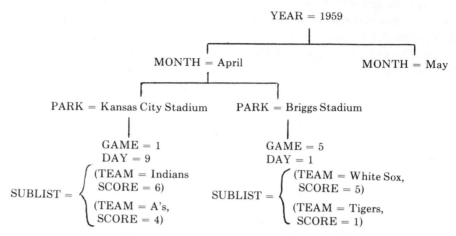

FIGURE 39. Baseball Data Base

The PARSER of *Baseball* consists of a dictionary lookup and a syntactic analysis component. The dictionary lookup accepts a given source language question, and assigns A-V pairs and parts of speech (PS) to each word in the question. For example, if the question contains "April," the A-V pair MONTH = April and the PS Noun will be assigned to the word. The syntactic component accepts as input the output of the dictionary lookup. This component is composed of six sequential units.

The first unit is an "ambiguity resolver," which selects the correct PS according to the given contexts for all words which have more than one definition in the dictionary. The second unit is the major one, the "bracketing routine" which, by means of a right-to-left scan of the sequence of PS's, isolates all noun phrases and all prepositional and adverbial phrases in the question. The words which remain unbracketed make up the verb, since only one-clause sentences are allowed.

In the example below, noun phrases are in square brackets, and the other phrases are in parentheses:

Did [any team] win [more than 6 home games] (by [a 3 run margin])?

This bracketing routing is essentially a context-free phrase structure analyzer.

The third unit of the syntactic analysis component is a "dangling preposition" routine, which connects unattached prepositions with the noun phrases to which they belong. For example:

INPUT: [How many runs] did [Boston] win by?

OUTPUT: (By [how many runs]) did [Boston] win?

Connecting prepositions to the proper noun phrases is essential if the subject-object locater is to work properly, and if the proper spec list is to be constructed during content analysis.

The next unit is the "active/passive test," which inspects the unbracketed words in the sentence and determines by the particular PS combination present whether the verb is active or passive. This information will be used in the next unit and also during one segment of the TRANSLATOR.

The fifth unit is the "subject-object locater," which isolates both the subject and object of the input question. The sixth and final unit is the "yes/no question test," which determines whether the RETRIEVER will have to supply a "yes/no" or "content" answer. The decision is made according to the presence or absence of a list of key words in the questions (e.g., "how many," "who," "what," etc.). Questions *not* containing any of these key words require a yes/no answer.

This completes the operation of the PARSER. The output of these six syntactic units described above are saved for use by the next step in the process, TRANSLATOR, whose task it is to form the query-language statement, called spec list, which will be used later by the RETRIEVER to retrieve the information requested by the question. To form this spec list, the TRANSLATOR operates on the bracketed question, utilizing both the A-V "meanings" of the words and the grammatical information provided by the syntactic component.

For example, the TRANSLATOR accepts as input

(a)   [Who]   beat   [the Tigers]   in   [Briggs Stadium]   in   [April]?

TEAM = ? SBR, TEAM = Tigers, PARK = Briggs Stadium, MONTH = April.

The subroutine for handling "beat" is executed, and (a) is changed into the spec list:

(b)   [Who]   beat   [the Tigers]   in   [Briggs Stadium]   in   [April]

[WINNING]TEAM = ?[LOSING]TEAM = Tigers? PARK = Briggs Stadium? MONTH = April

Now, the RETRIEVER accepts as input the spec list of (b), and searches the data base for the value of attribute [WINNING] TEAM which satisfies the other conditions ([LOSING] TEAM = Tigers, PARK = Briggs Stadium, MONTH = April).

Baseball, and all other existing question-answering systems, suffer from the following drawbacks:

(1) Each system can answer questions about a highly restricted subject with some degree of success, but does not seem to be extendable to subjects of different nature. For example, *Baseball* could be extended to other games whose records can be structured according to time, place, game number, teams, scores, etc., but not to subjects which do not have such

a structure. *Student*, likewise, can solve high school algebra problems, and only those. When a new scope of coverage is added to such a system, little of what is already in the system seems to be of any use for handling the added material. For example, if *Student* were to be extended to high school chemistry problems, the modifications required would be such that the new system would essentially consist of two disjoint components, the one for algebra, and the other for chemistry.

(2) Most existing systems use context-free phrase structure grammars for the PARSER, and thus have the following shortcomings:

(a) Only kernel or near-kernel sentences are accepted by the systems, with the exception of *Student*. If transformed sentences were to be accepted, a new routine would have to be added to the TRANSLATOR for each such transformed structure.

(b) The structure assigned to a question is in many cases *ad hoc* and contrived to fit the special structure of the data base used for their systems. Thus, generality of the systems is lost, and therefore, an entirely new grammar and a new translation algorithm have to be designed for answering questions pertaining to a data base of a different nature.

(c) In order to get an immediately operational question-answering system, quality has been sacrificed in both the syntactic analysis and the translation components. Therefore, it is not clear which component causes the limitations and drawbacks of a given question-answering system.

In the light of the above observations, researchers in this field should now play down practical applications, and concentrate on the design of a general question-answering system, by manually simulating an idealized analyzer which assigns to a given humanly unambiguous sentence a unique structural description and a unique correct semantic interpretation.

The structural description assigned to a sentence has to be the deep structure of the sentence: otherwise, as was pointed out in (2a) above, the TRANSLATOR would become inordinately complex as more and more types of transformed structures are allowed as input to the system. For example, assume that the question is: "Were the Orioles beaten by a team defeated by the Tigers in a game played in April in a park used by the Orioles and the Yankees?" An extention of *Baseball* would require special subroutines for dealing with these participial constructions:

Were	[the Orioles]	beaten by	[a team]	defeated by	[the Tigers]
	TEAM = Orioles	SBR1	TEAM = —	SBR1	TEAM = Tigers

in	[a game]	played in	[April]	in	[a park]	used by	[the Orioles]
	GAME = —		MONTH = April		PARK = —		TEAM = Orioles

and	[the Yankees]?
	TEAM = Yankees

Indeed, it is difficult to see how the Attribute-Value pairs associated with lexical forms in the question can be chained into a spec list with no embedded structure. A question-answering system based on a transformational grammar, on the other hand, would assign the deep structure informally represented in Figure 40 as one of its interpretations.

Now, notice that each embedded sentence plays the role of reducing the data base to its subdata base. The S_4 (the Orioles and the Yankees used *wh-* park), reduces the original data base (DB) to a portion which pertains to those games which were played in the parks which the Orioles and the Yankees used. Let us represent this subdata base as $R(\mathrm{DB}, S_4)$. Now, S_3 (someone played *wh-* game in April in a park) accepts $R(\mathrm{DB}, S_4)$ as input and reduces it to a portion which pertains to the games played in April. Thus, we obtain $R(R(\mathrm{DB}, S_4), S_3)$. Next, S_2 (the Tigers defeated *wh-* team in a game) is processed, yielding $R(R(R(\mathrm{DB}, S_4), S_3), S_2)$, the subdata base of the previous subdata base pertaining only to those games in which the Tigers is a winning team. Finally, S_1 (Q a team beat the Orioles) reduces this subdata base into a portion which pertains to those games in which the Orioles is a losing team. If $R(R(R(R(\mathrm{DB}, S_4), S_3), S_2), S_1)$ is null, the answer to the original question is no; otherwise, the answer is yes.

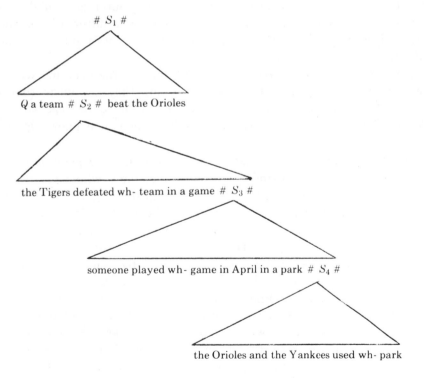

FIGURE 40. Deep Structure of a Question for a Question-Answering System

What is important to note here is that the same TRANSLATOR algorithm can be used for each embedded sentence, which is simple in its structure. Therefore, it does not matter how many embedded sentences a given question contains: the same algorithm would be used cyclically from bottom to top of the deep structures of the sentence.

Several research groups are making a pilot study of question-answering systems using a transformational grammar of English for the PARSER: the MITRE Corporation (Walker [53]), Technical Operations, Inc. (Langevin) and Harvard (Woods [54]). The results of such research will deserve careful attention since, to a certain degree, their success or failure can be used to help determine whether analysis of English motivated by the framework of a transformational theory of grammar is a sound basis for practical language data processing systems.

2.2. *Machine Translation.* Pessimism concerning the possibility of fully-automatic high-quality machine translation has been voiced emphatically by Bar-Hillel [2], Oettinger [39], [41] and Dreyfus [13]. The following is a quotation from Oettinger ([41], p. 11):

"Automatic language translation no longer holds the center of the stage. Progress continues to be made in the matter of machine aids to translation, but today no one seriously imagines that fully-automatic, high-quality machine translation is just around the corner. The automatic parsing of English, Russian and other languages continues to be a subject of active study throughout the world.

"Some serious scholars have a continuing faith in the eventual feasibility of economical, fully automatic translation but they recognize that considerable basic knowledge necessary for this goal to be reached is still lacking and they properly refuse to guess how soon such knowledge might be acquired. . . .

"Meanwhile, a dwindling lunatic fringe continue their periodic claims of perfect translation just around the corner, and many who have been unsuccessful in translating from Russian to English, English to Russian or in any other direction are now flocking to the study of translation from or to Chinese. One system long and loudly advertised as an automatic translation system is now in experimental operation for the United States Air Force but it acts—by necessity rather than by choice—as a machine aid to translation. Output of this system is placed in the hands of bilingual post-editors who prepare final translations with the original text, the machine output, and a variety of other aids at their command."

Dreyfus lists three factors which characterize human parsing of sentences and which doom machine translation to failure: fringe consciousness, essence/accident discrimination, and ambiguity tolerance. "Fringe consciousness makes us aware of cues in context which are too numerous to be made explicit. A pragramatic sense of what is essential in a given context allows us to ignore as irrelevant certain possible parsings of sentences and meanings of words which would be included in the output of a machine. Ambiguity tolerance then allows us to use this information about goals and context to narrow down the remaining spectrum of possible parsings and meanings as much as the situation requires without requiring the resulting interpretation to be absolutely unambiguous." He states that the user of a natural language is not aware of many of the cues to which he responds in determining the intended syntax and meaning of a given sentence. On the other hand, nothing indicates that he considers each of these cues unconsciously. Dreyfus suggests that these cues are not the sort that could be taken up and considered by a sequential or even parallel list-searching program for two reasons: First, there are too many possibly relevant cues; second, even if a manageable number of relevant cues existed, they would not help us: in order to use a computer to interpret these cues, we would have to formulate syntactic and semantic criteria in terms of strict rules: and our use of language with respect to situations in the real world, while precise, is not strictly rule-like. Dreyfus concludes that significant developments in artificial intelligence must await computers of an entirely different sort, of which the only existing prototype is the little-understood human brain.

That Bar-Hillel, Oettinger, and Dreyfus are pessimistic about machine translation does not mean they are pessimistic about computational linguistics in general. It is granted that our current understanding of *human* mental processes and the current state of the art of computer sciences do not allow us to simulate fringe consciousness, essence/accident discrimination and ambiguity tolerance. In fact, machine translation is too high a goal for computational linguistics. The goal of the field should be to explicate, with the use of computers, that portion of our use of language which is rule-governed. The field has a long way to go before achieving even this modest goal. Slowly but steadily, emphasis in computational linguistics research has been shifted from the original goal of machine translation to the more reasonable goal of the systematic and analytic study of the rules which govern the syntax and semantics of natural languages.

REFERENCES

1. R. Abbott and S. Kuno, *The predictive analyzer and context-free grammars,* Mathematical Linguistics and Automatic Translation, Rep. NSF-15, Harvard Computation Laboratory, Cambridge, Mass., 1965.

2. Y. Bar-Hillel, *Language and information.* III, Addison-Wesley, Reading, Mass., 1964.

3. J. B. Bessinger, Jr., S. M. Parrish and H. F. Arader, eds. *Literary data processing conference proceedings,* IBM, 1964.

4. T. G. Bever and P. Rosenbaum, *Two studies on syntax and semantics*, MITRE Tech. Rep., Bedford, Mass. (to appear)

5. D. G. Bobrow, *Syntactic analysis of English by computer—a survey*, AFIPS Conf. Proc. Vol. 24, Spartan, Baltimore, Md., 1963, pp. 365-387.

6. _____, *Natural language input for a computer problem-solving system*, AFIPS Conf. Proc., Vol. 26, Spartan, Baltimore, Md., 1964

7. D. Bolinger, *The atomization of meaning*, Language, (4) **41** (1965), 555-573

8. T. E. Cheatham, Jr. and K. Sattley, *Syntax-directed compiler*, AFIPS Conf. Proc., Vol. 25, Spartan, Baltimore, Md., 1964, pp. 31-57.

9. N. Chomsky, *Syntactic structures*, Mouton, The Hague, Netherlands, 1957.

10. _____, "Formal properties of grammar" in *Handbook of mathematical psychology*, edited by R. R. Bush, E. H. Galanter and R. D. Luce, Vol. 2, Wiley, New York, 1963.

11. _____, *Aspects of the theory of syntax*, MIT Press, Cambridge, Mass., 1965.

12. N. Chomsky and G. A. Miller, "Introduction to the formal analysis of natural languages" in *Handbook of mathematical psychology*, edited by R. R. Bush, E. H. Galanter and R. D. Luce, Vol. 2, Wiley, New York, 1963.

13. H. L Dreyfus, *Alchemy and artificial intelligence*, RAND Rep. p. 3244, RAND, Santa Monica, Calif., 1965.

14. J. Friedman, *An investigation of surface grammars*, MITRE, Bedford, Mass., 1965.

15. B. F. Green, Jr., A. K. Wolf, C. Chomsky and K. Laughery, "Baseball: an automatic question answering" in *Computers and thought*, edited by E. A. Figenbaum and J. Feldman, McGraw-Hill, New York, 1963, pp. 207-216.

16. S. Greibach, *Inverses of phrase structure generators*, Ph.D. Thesis, Mathematical Linguistics and Automatic Translation, Rep. No. NSF-11, Harvard Computation Laboratory, Cambridge, Mass., 1963.

17. _____, *Formal parsing systems*, Comm. Assoc. Comput. Mach. **7** (1964), no. 8, 346-353.

18. _____, *A new normal-form theorem for context-free phrase structure grammars*, J. Assoc. Comput. Mach. **12** (1965), no. 1, 42-52.

19. T. Griffiths, *Turing machine recognizers for general rewriting systems*, Proc. IEEE Sympos. on Switching Circuit Theory and Logical Design, Princeton Univ. Press, Princeton, N. J., 1964, pp. 47-56.

20. T. Griffiths and S. R. Petrick, *On the relative efficiencies of context-free grammar recognizers*, Comm. Assoc. Comput. Mach. (5) **8** (1965), 289-300.

21. L. Gross, *Design for a computer program to simulate the phonological component of a generative grammar*, 1966. (to appear)

22. M. Gross, *On the equivalence of models of language used in the fields of mechanical translation and information retrieval*, Information Storage and Retrieval **2** (1964), no. 1, 43-57.

23. P. Guiraud, *Bibliographie critique de la statistique linguistique*, Comité de la Statistique Linguistique, Conseil International de la Philosophie et des Sciences Humaines, Spectrum, Utrecht, 1954.

24. D. Hays, "Automatic language-data processing" in *Computer applications in the behavioral sciences*, edited by H. Borko, Prentice-Hall, Englewood Cliffs, N. J., 1962, pp. 394-421.

25. E. T. Irons, *An error-correcting parse algorithm*, Comm. Assoc. Comput. Mach. **6** (1963), no. 11, 669-673.

26. T. Kasami, *An efficient recognition and syntax-analysis algorithm for context-free languages*, Sci. Rep. No. 2, AFCRL-65-558, 1965.

27. J. J. Katz and J. A. Fodor, *The structure of a semantic theory*, Language **39** (1963), no. 2, 170-210.

28. M. Kay, *A general procedure for rewriting strings*, presented 1964 Annual Meeting, Assoc. Mach. Transl. Comput. Linguist., Indiana University, Bloomington, Ind., 1964.

29. S. Kuno, *The predictive analyzer and a path elimination technique*, Comm. Assoc. Comput. Mach. **8** (1965), no. 7, 453-462.

30. _____, *A system for transformational analysis*, The Mathematical Linguistics and Automatic Translation, Rep. NSF-15, Harvard Computation Laboratory, Cambridge, Mass., 1965.

31. _____, *The augmented predictive analyzer for context-free languages—its relative efficiency—*, Comm. Assoc. Comput. Mach. **9** (1966), no. 11, 810-823.

32. S. Kuno and A. G. Oettinger, *Multiple-path syntactic analyzer*, Information Processing-62, North-Holland, Amsterdam, 1963, pp. 306-312.

33. _____, *Syntactic structure and ambiguity of English*, AFIPS Conf. Proc., Vol. 24, Spartan, Baltimore, Md., 1963, pp. 397-418.

34. G. Lakoff, *On the nature of syntactic irregularity*, Ph.D. Thesis, Indiana University, Mathematical Linguistics and Automatic Translation, Rep. NSF-16, Harvard Computation Laboratory, Cambridge, Mass., 1965.

35. R. A. Langevin and M. F. Owens, "An application of computers to document analysis" in *Modern uses of logic in law*, 1964, pp. 72-81.

36. _____, *Computer analysis of the nuclear test ban treaty*, Science **146** (1964), no. 3648, 1186-1189.

37. G. H. Matthews, *Analysis by synthesis of sentences in a natural language*, 1961 International Conference on Machine Translation and Applied Language Analysis, Her Majesty's Stationery Office, London, England, 1962.

38. A. G. Oettinger, "Linguistics and mathematics" in *Studies presented to Josua Whatmough*, Mouton and Co., The Hague, Netherlands, 1957, pp. 179-186.

39. _____, "The state of the art of automatic language translation: an appraisal" in *Beiträge zur Sprachkunde und Informationsverarbeitung*, Vol. 2, Oldenboug Verlag, Munchen, 1963.

40. _____, *Computational linguistics*. II, Amer. Math. Monthly (2) **72** (1965), 147-150.

41. _____, *Automatic processing of natural and formal languages*, Proc. IFIP Congr. 65, Spartan Books, Inc., Washington, D. C., 1965, pp. 9-16.

42. S. R. Petrick, *A recognition procedure for transformational grammars*, Ph.D. Thesis, Massachusetts Institute of Technology, Cambridge, Mass., 1965.

43. W. Plath, "Mathematical linguistics" in *Trends in European and American linguistics*, Spectrum, Utrecht, 1961, pp. 21-57.

44. P. Postal, *Constituent structure: A study of contemporary models of syntactic description*. III, Internat. J. Amer. Linguist. **30** (1964), no. 1.

45. R. W. Ritchie and P. S. Peters, Jr., *On the generative capacity of transformational grammars*, Information and Control. (to appear)

46. J. Robinson, *Preliminary codes and rules for the automatic parsing of English*, RM-3339-PR, RAND, Santa Monica, Calif., 1962.

47. _____, *PARSE: a system for automatic syntactic analysis of English text*, Part I, RM-4654-PR, RAND, Santa Monica, Calif., 1965.

48. P. Rosenbaum and D. Lochak, *The core grammar*, and D. Lieberman, *Design of grammar tester*, Scientific Report for Contract AF-19 (628)-5127, 1966.

49. I. Sakai, *Syntax in universal translation*, Proc. 1961 International Conference on Machine Translation of Languages and Applied Language Analysis, Her Majesty's Stationery Office, London, England, 1962, pp. 593-608.

50. P. A. Shapiro, *The list-structured data-base question-answerer—a study of its evolution*, Papers presented at the Seminar in Mathematical Linguistics, conducted by A. G. Oettinger, S. Greibach and S. Kuno, The Computation Laboratory, Harvard University, 1966.

51. R. F. Simmons, *Answering English questions by computer: a survey*, Comm. Assoc. Comput. Mach. **8** (1965), no. 1, 53-70.

52. D. E. Walker and J. M. Bartlett, *The structure of languages for man and computer: problems in formalization,* First Congress on the Information Sciences, 1962.

53. _____ , *English preprocessor manual,* SR-132, MITRE, Bedford, Mass., 1964.

54. W. A. Woods, *Semantic interpretation of English questions on a structured data base,* Papers presented at the Seminar in Mathematical Linguistics, conducted by A. G. Oettinger, S. Greibach and S. Kuno, The Computation Laboratory, Harvard University, Cambridge, Mass. 1966.

55. D. H. Younger, *Context-free language processing in time* n^3, Proceedings 1966 Annual Symposium on Switching and Automata Theory, IEEE Conference Record 16 C 40, 1966, 7-20.

HARVARD UNIVERSITY
CAMBRIDGE, MASSACHUSETTS

P. Swinnerton-Dyer

THE USE OF COMPUTERS
IN THE THEORY OF NUMBERS

The customary reasons for using a computer are not very convincing when applied to pure mathematics. The function of a computer is to perform calculations on particular pieces of data, and thereby to produce particular new facts. The scheme of calculation may embody a general theorem, in which case the results will give a specific example of the theorem; but in pure mathematics examples simple enough to be illuminating are usually simple enough to be worked out by hand. A rather more promising line is to work out special cases of conjectures, in the hope of finding counter-examples: Lehmer has had some notable successes in this way. But as in backing horses, you only get a reward when you pick a winner; and when the conjecture is true there are no winners to pick.

The other thing to do is to pile up facts in the hope that if you look at them for long enough a pattern will emerge. Here I should emphasize that the magpie-like accumulation of facts for their own sake is worthless; what one is interested in is to elucidate the structure of the subject. In particular, such calculation is only profitable in a topic in which the theory appears to be incomplete—and incomplete not because new concepts are needed, but because there should exist as yet undiscovered relations between the existing concepts. In other words, one needs a topic in which there are a lot of loose ends crying out to be tied together. Such situations are relatively rare: one of them is the subject of my lecture.

Let $f(x, y) = 0$ be an inhomogeneous cubic equation with rational coefficients; can we find rational solutions of this equation, and if so, what can we say about the set of all its rational solutions? Put in geometric terms, we have a cubic curve and are interested in the rational points on it. This is a model for an important unsolved problem; in contrast, the theory for a quadratic equation is complete, and it is unlikely that there are any interesting theorems for quartic or higher curves. The main reason why the cubic is interesting is that the set of points on it form a commutative group in a natural way, and there is therefore a structure in terms of which results can be stated.

To simplify the description of the group law, assume that the cubic has the special form

(1) $$y^2 = x^3 - ax - b$$

with a, b integers (which is typical of the general case). Let the law of composition be denoted by an asterisk; then $A * B$ is defined to be the point M in the figure, where LM is vertical. It can be shown[1] that this

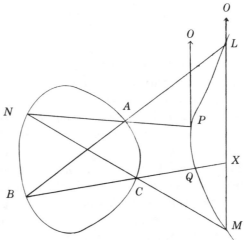

does give a commutative group law, with the point at infinity as the neutral element of the group. Obviously, if A and B are rational, so is $M = A * B$; thus the rational points on the curve themselves form a group. Mordell proved in 1922 that this group was finitely generated—that is, there are rational points $P_1, \cdots, P_g$ such that every rational point on the curve has the form

$$P_{i_1} * P_{i_2} * \cdots * P_{i_r}$$

for some $i_1, \cdots, i_r$. (If there are no rational points on the curve, except at infinity, we take $g = 0$.) His proof gives an upper bound for g (in terms of a and b); but it gives no way of finding the least value of g, still less the corresponding points $P_1, \cdots, P_g$ in any particular case. In practice one

---

[1] The only difficulty lies in proving the associative law $(A * B) * C = A * (B * C)$, which asserts that N—the point at which MC meets the curve again—lies on AP. To prove this, let O be the point at infinity on the curve, so that O lies on PQ and LM. There is a pencil of cubics generated by $f = 0$ and the degenerate cubic consisting of the three lines LAB, NCM and OPQ. Let $g = 0$ be that cubic in the pencil which contains X, the intersection of BC and LM; then $g = 0$ passes through all ten named points. Since it has four points in common with each of the lines $OLXM$ and $BCQX$, it contains each of them; hence it splits into three lines, and the third line must contain the remaining points N, A and P. Thus these three points are collinear.

can usually find these, by methods which I shall outline below; but there is no wholly reliable way of finding them, or even of deciding whether there are rational points on the curve at all.

What can we hope to express g in terms of? We must look for something which is large when there ought to be a lot of rational points on the curve; and we get a hint towards this from the known theory for the quadratic case. Clearly we can only solve $f(x,y) = 0$ if we can solve the congruences

$$(2) \qquad\qquad f(x,y) \equiv 0 \bmod p^m$$

for each prime p and each integer $m > 0$. If f is quadratic this condition is sufficient as well as necessary; but for a cubic equation we have to be more subtle. Indeed for the special Equation (1) the congruences are always all soluble. But one can argue heuristically as follows. To find a rational solution of (1) is the same as finding a compatible set of solutions of the congruences (2); and this will be comparatively easy to do if the congruences have on the average a large number of solutions, and comparatively hard if they have on the average rather few. Let $N(p^m)$ be the number of solutions of

$$y^2 \equiv x^3 - ax - b \bmod p^m$$

and suppose for simplicity that p does not divide $6(4a^3 - 27b^2)$. If c is prime to p and is a square $\bmod p$, then it is a square $\bmod p^m$; hence the integral solutions of $y^2 \equiv x^3 - ax - b \bmod p$ each give rise to p^{m-1} solutions $\bmod p^m$ provided y is prime to p, since each congruence class for $x \bmod p$ gives rise to p^{m-1} congruence class for $x \bmod p^m$. A similar argument works for the case when p divides y, and we deduce

$$N(p^m) = p^{m-1}N(p).$$

But the expected value of $N(p^m)$ is just p^m; for there are p^{2m} possible pairs $(x,y) \bmod p^m$ and p^m values which $y^2 - (x^3 - ax - b)$ can take $\bmod p^m$. Hence the ratio

(actual number of solutions of (2))/(expected number of solutions of (2))

is $p^{-1}N(p)$, which does not depend on m. This suggests that we should look at the product $\prod \{ p^{-1}N(p) \}$, but this is in fact an over-simplification. It would be equally plausible to allow for the fractional solutions of (2), which correspond to the point at infinity on (1); and this leads us to consider

$$(3) \qquad\qquad \prod \{ (N(p) + 1)/p \}.$$

At this level of argument, the choice between these two expressions is a matter of taste; what is decisive is that (3) can be expressed in terms of things which already turn up in the theory, and its rival cannot be.

It is not hard to calculate the individual terms of this product—one forms the possible values of $y^2 \bmod p$ and of $x^3 - ax - b \bmod p$, and compares them; and in this way $N(p)$ can be found in a number of operations proportional to p. Experiment showed that the partial product of the first thousand or so terms is large when g is large; but it also showed that the product behaved rather badly. It is known that

$$|N(p) - p| < 2p^{1/2}$$

and that no stronger statement need be true; and it is also known that

$$\prod_{p<P} \left(1 + \frac{1}{p}\right) \sim C \log P$$

for a certain constant C whose value is unimportant. Coupled with the numerical evidence, these facts led to the conjecture that

$$(\log P)^{-g} \prod_{p<P} \left\{\frac{N(p) + 1}{p}\right\}$$

is finitely oscillatory; there are good reasons why nothing stronger than this could reasonably hold. On the strength of this, Birch and I were able to predict the values of g from the behaviour of the partial products for a curve with almost invariable success; but we could not make our technique objective, and to our more sceptical pure mathematical friends the evidence was unconvincing.

Fortunately there is one type of equation for which one can go further than in the general case; this is the equation

$$y^2 = x^3 - ax$$

for which $b = 0$. It is now trivial that $N(p) = p$ for $p \equiv 3 \bmod 4$; for in this case -1 is not a square $\bmod p$ and so x and $-x$ together give just two solutions of the congruence. Moreover if $p \equiv 1 \bmod 4$, then it is possible to write $p = u^2 + v^2$ with u, v integers, and it is known that $N(p) = p + 2u$. (There are four possible values of u, but the rules for choosing the correct one are known.) Thus

$$(N(p) + 1)/p = 1 + p^{-1} \qquad\qquad \text{for } p \equiv 3 \bmod 4,$$

$$= (1 + 1/(u + iv))(1 + 1/(u - iv)) \quad \text{for } p \equiv 1 \bmod 4.$$

After some manipulation one can obtain the formal identity

$$(4) \qquad\qquad \prod \left\{\frac{N(p) + 1}{p}\right\}^{-1} = \underset{m,n}{\sum\sum}' \frac{\chi_a(m + in)}{m + in}$$

in which the sum is over all integers m, n with n even and $m - n \equiv 1 \bmod 4$; here χ_a is the biquadratic residue symbol (arising from the ambiguity in the choice of u), whose essential properties are that it is a fourth root of unity and that it depends only on a and the residue classes of m and n mod $4a$. (I have described this as formal, since the right-hand side only converges conditionally, and the left-hand side probably does not converge at all. One can rewrite (4) in wholly respectable terms, but it then becomes much more complicated.) We can express the right-hand side in finite terms by writing

$$m = 4ar + \mu, \qquad n = 4as + \nu$$

where r, s run through all integers and μ, ν through a finite set of values. Thus

$$(5) \quad \sum_{m,n}{}' \frac{\chi_a(m + in)}{m + in} = \sum_{\mu,\nu} \frac{\chi_a(\mu + i\nu)}{4a} \sum_{r,s} \left\{ r + is + \frac{\mu + i\nu}{4a} \right\}^{-1};$$

here the inner sum is a doubly periodic function of $\mu + i\nu$ and can therefore be expressed in terms of Weierstrass elliptic functions. Since the outer sum is finite, the right-hand side is effectively computable.

We can now put the conjecture into a form in which it can be tested on a computer; for it asserts that the right-hand side of (5) vanishes if and only if $g > 0$. In practice it is possible to calculate this to about seven significant figures, for Weierstrass elliptic functions are not very easy to deal with. But unexpectedly one can show that the value of the right-hand side is the product of an integer and a straightforward factor (which is in fact a constant multiple of $a^{-1/4}$); the integer can therefore be found exactly, and in this way the conjecture has been verified in several hundred cases.

Of course this is not the end of the story. The integer which has just turned up in the case $g = 0$ can be fitted into the theory; and much more detailed statements can be given in the case $g > 0$. But I have no time to say more about this now. The original conjectures, the numerical evidence, and the theory which underlies them, can be found in [1]. Far-reaching generalizations of them have been given by Tate in [2] and [3]. So far as I know, nobody doubts their truth; but also nobody has any idea of how to set about proving them.

For completeness, I should give some indication of how one finds g in practice; and for simplicity I will give a typical case in which one proves that $g = 0$. (One proves that $g > 0$ by actually exhibiting a solution, having found it by search: this is very dull.) Consider the case $a = 3$ and write $x = X/Z$, where X and Z are coprime integers. I wish to show that

(6) $$Y^2 = XZ(X^2 - 3Z^2)$$

has only the trivial solutions given by $X = 0$ or $Z = 0$. Since X and Z are coprime the highest common factor of XZ and $X^2 - 3Z^2$ is 3 if 3 divides X, and 1 otherwise. Hence we have either

(7) $$|X| = 3U_1^2, \quad |Z| = V_1^2, \quad |X^2 - 3Z^2| = 3W_1^2$$

for some integers U_1, V_1, W_1, or else

(8) $$|X| = U_2^2, \quad |Z| = V_2^2, \quad |X^2 - 3Z^2| = W_2^2.$$

But (7) implies $3U_1^4 - V_1^4 = \pm W_1^2$ with V_1 prime to 3; and since squares are congruent to 0 or 1 mod 3 the upper sign is impossible. Similarly (8) implies $U_2^4 - 3V_2^4 = \pm W_2^2$ in which the lower sign is impossible. Hence in either case we have coprime integers U, V, W such that

(9) $$U^4 - 3V^4 = W^2$$

and $0 < |UV| < |XZ|$. Congruences mod 8 show that U must be odd and V even. Thus if we write (9) in the form

$$(U^2 - W)(U^2 + W) = 3V^4$$

the highest common factor of the expressions on the left is 2. We can now repeat the type of argument above. After four such steps we obtain integers X_1, Y_1, Z_1 such that

$$Y_1^2 = X_1 Z_1 (X_1^2 - 3Z_1^2)$$

and $0 < |X_1 Z_1| < |XZ|$. If we start with the solution of (6) which minimizes $|XZ|$ —which we can do since this is an integer— then $0 < |X_1 Z_1| < |XZ|$ is impossible and we have obtained a contradiction. Hence there is no nontrivial solution of (6).

This sort of argument is tedious to repeat by hand for a large number of cases, but it can be completely mechanized.

REFERENCES

1. B. J. Birch and H. P. F. Swinnerton-Dyer, *Notes on elliptic curves. II*, J. für Math. **218** (1965), 79-108.

2. J. Tate, *Algebraic cycles and poles of zeta functions*, Proc. Purdue Conf. on Arithmetical Algebraic Geometry, 1965.

3. ———, *On the conjectures of Birch and Swinnerton-Dyer and a geometric analog*, Seminaire Bourbaki **306** (1966), 1-26.

TRINITY COLLEGE
CAMBRIDGE, ENGLAND

M. E. Mahowald
M. D. MacLaren[1]

A MACHINE CALCULATION
OF A SPECTRAL SEQUENCE

1. **Introduction.** Mathematicians interested in computing have, over the years, pointed out that computing machines can and should play a more extensive role in pure mathematical research than is true at present. Machines can be used by running a calculation to test a conjecture or by performing routine tasks. From both points of view homotopy theory is a reasonable area for such machine use. It is felt that the stable homotopy problem for spheres (see §2 for some definitions) could be solved if one had enough data in order to guess at an answer. It is not clear how much data would suffice but there are several efforts in this direction now. Our approach is to study spaces, the Stiefel manifolds, which in a certain sense are approximations to spheres, hoping to uncover some internal structure. This has been reasonably successful, and the machine computation played a strong role in this matter. It turns out that these spaces also are important in unstable groups (compare §2). The topological results and details are to be discussed elsewhere [5]. Here we will content ourselves with a short description of the topology which leads to the specific problem run on a machine. We will then discuss some of the details of the computation which was done. In a sentence: we used the machine to do most of the drudgery in computing $\pi_{k+p}(V_{k+m,m})$ for $m \geq p - 2$, $p \leq 28$, $k > p - 1$. The machine program would do the job for all m, but the restriction on p ($p < 28$) is a limit on our ambition, while the last inequality is important for theoretical reasons.

A totally different approach to the machine computation of this problem is due to Liulevicius [3].

2. **The topological problem.** Each topological space has certain algebraic invariants which play an important role in analyzing many mathematical problems. Probably the most familiar one involves a disk D in the complex plane. The notion of a winding number about a point gives an explicit

[1] Work supported by the U.S. Atomic Energy Commission and the U.S. Army Research Office (Durham). In addition the first named author is an Alfred P. Sloan Fellow.

representation of $\pi_1(D - pt)$, the fundamental group of $D - pt$. In an analogous fashion one can define groups $\pi_k(X)$ for each integer k and any reasonable topological space. These always are abelian if $k > 1$. As frequently happens in mathematics, the definition of the homotopy groups $\pi_k(X)$ is easy and intuitive. The determination of them is hard, and only for very few finite complexes has it been done. In particular if $n > 1$, then $\pi_k(S^n)$ is known only for a few values of k for each n, (actually $k - n \leq 44$, $k < 2n - 1$, and if $k - n \leq 22$ for a large number of n). The group $\pi_k(S^n)$ depends only on $k - n$ if $k < 2n - 1$ and is called the stable $(k - n)$-stem. If $k \geq 2n - 1$, then $\pi_k(S^n)$ is called an unstable group.

The object of the research effort which lead to this calculation is to better understand the homotopy problem. There are two reasons why knowledge of the homotopy of Stiefel manifolds, $V_{k+m,m}$, is useful for this. The first is that these groups are closely related to $\pi_k(S^n)$ for $4n - 3 > k > 2n - 2$. The second is that for $k = 2^i + 1$ and m large, $V_{k+m,m}$ is, in a theoretical sense, an approximation to a sphere. Just how is rather complicated, and the interested reader is referred to [5], Chapter II.

Adams has succeeded in breaking down the homotopy problem into two parts. The first part is a purely algebraic one and is very computational. The second is highly geometrical and so has not lent itself to much systemization. The machine calculation is concerned with the algebraic part only.

3. **The algebraic problem.** Let $H^*(X) = \sum_{i \geq 0} \tilde{H}^i(X, Z_2)$ where $\tilde{H}^i(X, Z_2)$ is the augmented cohomology with Z_2 $(= Z/2Z)$ for coefficients [4]. There is a homological functor called Ext [4] which may be applied to $H^*(X)$. The result, $\mathrm{Ext}(H^*(X), Z_2)$, is a bigraded algebra over Z_2, i.e., $\mathrm{Ext} = \sum_{s,t} \mathrm{Ext}^{s,t}$ where each component $\mathrm{Ext}^{s,t}$ is a finite dimensional vector space. If $\alpha \in \mathrm{Ext}^{s,t}$ and $\beta \in \mathrm{Ext}^{p,q}$, then $\alpha\beta \in \mathrm{Ext}^{s+p,t+q}$.

Adams has shown [1] that there is a spectral sequence of which the E_∞ term is associated with the stable homotopy groups of X and whose E_2 term is $\mathrm{Ext}(H^*(X), Z_2)$. In [5] a second spectral sequence is introduced whose E_∞ term is related to $\mathrm{Ext}(H^*(V_{k+m,m}), Z_2)$. It is this spectral sequence which is computed using the machine.

Before we continue we should discuss spectral sequences a bit. A spectral sequence is a sequence $E_1, E_2, \cdots$, of graded algebras and a sequence of maps $d_1, \cdots, d_r, \cdots$ such that $d_r: E_r \to E_r$, $d_r d_r = 0$, and d_r is a differential, $d_r(\alpha\beta) = d_r(\alpha)\beta + \alpha d_r(\beta)$. Anytime one has a map such as $d_r: E_r \to E_r$ one can define the homology group $\ker d_r / \mathrm{im}\, d_r$.[2] This new group is required to be E_{r+1} and d_{r+1} is the induced differential. In cases of interest it usually happens that the spectral sequence converges, i.e., $E_{r+1}^{s,t} = E_r^{s,t}$ for $r \geq r_0$, where r_0 usually depends on s and t. Note that the graded algebra may

---

[2] $\ker d_r = \{\alpha; d_r(\alpha) = 0\}$ and $\mathrm{im}\, d_r = \{\alpha; d_r\beta = \alpha \text{ for some } \beta\}$. Because $d_r^2 = 0$ $\mathrm{im}\, d_r$ $\subset \ker d_r$ and so $\ker d_r / \mathrm{im}\, d_r$ is defined.

have an infinite number of nonzero components. For fixed s_0 and t_0 it is only necessary to consider a finite part, say $s < n$ and $t < m$ to get $E_r^{s_0,t_0}$ and so on to get $E_\infty^{s_0,t_0}$.

Now we will describe the second spectral sequence which converges to Ext and whose computation is described in this note. The E_1 term of the spectral sequence is

$$E_1 = \sum_{n < m, s \geq 0, t \geq 0} E_1^{s,t,n}$$

where

$$E_1^{s,t,n} = \mathrm{Ext}^{s,t-n}(Z_2, Z_2).$$

The E_1 term depends only on m while the differentials depend only on the congruence class of $k + n \bmod$ an appropriate power of two. This means that the theoretical calculation for one Stiefel manifold implies the homotopy structure of all of them. Therefore one calculation is made by hand, the differentials are tabulated, and the machine produces all the remaining calculations.

4. **The calculation.** Just like E_1 each term E_r in the spectral sequence is a direct sum:

$$E_r = \sum_{s,t,n} E_r^{s,t,n}.$$

In the calculation we use only a finite part: $0 \leq s \leq s_{\max}$, $0 \leq t \leq t_{\max}$, $n < m$.[3] Since all the nonzero terms in E_1 are one or two dimensional, the same is true for the E_r. Therefore if $E_{r+1}^{s,t,n}$ is nonzero it is isomorphic either to $E_r^{s,t,n}$ or $E_r^{s,t,n}/\alpha$, where α is an element of $E_r^{s,t,n}$ such that $d_r(\alpha) \neq 0$ or $\alpha = d_r(\beta)$. Moreover the case $E_{r+1}^{s,t,n} \cong E_r^{s,t,n}/\alpha$ can only occur if $E_r^{s,t,n}$ and hence $E_1^{s,t,n}$ is two dimensional. From this it is clear that to represent E_r we need only keep a list of all triples (s, t, n) for which $E_r^{s,t,n} \neq 0$ and, in addition, note with each triple which element α, if any, is factored out.

Now to go from E_r to E_{r+1}, we take, one by one, the triples (s, t, n) on the list representing E_r and look at d_r applied to $E_r^{s,t,n}$. For the moment consider only the simple case where $E_1^{s,t,n}$ is one dimensional. Then, because E_r is an algebra over Z_2, $E_r^{s,t,n}$ contains a single nonzero element α. If $d_r(\alpha) = 0$, we simply pass on to the next triple on the list. Otherwise we must "kill" both α and the element $\beta = d_r(\alpha)$. Since $E_r^{s,t,n}$ is one dimensional, the triple (s, t, n) is simply deleted from the list. The element β is contained in $E_r^{s',t',n'}$, where $s' = s + 1$, $t' = t - 1$, $n' = n - r$. If this is one dimensional, either because $E_1^{s',t',n'}$ is one dimensional, or because an element has been factored out, then the triple (s', t', n') is deleted from the list. If $E_r^{s',t',n'}$ is two dimensional, we must record the fact that β is factored out. As $E_1^{s',t',n'}$ then

---

[3] For convenience in the calculation we replace the normal index t of the gradation by $t - s$.

contains just three distinct nonzero elements, this is quite simple. There is a code associated with the triple (s', t', n'), which is originally set equal to zero. When an element is factored out, the code is set equal to 1, 2, or 3 to indicate which element is involved.

The case where $E_1^{s,t,n}$ is two dimensional is slightly more complicated. Either $E_r^{s,t,n}$ is two dimensional or an element β has been factored out. In the first case, we simply check $d_r(\alpha)$ for all three elements α in $E_r^{s,t,n}$, then delete (s, t, n) if $d_r(\alpha) \neq 0$ for two of the elements, or factor out α if $d_r(\alpha) \neq 0$ for exactly one element. When an element β has been factored out, the two remaining elements are identified, so $d_r(\alpha)$ is checked for both of the elements α, and $E_r^{s,t,n}$ is deleted if either is nonzero.

In the above we have not said how $d_r(\alpha)$ is evaluated. Since $d_r(\alpha)$ must be in $E_r^{s+1,t-1,n-r}$, a series of tests is made: $s + 1 \leq s_{\max}$, $t - 1 \geq 0$, $n - r \geq 0$, $E_r^{s+1,t-1,n-r} \neq 0$. If any of these tests fail $E_r^{s+1,t-1,n-r}$ is zero, and hence $d_r(\alpha) = 0$. If all the tests are passed, $d_r(\alpha)$ must be evaluated symbolically. This symbolic calculation is done in Ext, and to describe it, we must discuss the structure of Ext in more detail.

Besides the ordinary algebraic structure, Ext has a special set of operators. These operators are really Massey products, but we only consider them as operators, each one being represented by some convenient symbol. Ext contains a set of elements $h_0, h_1, h_2, \cdots$ which are generators, in the sense that any element can be obtained from the h_i by taking products and applying operators. Now the map d_r from $E_r^{s,t,n}$ to $E_r^{s+1,t-1,n-r}$ can also be viewed as a map d_r' from $\text{Ext}^{s,t-n}$ to $\text{Ext}^{s+1,t-1-n+r}$, and it turns out that d_r' is either zero, multiplication by one of the generators, or multiplication by one of the operators. Exactly which depends on the congruence class of $k + n \bmod M$, where $r < M$, M is a power of two, and k is a parameter of the Stiefel manifold $V_{k+m,m}$. Thus to evaluate $d_r(\alpha)$, the congruence class of $k + n \bmod M$ is computed. Then, if this corresponds to a nonzero multiplier γ, the symbolic product $\beta = \gamma\alpha$, which is in $\text{Ext}^{s+1,t-1-n+r}$, is checked to see if it is nonzero.

The final problem in the calculation is then to determine which symbolic products are nonzero, or more generally to recognize different symbolic representations of the same element. Our solution to this problem is rather unsatisfying but at least workable. The input to the program includes a canonical symbolic representation for each nonzero element of Ext. In addition a list of equivalent representations is given. The list gives those equivalent representations which might occur in the calculation, i.e., those which are the product of a canonical representation and a multiplier corresponding to some d_r. In evaluating the differential d_r, the symbolic product $\beta = \gamma\alpha$ is compared with all the given symbolic representations of elements in $\text{Ext}^{s+1, t-1-n+r}$.

5. **Notes on the programming and execution of the calculation.** The computation was programmed for the CDC 3600 computer using the COGENT
programming system [6, 7]. This new system has several features which
were of significant value in carrying out the computation and it is perhaps
appropriate to say something about them.

The set of triples (s, t, n) for which $E_1^{s,t,n} \neq 0$ is rather sparse. This naturally
suggests using list processing techniques in order to effectively use the
computer memory. The COGENT system provides multiword list elements
(plexes) and automatically handles the recovery of unused storage. This
simplifies the programming and allows one a great deal of flexibility in
representing, within the machine, the structures to be manipulated. A
simple example is the representation of E_r—obviously not the best possible—shown in Figure 1.

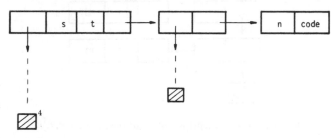

FIGURE 1. Internal representation of E_r by a list structure

As indicated earlier the differentials, d_r, were computed by hand and
this calculation was roughly equivalent to computing the spectral sequence
for one value of the parameter k. Examination of the results of the machine
computation for the same value of k provided a check on the differentials,
the program, and the input to the program. In this checking, which turned
up errors in all three areas, there was a great deal of interaction between
the machine computation and the hand computation. Obviously this was
a situation where it was important for the input and output of the machine
to be in a form convenient to the human user. COGENT has features
which are of great value in this connection, the most unusual being its
syntax analyzer.

The syntax analyzer is a routine which converts character strings, the
input to the machine, into list structures in the computer's memory.
COGENT will produce such a syntax analyzer from a set of productions,
which describe the desired translation process. The productions are written
in what is essentially the familiar Backus form [2]. In the course of its

---

[4] This symbol indicates the end of a list.

operation the syntax analyzer may call routines written by the programmer to perform manipulations on the list structures. An example of the sort of conversion that can be performed, with very little programming effort, is shown in Figure 2. This gives the internal representation of the symbolic product $P_1 h_0^3 h_3$. This is entered into the machine as "$P1(H0*3)H3$." For efficiency in comparing symbolic products, the set of triples representing a product is ordered by rank, the rank being a unique positive integer assigned automatically to each of the elementary symbols P_1, h_0, h_3, etc. In Figure 2 the rank is the first integer in each triple and has been chosen arbitrarily.

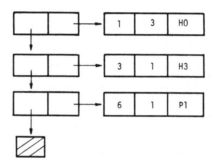

FIGURE 2. Internal representation of the product $P_1 h_0^3 h_3$

The output procedures of COGENT are very flexible. Using these it is possible to produce symbolic output in an efficient block-tabular form, even though the size of the blocks is variable and cannot be determined ahead of time. A sample of the output for E_{16} is shown in Figure 3. The leftmost column gives the index s and the top row the index t. Each block gives the values of n for which $E_{16}^{s,t,n} \neq 0$ and, in symbolic form, the corresponding element in Ext. The more complicated entry "$1..P2H3 + P1H1D0/(H0*2)I$" in block 9,24 indicates that $E_1^{9,28}$, was two dimensional, containing elements $P_2 h_3, P_1 h_1 d_0$, and $h_0^2 i$, and that $h_0^2 i$ has been factored out.

We might close with a few statistics on the computation. Compilation and assembly of the complete program required approximately seven minutes. Once all corrections to the program and input were made, the calculation of E_{16} for all values of k from 1 to 16 required approximately fifty-five minutes. A sizeable fraction of this time was used in the output routines, which, in their present form, do a lot of computation in an inefficient manner. Less than two minutes of the time was spent in storage recovery, proving that there are interesting symbolic computations in which storage recovery is not the main problem. The program was certainly

	18	19	20	21	22	23	24
0							
1	11..H3 3..H4				7..H4		
2	10..H1H3 2..H1H4 0..H2H4	5..(H3*2) 1..H2H4		7..(H3*2) 3..H2H4	6..H1H4	5..H2H4	
3	9..(H2*3) 4..H0(H3*2) 1..(H1*2)H4 0..H0H2H4	0..C1	6..H0(H3*2) 1..C1	2..C1 0..(H3*3)	5..(H1*2)H4 3..C1 1..(H3*3)	4..C1 2..(H3*3)	10..H0(H3*2) 3..(H3*3)
4	1..E0 0..(H0*2)H2H4, F0	1..F0	3..E0 0..G	3..F0 1..G	4..(H0*2)H2H4 0..H2C1	5..F0 3..G 1..H2C1 0..H4C0	2..H2C1 1..H4C0
5	0..H0F0		2..H0F0 0..H0G	0..H1G	1..H1G	2..H1G 0..H2G	1..H2G 0..H1H4C0
6			0..(H0*2)G			13..P1(H1*2) 0..H0H2G	
7					6..P1C0	12..P1(H0*2)H2 0..I	
8		4..(H0*7)H4			5..P1H1C0 0..P1D0	8..(H0*7)H4 1..P1D0 0..H0I	
9	1..P2H1	2..P2H1 0..P2H2			3..P2H2 0..P1H0D0	6..P2H1 0..P2H3, P1H1D0	1..P2H3+P1H1D0/(H0*2)I
10	0..P2(H1*2)	1..P2(H1*2) 0..P2H0H2			0..P1(H0*2)D0	5..P2(H1*2) 0..P2H0H3	2..P1(H0*2)D0 0..P1(H1*2)D0

FIGURE 3. Sample of printout of E_{16} with parameters $k = 16$ and $m = 30$

not written in an efficient fashion; efficiency was simply not important. The greatest gain in efficiency would come from using some sort of binary search procedure to locate given triples (s, t, n). The actual program simply does a linear search to find (s, t), then another one to find n. The computation did, however, take advantage of the periodicity of the d_r.

References

1. J. Frank Adams, *On the structure and applications of the Steenrod algebra*, Comment. Math. Helv. **32** (1958), 180-214.

2. J. W. Backus, *The syntax and sematics of the proposed international algebraic language of the Zurich ACM-GAMM Conference*, Proc. Internat. Conf. on Information Processing, UNESCO, Paris, June 1959, pp. 125-131.

3. A. Liulevicius, *Coalgebras, resolutions, and the computer*, Math. Algorithms **1** (1966), 4-12.

4. Saunders MacLane, *Homology*, Academic Press, New York, 1963.

5. Mark Mahowald, *The unstable homotopy of S^n*, Mem. Amer. Math. Soc. (to appear).

6. J. C. Reynolds, *COGENT programming manual*, Argonne National Laboratory, Lewis Winner, New York, 1965.

7. _____ , *An introduction to the COGENT programming system*, Proc. Nat. ACM Conf., 1965.

Northwestern University
    Evanston, Illinois

Argonne National Laboratory
    Argonne, Illinois

C. E. Leith[1]

NUMERICAL HYDRODYNAMICS
OF THE ATMOSPHERE

Introduction. By the end of the nineteenth century it was believed that the thermodynamic and hydrodynamic equations determining the flow of the earth's atmosphere were sufficiently well known to reduce the problem of weather prediction to a calculational process. Richardson's [1] attempt of 1911-1922 to carry out such a prediction met with unexplained failure after an enormous amount of hand calculation. In the 1940's using the electronic computer then available it was possible for a group of people under von Neumann's guidance to tackle this problem again, this time with such success that the use of numerical computation is at present the basis of routine 3-day weather prediction.

In trying to extend such calculations from a few days to many months it is necessary to take into account physical processes which are safely ignored for the shorter period. There arise also numerical difficulties which must be understood and overcome. Yet it is by long term numerical models that it is hoped some insight may be achieved into the importance of various external influences on the climate. Several groups [2, 3, 4] are working on this long-term problem with considerable success. There will be described here one numerical model and some of the mathematical and physical problems that arose in its construction.

Representation of state functions. The first question that arises in the planning of a numerical model of fluid flow concerns the most suitable numerical representation for the functions describing the hydrodynamic and thermodynamic state of the flow. Any choice represents of necessity a compromise, for any finite representation must be an approximation to the infinite amount of information characterizing the true state.

If the equations describing the evolution of the flow were a set of linear differential equations then linear theory suggests that a most natural choice would be a representation of the state functions by expansion on a

---

[1] This work was performed under the auspices of the U.S. Atomic Energy Commission.

basis of characteristic functions of the spatial differential operators involved. (To describe a flow confined to a spherical surface, for example, it would be natural to use surface spherical harmonics as a basis.) The original partial differential equations would be transformed thus into a set of ordinary time differential equations describing the evolution of the expansion coefficients, and in fact the state at any time could be computed as a sum of contributions from independently evolving components. This lacks being a complete solution to the problem in that we are restricted to a finite and incomplete basis. We only know (and perhaps need to know) the solution in a finite dimensional manifold, but the manifold is invariant and we can safely ignore the rest. We might call this process of decomposing the function space into a known and unknown manifold as linear truncation.

Unfortunately the equations for the flow include important nonlinear terms and the methods of linear analysis lose much of their effectiveness. If one proceeds as for the linear problem to make an expansion in functions characteristic for the linear spatial derivatives then the nonlinear terms are transformed into nonlinear sum relations linking the evolution of the coefficients. No longer is it possible to find an invariant finite dimensional known manifold without artifically cutting off the links to the unknown manifold. This further cutting off might be called then nonlinear truncation. Such "wave-number space" representations have been found useful in many investigations of the hydrodynamics of the atmosphere [5, 6, 7].

Perhaps the more common representation of the state functions is by their evaluation at a finite number of mesh points more or less uniformly distributed throughout the space-time domain of the original differential equations. The partial differential operators are then approximated by finite difference expressions reducing thereby the integration of the evolution equations to a numerical process. It is this approach which is followed in the model to be described here.

This configuration space representation has clearly also defined a known manifold in the function space; the unknown manifold contains functions which vanish at the mesh points. Unfortunately, even for the linear terms this known manifold is no longer invariant and there remain the further troubles of nonlinear interaction between manifolds. It would seem then that the configuration space approach has little to recommend it. Its principal virtue is that the nonlinear terms are differential and thus local in configuration space, while being nonlocal in wave number space. Nonlocal terms involve for their evaluation many more arithmetic operations than local terms; the ratio of arithmetic requirements being proportional to the dimension of the known manifold. This typically can be 10^5.

It has been pointed out that the configuration space mesh should be more or less uniformly distributed. No problem arises here if the spatial domain is a rectangular box for then each dimension can be subdivided uniformly into a mesh of equal intervals in the three space coordinates. Unfortunately the domain of the flow of the earth's atmosphere is more nearly a spherical shell. The choice of distribution of mesh points over the surface of a sphere involves further compromise. A natural choice of horizontal coordinates is latitude and longitude; the difference equations have a simple form for equal mesh intervals in these coordinates. This leads, however, to singularly narrow mesh zones in the polar region. Not only is this wasteful of computing power, but can for common and efficient choices of difference equations impose a too severe restriction on the choice of mesh time interval. The mesh which has been used for the model described here divides the region between 60°N and 60°S latitude into a horizontal mesh of 5° spacing in latitude and longitude. Between latitudes 60° and 75°, however, there is a coarsening of the longitudinal mesh to an interval of 10°. Between 75° and 80° the longitudinal interval is 20° and finally from 80° to 90° the interval is 40°. Such a choice introduces discontinuities in the mesh at the transition latitudes of 60°, 75°, and 80° which complicate the difference equations and introduce new sources of error. The pole is surrounded by nine triangular zones and requires special difference equations.

Another approach to this problem used by Smagorinsky [2] has been to carry out a coordinate transformation corresponding to a polar stereographic projection for, say, the northern hemisphere. Subdividing the projected map into a square mesh leads to reasonably uniformly shaped mesh elements with a factor of two variation in linear dimension between the pole and the equator. For global coverage it is necessary to use also a southern hemisphere projection and to carry information from one mesh to another at the equator by an interpolation process. This interpolation process is probably the weakest link in the procedure but this technique has been used successfully.

Another variant due to Phillips [8] has involved the similar patching together of polar stereographic projections for the polar regions to a Mercator projection for the equatorial zones, the connection being made at middle latitudes.

The most recent and potentially the most satisfactory solution to the mapping problem is one due to Kurahara [9] in which the discontinuous transitions of the first scheme are smoothed out so that each latitude circle has its own choice of longitudinal interval. The resulting mesh leads of course to more complicated finite difference equations and thus to more arithmetic operations.

The specification of the mesh intervals in the vertical direction is more straightforward. Although the earth's atmosphere extends tenuously indefinitely outward the part of it of greatest concern is where most of its mass is to be found. It is convenient and a good approximation for global models to assume that the atmosphere is in hydrostatic equilibrium. This means that the pressure at any particular point is due only to the weight per unit area of the air above that point and permits pressure to be used as a vertical (mass-like) coordinate. In this model the vertical mesh division is into six pressure layers. Such a coordinate scheme has removed the problem of an ill-defined upper boundary for the atmosphere, but it has replaced it with the problem of computing the position (i.e., pressure) of the lower boundary, the earth's surface, which now becomes a free boundary changing in space and time.

Differential equations. The dependent variables of the numerical model fall into two general classes called prognostic and diagnostic. The prognostic variables are those for which the time evolution is explicitly computed. At a given time the complete specification of all prognostic variables is necessary and sufficient to define the thermodynamic and hydrodynamic state of the model. The diagnostic variables on the other hand are derivable at a given time from the full set of prognostic variables at that time. As such they play a subsidiary role and are computed either for their own interest or for simplifying the calculational cycle. There is no unique way, of course, of choosing which variables are to be prognostic.

The choice made in this case is of prognostic variables specifying temperature, T; relative fraction of water vapor, μ; horizontal velocity components, u (west wind), v (south wind); and surface pressure p_s. The corresponding prognostic equations are the physical conservation laws for energy, water substance, momentum, and mass. These have been described fully elsewhere [4] and will only be listed here.

Independent Variables

t, time

θ, latitude

λ, longitude

p, pressure

Dependent Variables

Prognostic

T, temperature

μ, water vapor

u, west wind

v, south wind

p_s, surface pressure

Diagnostic

D, horizontal wind divergence

ω, vertical "velocity" dp/dt

ϕ, geopotential gz where z is height

θ, potential temperature (a measure of entropy)

T', virtual temperature

Constants

Geophysical

a, radius of the earth

Ω, angular velocity of the earth's rotation

g, acceleration of gravity

Thermodynamic

C_p, specific heat at constant pressure for dry air

R, gas constant for dry air

$\kappa = R/C_p$

$R' = $ gas constant for water vapor

$\sigma = R/R'$

Equations

Prognostic

$$\frac{\partial T}{\partial t} + u\frac{1}{a\cos\theta}\frac{\partial T}{\partial \lambda} + v\frac{1}{a}\frac{\partial T}{\partial \theta} + \omega\frac{T}{\theta}\frac{\partial \theta}{\partial p} = \frac{1}{C_p}\dot{q},$$

$$\frac{d\mu}{dt} = \frac{\partial \mu}{\partial t} + u\frac{1}{a\cos\theta}\frac{\partial \mu}{\partial \lambda} + v\frac{1}{a}\frac{\partial \mu}{\partial \theta} + \omega\frac{\partial \mu}{\partial p} = \dot{r},$$

$$\frac{du}{dt} - \left\{2\Omega\sin\theta + \frac{u\tan\theta}{a}\right\}v = -\frac{1}{a\cos\theta}\frac{\partial \phi}{\partial \lambda} + F_\lambda,$$

$$\frac{dv}{dt} + \left\{2\Omega\sin\theta + \frac{u\tan\theta}{a}\right\}u = -\frac{1}{a}\frac{\partial \phi}{\partial \theta} + F_\theta,$$

$$\frac{\partial p_s}{\partial t} + u_s\frac{1}{a\cos\theta}\left(\frac{\partial p_s}{\partial \lambda}\right)_s + v_s\frac{1}{a}\left(\frac{\partial p_s}{\partial \theta}\right)_s = \omega_s.$$

Diagnostic

$$D = \frac{1}{a\cos\theta}\left[\frac{\partial u}{\partial \lambda} + \frac{\partial v\cos\theta}{\partial \theta}\right],$$

$$\omega = -\int_0^p D(p')\,dp',$$

$$\phi = \phi_s - R\int_{p_s}^p T'\,d(\ln p'),$$

$$\theta = Tp^\kappa,$$

$$T' = (1 + ((1-\sigma)/\sigma)\,\mu)\,T.$$

Here the operator d/dt indicates the individual or Lagrangian time deriva-
tive defined as for $d\mu/dt$ above, and the subscript s indicates evaluation
at the earth's surface.

The term $\dot{q}/C_p$ on the right-hand side of the temperature equation
includes calculated eddy diffusion and convective processes as well as
various energy sources and sinks. There are computed contributions to
this term from the absorption of solar radiation, release of latent heat
when condensation occurs, and the divergence of infrared radiation flux.

The term $\dot{r}$ on the right-hand side of the water vapor equation likewise
includes calculated eddy diffusion and convective processes, condensation
and precipitation, and in the lowest layer the evaporation of water from
ocean surfaces.

The terms F_λ, F_θ on the right-hand side of the momentum equation
include calculated frictional stresses both internal and at the earth's
surface.

The last prognostic equation for surface pressure change describes the
conservation of mass. For this there are no external sources or sinks.

The surface temperature and moisture are specified as time-independent
functions of latitude and longitude and serve as boundary conditions for
the model. The geography of the distribution of continents and oceans is
specified only through these functions.

Difference equations. Although there seems to be no single way of choosing
among the various finite difference approximations to the differential
equations of the system, there are a number of important pitfalls to avoid
and guides to follow. We may write the original differential equation
system as

$$(1) \qquad\qquad d\Psi/dt = \mathfrak{A}\Psi$$

where Ψ is the state function vector in an appropriate function space of
solutions and $\mathfrak{A}$ is an operator which is not necessarily linear nor bounded.
Our choice of finite difference approximation whatever it may be leads to
an approximation to (1) by

$$(2) \qquad\qquad d\psi/dt = A\psi$$

where now ψ is the state vector in the finite dimensional known manifold
M and A is an operator on M. It is evident that in some sense A should
as closely approximate $\mathfrak{A}$ as possible. If we consider next the finite sub-
division of the time variable t into discrete time points, $\cdots, t^{n-1}, t^n, t^{n+1}, \cdots$
we typically approximate (2) still further by

$$(3) \qquad\qquad (\psi^{n+1} - \psi^n)/(t^{n+1} - t^n) = A\psi^n$$

or sometimes by

(4) $$(\psi^{n+1} - \psi^n)/(t^{n+1} - t^n) = A(\psi^n + \psi^{n+1})/2.$$

For nonlinear systems A is nonlinear, a function of ψ, but we may consider it evaluated for $\psi = \psi^n$ and treat it for the moment as linear. Since M is finite dimensional A is in fact a matrix.

Letting $\Delta t = t^{n+1} - t^n$ we see then that either for (3)

(5) $$\psi^{n+1} = (I + A\,\Delta t)\,\psi^n$$

or for (4)

(6) $$\psi^{n+1} = (I - A\,\Delta t/2)^{-1}(I + A\,\Delta t/2)\,\psi^n$$

where I is the identity matrix. In either case we may write

(7) $$\psi^{n+1} = R\psi^n$$

where the recursion matrix R is, in some sense, close to the identity.

During the interval $\Delta t = t^{n+1} - t^n$ the original differential equation could be integrated (letting $\mathfrak{A}$ be linear and normal for the moment) to give

(8) $$\Psi^{n+1} = \exp(\mathfrak{A}\,\Delta t)\,\Psi^n.$$

For many physical problems the operator $\exp(\mathfrak{A}\Delta t)$ has norm $\|\exp(\mathfrak{A}\Delta t)\| \leq 1$. Thus for any Ψ^n we have $|\Psi^{n+1}| \leq |\Psi^n|$. In these cases it is important that the approximating operator R also have norm $\|R\| \leq 1$, i.e., that the spectrum of R lie on or in the unit circle. For otherwise for some characteristic vector ϕ

$$|\phi^{n+1}| = |r|\,|\phi^n| \quad \text{with} \quad |r| > 1$$

and $|\phi^{n+m}| = |r|^m|\phi^n|$ leading to exponential growth. Even though $\phi^0 = 0$ at time $t = 0$ errors due to arithmetic rounding could introduce some nonzero component in the ϕ direction which would eventually erroneously dominate the solution. A finite difference approximation that errs in this way is called unstable and is obviously to be avoided. The ease of naively choosing an unstable differencing scheme can be illustrated by considering an operator $\mathfrak{A}$ in Equation (1) whose spectrum is pure imaginary. Then the operator $\exp(\mathfrak{A}\Delta t)$ in (8) is unitary, its spectrum lies on the unit circle and we run the greatest risk of instability in any approximation. Even though we choose an approximation A whose spectrum is pure imaginary we arrive at an unstable differencing scheme with Equations (3) and (5) but a stable scheme with Equations (4) and (6).

In practice it is often very difficult to determine the spectral characteristics of the operator $\mathfrak{A}$ or even of a finite difference approximation A to it. What is done is to write $\mathfrak{A}$ as a sum

$$\mathfrak{A} = \mathfrak{A}_1 + \mathfrak{A}_2 + \cdots + \mathfrak{A}_m$$

of operators corresponding in our case to terms or groups of terms appearing on the right-hand side of the prognostic equations. We have then broken the approximation problem into analyzable pieces, and we make corresponding choices $A_1, A_2, A_3, \cdots, A_m$. Perhaps the most natural choice of the composite operator A is

$$(9) \qquad\qquad A = A_1 + A_2 + \cdots + A_m.$$

Unfortunately the stability of any scheme leading to some R_i with $\|R_i\| \leq 1$ for each A_i does not guarantee the stability of the corresponding scheme for A. However, if we combine the separate schemes not by Equation (9) but rather by

$$(10) \qquad\qquad R = R_1 \cdot R_2 \cdot \cdots \cdot R_m,$$

it is easy to see that since $\|R_i\| \leq 1$ then so is also $\|R\| \leq 1$, and the composite scheme retains the stability of the parts. This is the basis for the method of splitting or the method of fractional time steps [10, 11] so called because the calculational time step can be considered to be composed of a series of fractional time steps in each of which is evaluated

$$(11) \qquad\qquad \psi^{n+l/m} = R_l \psi^{n+(l-1)/m}.$$

Nonlinear problems. It has already been pointed out that nonlinear terms in the differential equations of hydrodynamic flow lead to an interaction between the known and unknown manifold in a wave number space representation, and that this difficulty is not removed by using a configuration space representation.

In the case of a numerical model of the atmosphere we may view this difficulty as being due to the turbulent nature of the flow. It is clearly impossible to define and compute all motions on all scales. The detailed motion of a dust devil whirling down an alley in Calcutta or of the air currents swirling about a mountain peak in the Sierra Nevada of North America must remain undescribed in any global model. In fact with a horizontal mesh interval of the order of 500 kilometers we can only hope to explicitly describe scales of motion of horizontal dimensions of the order of 1000 kilometers and larger. The influence of the smaller scales of motion on the behavior of the larger explicitly computed scales must be treated statistically. Turbulence theory in its present state gives no clear answer as to how this should be done, only a few suggestions, which are being followed.

In a three-dimensional isotropic and homogeneous turbulent flow the effect of nonlinear terms is to permit large scale motions to interact in such a way that there tends to be a transfer of energy to smaller scales. Any finite difference model of such a flow should also lead to such an energy cascade but now a natural limit is imposed by the mesh interval on how far this process can be properly computed. It has been observed [2] that in finite difference models energy transfer to scales outside the describable range does not simply vanish from the system but rather through an "aliasing" process reappears erroneously as an increase in energy at the low wave number (large scale) alias of the proper wave number. The low wave numbers are hopefully those of greatest significance in the calculation, and the first problem is to try to prevent their being contaminated by this aliasing error. To the extent that the nonlinear processes are removing energy from describable wave numbers the effect may be likened to a dissipation, and it is tempting to introduce an "artificial" viscosity term in such a way that it will remove that amount of energy which in fact is being removed by nonlinear transfer processes. Such an approach has been taken by Smagorinsky [2] and Lilly [14].

The artificial (kinematic) viscosity coefficient ν so introduced should depend on some limit scale λ and on the rate of energy removal ϵ. If it depends only on these quantities, then dimensional arguments suggest the form

$$\nu = \alpha \epsilon^{1/3} \lambda^{4/3}$$

where α is a dimensionless coefficient to be determined by numerical experiment. This is in fact the eddy diffusion or viscosity coefficient discovered by Richardson [15] who observed that larger clusters of mass points embedded in a turbulent flow of air or water are dispersed more rapidly by the inclusion within the cluster of a wider range of scales of random motion. Thus eddies of 1 meter dimension will contribute to the dispersal of a 3 meter diameter cluster but will only transport a 30 cm diameter cluster.

The limit scale λ can be taken as proportional to the linear dimension of the mesh interval or in fact equal to it since α is adjustable. The choice of ϵ is less straightforward.

One can take ϵ to be the average value over the whole flow of the dissipation rate. For the atmosphere this has been estimated as about 5 ergs/gram second. Once such a choice has been made, the artificial viscosity coefficient is seen to be a constant. Its value is in fact determined by what is required to maintain relatively meaningful flow in the numerical model.

A more sophisticated approach to the evaluation of ϵ is to take it as locally computed for each mesh interval. Then

$$\epsilon = \nu D^2$$

where D^2 is the finite difference approximation to a deformation rate and as such accounts only for large scale motions. But then

$$v = \alpha v^{1/3} D^{2/3} \lambda^{4/3}$$

or

$$v = \alpha^{3/2} |D| \lambda^2.$$

These estimates of the eddy viscosity coefficient are based on theories of the nature of turbulence in three-space dimensions. For the scales of motion of concern in atmospheric models the turbulent flow is confined more nearly to two dimensions, and many of the ideas of three-dimensional turbulence are no longer appropriate. In particular the vorticity conservation constraint imposed on two-dimensional flows is known [16, 17] to seriously alter the energy cascade process. Although the nature of two-dimensional turbulence is even less well understood than that of three-dimensional turbulence yet this constraint may well have an important effect in decreasing the rate of nonlinear energy transfer to larger wave numbers. Such a hope is the basis for choosing a finite difference scheme [18] which identically preserves the constraint and which seems to have been successful in decreasing the "artificial" viscosity coefficient needed for satisfactory integrations.

In the case of flow in one-space dimension turbulence as such can not develop, but the development of shock fronts has somewhat the same aspect of an energy cascade into higher wave numbers. We may now compute

$$|D| = |\Delta u / \Delta x|$$

where x is the space coordinate, u the velocity. The artificial pressure q produced by the artificial viscosity becomes then

$$q = -v \Delta u / \Delta x = -\alpha^{3/2} \lambda^2 \Delta u |\Delta u| / (\Delta x)^2$$

$$= -\alpha^{3/2} \Delta u |\Delta u|$$

which is the form proposed by von Neumann and Richtmyer [19] and used successfully in shock hydrodynamics calculations for 15 years.

Convection problems. An aspect of the influence of unknown small scales on known large scales which is specifically encountered in atmospheric models is that of convection. A familiar sight under certain atmospheric conditions is the towering cumulus convection cells of thunderstorms. These transport upward vast quantities of heat and moisture. Yet being only a few kilometers in size they evidently cannot be explicitly described by the model. The largest single energy source to the whole atmosphere is the release of latent heat in convection cells in the tropics. Unless this source can be computed with reasonable accuracy the model must remain inaccurate. In particular in models with a resolution of the vertical dimension into many layers the vertical transport by convection can be far more important than by explicitly described motions in determining the vertical temperature and moisture distribution. The solution to this problem consists in knowing the statistical laws for average convective transport given as functions of the large scale average moisture, temperature, and wind distributions. Such statistical laws are not yet well known either from theoretical prediction or from observation.

The problem of thermal convection has been worked on theoretically continuously since Rayleigh's solution of the problem of the onset of Bernard cell convection. Recent work [20, 21] on convection in a single fluid such as dry air has extended the theory into the more pertinent domain of fully developed, large amplitude, nonlinear convection. Convection in the atmosphere is further complicated by the possible phase change from water vapor to liquid with associated latent heat release. A linear theory of such moist convection has been worked on recently by Kuo [22].

While waiting for the solution to this problem it is possible to formulate some likely convective laws which include a few undetermined parameters. Such tentative laws can be introduced into the numerical models and the parameters adjusted until the model agrees with the real atmosphere in its behavior. There is, of course, the danger in this procedure that one can obtain the correct behavior for the wrong reasons. It is clear also that no longer can it be said that the complicated behavior of the atmosphere is being deduced from a set of simple fundamental physical laws but rather that the fundamental laws are being induced from the observed behavior.

It is hoped that a part of some final theory of convection will be an accurate prediction of cloud amount for this in turn influences the calculation of the heating by solar radiation and even more important the energy transfer by infrared radiation.

Results of calculation. Many years ago it was pointed out that a certain paradox existed in the search for an accurate numerical model of the atmosphere for, should it be found, its behavior would be just as complicated and just as little understood as that of the real atmosphere. In what sense could it then be said that the equations of atmospheric motion had been solved? The answer could be that an algorithm had been found that permits in any particular case the prediction of resulting behavior. The algorithm is, however, unusually time consuming and expensive to carry out, and the results are too complex to be readily comprehended.

The model state vector has some 50,000 components and the listing of these as a function of time is overwhelmingly noninformative. Much effort is being expended on this information problem; the natural first step is to represent the fields of meteorological variables as contour maps similar to the surface-pressure maps published in the daily newspaper. Experience has shown that one can thus display the information contained in about 1000 components as a single map (in agreement with an early estimate credited to Confucius). By superposition in different colors two or three such maps may be displayed together, and finally by use of successive maps as motion picture frames a time lapse motion picture can be produced. Even all this technique involves the selection of only a part of the total information contained in the model. It is enough, however, to show that the model simulates many of the observed features of the real atmosphere. Calculations carried out for external conditions corresponding to mid-January have shown the development of characteristic surface low-pressure regions around Iceland and the Aleutians, a well developed and maintained jet stream, trade winds and convergence zones in the tropics, and the birth, motion, and death of cyclonic disturbances in mid-latitudes.

The results of the calculation are seen to be then animated color cartoons of the behavior of a more or less realistic model of the earth's atmosphere. If this were all it would seem an amusing but expensive toy. The more important benefit is the ability to carry out experiments with the model that would be impossible or irresponsible with the real atmosphere. These can determine the relative importance of various external influences on the behavior of the atmosphere. The model also serves to exhibit by its limitations those areas of significant ignorance (such as moist convection) for which the rewards of further research may prove the greatest.

References

1. L. F. Richardson, *Weather prediction by numerical process,* Cambridge Univ. Press, New York; 1922, p. 236; reprint, Dover, New York, 1965.

2. J. Smagorinsky, S. Manabe and J. L. Holloway, Jr., *Numerical results from a nine-level general circulation model of the atmosphere,* Monthly Weather Rev. 93 (1965), 727-768.

3. Y. Mintz, *Very long-term global integration of the primitive equations of atmospheric motion,* WMO Technical Note No. 66, WMO-IUGG Symposium on Research and Development Aspects of Long Range Forecasting, Boulder, Colo., 1964, Geneva, 1965, pp. 141-167.

4. C. Leith, *Numerical simulation of the earth's atmosphere,* Methods in Computational Physics, Vol. IV, Academic Press, New York, 1965, pp. 1-28.

5. G. Platzman, *The analytic dynamics of the spectral vorticity equation,* J. Atmospheric Sci. 19 (1962), 313-328.

6. F. Baer, *Integration with the spectral vorticity equation,* J. Atmospheric Sci. 21 (1964), 260-276.

7. H. W. Ellsaesser, *Evaluation of spectral versus grid methods of hemispheric numerical weather prediction,* J Appl. Meteor. 5 (1966), 246-262.

8. N. Phillips, *A map projection system suitable for large scale numerical weather prediction,* J. Meteor. Soc. Japan 75 (1957), 262-267.

9. Y. Kurahara, *Numerical integration of the primitive equations on a spherical grid,* Monthly Weather Rev. **93** (1965), 399-415.

10. K. Bagrinovsky and S. Godunov, Dokl. Akad. Nauk SSSR **115** (1957), 3.

11. G. I. Marchuk, *A new approach to the numerical solution of differential equations of atmospheric processes,* WMO Technical Note No. 66, WMO-IUGG Symposium on Research and Development Aspects of Long Range Forecasting, Boulder, Colo. 1964, Geneva, 1965, pp. 212-226.

12. N. A. Phillips, *An example of nonlinear computational instability,* Rossby Memorial Volume, Rockefeller Inst. Press, New York, 1959.

13. J. Smagorinsky, *General circulation experiments with the primitive equations.* I, *The basic experiment,* Monthly Weather Rev. **91** (1963), 99-164.

14. D. Lilly, *On the numerical simulation of buoyant convection,* Tellus **14** (1962), 148-172.

15. L. F. Richardson, *Atmospheric diffusion shown on a distance-neighbor graph,* Proc. Roy. Soc. London Ser. A **110** (1926), 709.

16. T. D. Lee, *Difference between turbulence in a two-dimensional fluid and in a three-dimensional fluid,* J. Appl. Phys. **22** (1951), 524.

17. R. Fjortoft, *On the changes in the spectral distribution of kinetic energy for two-dimensional, nondivergent flow,* Tellus **5** (1953), 225-230.

18. A. Arakawa, *Computational design for long-term numerical integration of the equations of fluid motion: two-dimensional incompressible flow.* Part I, J. Comput. Phys. **1** (1966), 119-143.

19. J. von Neumann and R. D. Richtmyer, *A method for the numerical calculation of hydrodynamic shocks,* J. Appl. Phys. **21** (1950), 232-237.

20. E. A. Spiegel, *Thermal turbulence at very small Prandtl number,* J. Geophys. Res. **67** (1962), 3063-3070.

21. L. N. Howard, *Heat transport by turbulent convection,* J. Fluid Mech. **17** (1963), 405-432.

22. H. L. Kuo, *Further studies of the properties of cellular convection in a conditionally unstable atmosphere,* Tellus **17** (1965), 413-433.

LAWRENCE RADIATION LABORATORY
UNIVERSITY OF CALIFORNIA
LIVERMORE, CALIFORNIA

J. F. Traub

THE CALCULATION
OF ZEROS OF POLYNOMIALS
AND ANALYTIC FUNCTIONS

1. **Introduction.** We study a class of new methods for the calculation of zeros. In §§2 through 8 we treat the case of a polynomial with all distinct zeros and one zero of largest modulus. We studied this case in detail in [16]. Here we give a simplified treatment and also obtain some new results. In §§9 and 10 we treat the case of a zero of smallest modulus.

In the remaining sections we discuss the calculation of multiple zeros and equimodular dominant zeros of polynomials and zeros of analytic functions. Detailed analysis of these matters as well as material concerning the calculation of subdominant zeros will appear elsewhere.

2. **Description of the basic algorithm for the dominant zero of a polynomial.** Let

$$(2.1) \qquad P(t) = \sum_{j=0}^{n} a_j t^{n-j}, \ a_0 = 1$$

be a polynomial with complex coefficients and with zeros $\rho_1, \rho_2, \cdots, \rho_n$. In §§2 through 8 we assume the zeros are distinct and $|\rho_1| > |\rho_i|$, $i > 1$. We generate a sequence of polynomials as follows. Let $B(t)$ be an arbitrary polynomial of degree at most $n - 1$ such that $B(\rho_1) \neq 0$. Define

$$(2.2) \qquad \begin{aligned} G(0, t) &= B(t), \\ G(\lambda + 1, t) &= tG(\lambda, t) - \alpha_0(\lambda) \, P(t), \end{aligned}$$

where $\alpha_0(\lambda)$ is the leading coefficient of $G(\lambda, t)$. Then all the $G(\lambda, t)$ are polynomials of degree at most $n - 1$.

We generate the $G(\lambda, t)$ until we have calculated, say, $G(\Lambda, t)$. We use $G(\Lambda, t)$ to construct an iteration function. (In the remainder of this paper we do not distinguish between the running index λ and a fixed value of λ equal to Λ.) We choose an initial approximation t_0 and generate a sequence $\{t_i\}$ by

$$(2.3) \qquad t_{i+1} = \phi(\lambda, t_i)$$

where

$$(2.4) \qquad \phi(\lambda, t) = t - \alpha_0(\lambda) \, P(t)/G(\lambda, t).$$

The t_i form the approximating sequence for ρ_1.

We have described a two-stage algorithm.

a. Preprocessing stage: This is specified by the recursion for the G polynomials given by (2.2).

b. Iteration stage: This is specified by (2.3) and (2.4).

3. **A numerical example.** For illustration we calculate the dominant zero of

$$P(t) = (t + 1)(t - 2)(t + 3) = t^3 + 2t^2 - 5t - 6.$$

We choose

$$G(0, t) = t^3 - P(t) = -2t^2 + 5t + 6.$$

(The reason for this choice of $G(0, t)$ is explained in §4.) Then

$$G(1, t) = 9t^2 - 4t - 12$$

$$\vdots$$

$$G(9, t) = 53417t^2 - 52052t - 105468.$$

We now iterate using

$$\phi(9,t) = t - P(t)\,\alpha_0(9)/G(9,t),$$

and choosing $t_0 = 100000$ as our initial approximation. We calculate the sequence of approximations exhibited in Table 1. The sequence is converging alternatingly towards the zero at -3 which is the largest zero in modulus. In the right-hand column we exhibit the ratios of successive errors. After the first iteration these ratios are constant. This is as expected because the method used here is first order. (The extension to higher order is described in §4.) Observe that all the ratios are small and that the initial ratio is particularly small. These facts are characteristic of the method and are quantitatively explained in §7.

TABLE 1. Sequence of Approximants

i	t_i	$(t_{i+1} - \rho_1)/(t_i - \rho_1)$
0	100000.	
1	-2.97	2.6×10^{-7}
2	-3.0001	-5.2×10^{-3}
3	-2.9999993	-5.1×10^{-3}
4	-3.000000003	-5.1×10^{-3}
5	-2.99999999998	-5.1×10^{-3}
6	-3.00000000000009	-5.1×10^{-3}

$$\rho_1 = -3.$$

Note that the rate of convergence of the iteration "looks" numerically quadratic over the entire range of the iteration even though it is asymptotically a first-order process. The explanation for this lies in that the error at each step is the product of two small errors, one of which is the error at the previous step. See §7. This should be contrasted with the behavior of, say, the Newton-Raphson iteration which is asymptotically quadratic but which behaves linearly when the approximations are far from the zeros. (The reader is referred to Forsythe [6] for an example of this.)

4. **Comments on and extensions of the basic algorithm.** Note that the recursion for the G polynomials defined by (2.2) is easily performed by hand or machine. The multiplication by t is only a shift. All that is then required is a scalar-vector multiplication at each step. Another method for generating the $G(\lambda,t)$ which calculates $G(2\lambda,t)$ directly from $G(\lambda,t)$, $G(\lambda+1,t), \cdots, G(\lambda+n-1,t)$ is described in Traub [16, pp. 126-129].

From (2.2) it follows that $\phi(\lambda,t)$, which is defined by

(4.1) $$\phi(\lambda,t) = t - P(t)\,\alpha_0(\lambda)/G(\lambda,t),$$

may also be written as

(4.2) $$\phi(\lambda, t) = G(\lambda + 1, t)/G(\lambda, t).$$

Since, as we verify in §6, $\alpha_0(\lambda)$ does not vanish for λ sufficiently large, (4.2) exhibits the iteration function as the ratio of polynomials of degree exactly $n - 1$. This form is used when t is large. Equation (4.1) exhibits $\phi(\lambda, t)$ in incremental form.

It may be shown that if any of the zeros of P have magnitude greater than unity, then the coefficients of $G(\lambda, t)$ increase without limit. On the other hand, if all the zeros lie within the unit circle, $G(\lambda, t)$ converges to the zero polynomial. This difficulty is taken care of as follows: Let $\bar{h}(t)$ denote a polynomial $h(t)$ divided by its leading coefficient. We show in §6 that

$$\lim_{\lambda \to \infty} \bar{G}(\lambda, t) = \frac{P(t)}{t - \rho_1}.$$

Hence $\bar{G}(\lambda, t)$ has well-behaved coefficients. The $\bar{G}(\lambda, t)$ satisfy the recursion

(4.3)
$$\bar{G}(\lambda + 1, t) = t\overline{\bar{G}(\lambda, t) - P(t)} \quad \text{if} \quad \alpha_0(\lambda) \neq 0,$$
$$\bar{G}(\lambda + 1, t) = t\overline{\bar{G}(\lambda, t)} \quad \text{if} \quad \alpha_0(\lambda) = 0.$$

We can write the iteration function as

(4.4) $$\phi(\lambda, t) = t - P(t)/\bar{G}(\lambda, t).$$

We turn to the question of choosing the arbitrary polynomial $B(t)$ that appears in (2.2). Recall that $B(t)$ can be any polynomial of degree at most $n - 1$ such that $B(\rho_1) \neq 0$. Two natural choices for $B(t)$ are $B(t) = P'(t)$ and $B(t) = 1$. If $B(t) = G(0, t) = 1$, it is easy to show that $G(n, t) = t^n - P(t)$. Hence we might as well take $B(t) = G(0, t) = t^n - P(t)$ and this was done in the numerical example of §3. Additional discussion of the choice of $B(t)$ may be found in §11.

The iteration function $\phi(\lambda, t)$ is first order. From $G(\lambda, t)$ and its derivatives and $P(t)$ and its derivatives one may construct iteration functions of arbitrarily high order. A general treatment is presented in Traub [16], pp. 116-119.

Because of the rapidity of convergence of this type of method we would generally not use an iteration function of order greater than two. The second-order iteration function is given by

$$\phi_2(t) = t - P(t) G(\lambda, t)/(P'(t) G(\lambda, t) - P(t) G'(\lambda, t)).$$

We give a simple numerical example of a second-order iteration. Let $P(t) = t^4 - 46t^3 + 528t^2 - 1090t + 2175$. The zeros are $\rho_1 = 29$, $\rho_2 = 15$, $\rho_{3,4} = 1 \pm 2i$. We take $B(t) = 1$, $\lambda = 16$ and choose our initial approximation as $t_0 = 100000$. We calculate

$$t_1 = 28.9996,$$

$$t_2 = 28.9999999999997.$$

The other iteration functions discussed in later sections of this paper could also be made of arbitrary order. For the sake of simplicity of exposition we shall confine ourselves to the first-order case.

5. **Global convergence.** We state without proof the theorem of global convergence for the iteration functions $\phi(\lambda, t)$. A proof of this theorem in a form which covers the extension to iteration functions of arbitrary order may be found in Traub [16], pp. 121-122.

THEOREM. *Let the zeros ρ_i of the polynomial P be distinct with $|\rho_1| > |\rho_i|$, $i = 2, 3, \cdots, n$. Let t_0 be an arbitrary point in the extended complex plane such that $t_0 \neq \rho_2, \rho_3, \cdots, \rho_n$ and let $t_{i+1} = \phi(\lambda, t_i)$. Then for all sufficiently large but fixed λ, the sequence t_i is defined for all i and $t_i \to \rho_1$.*

The phrase "global convergence" is used in the following sense. For any polynomial whose zeros are distinct and which possesses a largest zero and for any choice of t_0 which does not coincide with a subdominant zero, we can conclude that for all sufficiently large λ the sequence t_i defined by $t_{i+1} = \phi(\lambda, t_i)$ exists and converges to ρ_1. The size of λ depends on P and t_0. It is determined primarily by the ratio of the magnitude of the largest subdominant zero to the magnitude of the dominant zero.

6. **Properties of the G polynomials.** We obtain the principle properties of the G polynomials from the defining recursion

$$
(6.1) \qquad \begin{aligned} G(0, t) &= B(t), \\ G(\lambda + 1, t_0) &= t\, G(\lambda, t) - \alpha_0(\lambda)\, P(t), \end{aligned}
$$

where $\alpha_0(\lambda)$ is the leading coefficient of $G(\lambda, t)$.

The G polynomials can be introduced in a number of different ways. In [16], p. 114, we define $G(\lambda, t)$ as the remainder of the division of $B(t) t^\lambda$ by $P(t)$. The G polynomials can also be defined as the sequence generated by a Bernoulli recurrence with initial conditions which depend on the choice of $B(t)$.

From (6.1) it follows that $G(\lambda + 1, \rho_i) = \rho_i G(\lambda, \rho_i)$. Hence

$$
(6.2) \qquad G(\lambda, \rho_i) = \rho_i^\lambda G(0, \rho_i) = \rho_i^\lambda B(\rho_i).
$$

Since $G(\lambda, t)$ is a polynomial of degree at most $n - 1$, we conclude from Lagrange's interpolation formula that

$$
(6.3) \qquad G(\lambda, t) = \sum_{i=1}^{n} c_i \rho_i^\lambda \frac{P(t)}{t - \rho_i}, \qquad c_i = \frac{B(\rho_i)}{P'(\rho_i)}.
$$

Since $B(\rho_1) \neq 0$ by hypothesis, $c_1 \neq 0$.

Let $\beta(\lambda)$ be the weighted power sum

$$
(6.4) \qquad \beta(\lambda) = \sum_{i=1}^{n} c_i \rho_i^\lambda.
$$

From (6.3)

(6.5) $$\alpha_0(\lambda) = \beta(\lambda).$$

Hence for λ sufficiently large, $\alpha_0(\lambda) \neq 0$.

From (6.3), (6.4) and (6.5) we obtain immediately the most important property of $G(\lambda, t)$, namely

(6.6) $$\lim_{\lambda \to \infty} \bar{G}(\lambda, t) = \lim_{\lambda \to \infty} \frac{G(\lambda, t)}{\alpha_0(\lambda)} = \frac{P(t)}{t - \rho_1},$$

for all finite t.

Furthermore the rate of convergence depends on the ratio of the magnitude of the largest subdominant zero to the magnitude of the dominant zero.

To see the importance of (6.6), consider a general iteration function,

$$\psi(t) = t - P(t)/V(t)$$

where $V(t)$ is some function which is yet to be specified. If

(6.7) $$V(t) = P(t)/(t - \rho_1)$$

then $\psi(t) = \rho_1$ and we always obtain the answer in one step. In the Newton-Raphson method, $V(t) = P'(t)$ and (6.7) is satisfied only at $t = \rho_1$. Equation (6.6) shows that when $V(t) = \bar{G}(\lambda, t)$, then (6.7) is satisfied for all finite t as λ goes to infinity and is satisfied arbitrarily closely for λ sufficiently large.

We obtain an interesting interpretation of the recursion for the G polynomials by considering the Laurent expansion of $G(\lambda, t)/P(t)$. Let

(6.8) $$\frac{G(\lambda, t)}{P(t)} = \sum_{k=0}^{\infty} \frac{d_k(\lambda)}{t^{k+1}}.$$

Clearly, $d_0(\lambda) = \alpha_0(\lambda) = \beta(\lambda)$. Write the recurrence for $G(\lambda, t)$ as

(6.9) $$G(\lambda + 1, t)/P(t) = tG(\lambda, t)/P(t) - \alpha_0(\lambda).$$

Then we conclude that

(6.10) $$d_{k+1}(\lambda) = d_k(\lambda + 1).$$

Hence the right side of (6.9) may be viewed as the operation of performing a left shift upon the vector of coefficients of the Laurent expansion. From (6.10),

$$d_k(\lambda) = d_0(\lambda + k) = \beta(\lambda + k),$$

a result which could also have been obtained directly from the partial fraction expansion of $G(\lambda, t)/P(t)$.

Hence

(6.11) $$\frac{G(\lambda, t)}{P(t)} = t^\lambda \left[\frac{B(t)}{P(t)} - \sum_{k=0}^{\lambda-1} \frac{\beta(k)}{t^{k+1}} \right].$$

Thus, except for a factor of t^λ, $G(\lambda, t)/P(t)$ is just the remainder of the series for $G(0, t)/P(t)$ after λ terms.

Finally we mention that the recursion for the G polynomials may be cast as a matrix-vector multiplication where the matrix is the companion matrix of P. We do not pursue this here. The interested reader is referred to the papers by Bauer in the bibliography.

7. **The behavior of the error.** In the numerical example of §3 we noted that the ratios of successive errors were small, and that the initial ratio was particularly small when t_0 was large. We now study the behavior of the error quantitatively.

Let

$$E(\lambda, t) = (\phi(\lambda, t) - \rho_1)/(t - \rho_1).$$

From (4.2) and (6.3),

$$(7.1) \qquad E(\lambda, t) = \frac{\sum_{i=2}^{n} d_i(\rho_i/\rho_1)^\lambda(\rho_i - \rho_1)/(t - \rho_i)}{1 + \sum_{i=2}^{n} d_i(\rho_i/\rho_1)^\lambda(t - \rho_1)/(t - \rho_i)}, \qquad d_i = c_i/c_1.$$

This result is exact. We draw a number of conclusions.

$E(\lambda, t)$ is of order $(\rho_2/\rho_1)^\lambda$ and can be made arbitrarily small. For the remainder of this section we strengthen our assumption to $|\rho_1| > |\rho_2| > |\rho_j|$, $j > 2$. Then

$$(7.2) \qquad \lim_{\lambda \to \infty} \frac{E(\lambda, t)}{(\rho_2/\rho_1)^\lambda} = d_2 \frac{(\rho_2 - \rho_1)}{t - \rho_2}.$$

The asymptotic error constant (Traub [14, p. 9]) is defined by

$$C(\lambda) = \lim_{t \to \rho_1} E(\lambda, t).$$

We conclude

$$(7.3) \qquad \lim_{\lambda \to \infty} \frac{E(\lambda, t)}{C(\lambda)} = \frac{\rho_1 - \rho_2}{t - \rho_2}.$$

This result explains why the initial error ratio in the example of §3 is so small. For that example, $\rho_1 = -3$, $\rho_2 = 2$, $t = 100000$ and the initial ratio should be smaller than the asymptotic ratio by about -5×10^{-5}. This is indeed the case in the example.

If $B = P'$ we can draw an additional conclusion from (7.2). In this case $d_2 = 1$. Let $P(t)$ and $Q(t)$ be two polynomials with the same dominant zeros ρ_1 and ρ_2. We calculate the approximating sequences for ρ_1, both starting at t_0 but with one sequence calculated from P and the other from Q. On a computer, for λ sufficiently large, the two sequences are essentially identical. To put it another way, the sequence of approximants depends only on the two dominant zeros of P and is essentially independent of the remaining zeros.

8. **Two variations of the basic algorithm.** In the following two variations the same sequence of approximants t_i, except for roundoff, is calculated as in the basic method described in §2. However the way in which the t_i are obtained is different.

Both variations are based on the following analysis. In §6 we showed that

(8.1) $$\frac{G(0,t)}{P(t)} = \frac{B(t)}{P(t)} = \sum_{k=0}^{\infty} \frac{\beta(k)}{t^{k+1}}.$$

Let $B(t) = \sum_{i=0}^{n-1} b_i t^{n-1-i}$. By comparing coefficients in (8.1), we conclude that for $B(t)$ given, $\beta(0)$, $\beta(1)$, $\cdots$, $\beta(n-1)$ are determined by

(8.2) $$\sum_{r=0}^{j} a_r \beta(j-r) = b_j, \qquad j = 0, 1, \cdots, n-1.$$

For $j \geq n$ the $\beta(j)$ satisfy

(8.3) $$\sum_{r=0}^{n} a_r \beta(j-r) = 0.$$

We can now associate $\beta(0), \beta(1), \cdots, \beta(n-1)$ with $B(t)$ in either of two ways. We can choose either the set $\beta(0), \beta(1), \cdots, \beta(n-1)$ or $B(t)$ arbitrarily and determine the other by (8.2). In either case $\beta(j)$, $j \geq n$, is calculated using (8.3). (We might add parenthetically that if $B = P'$, then (8.2) are Newton relations for the power sums $\beta(\lambda)$.)

We now turn to variation one. Define $\alpha_j(\lambda)$ by

$$G(\lambda, t) = \sum_{j=0}^{n-1} \alpha_j(\lambda) t^{n-1-j}.$$

It follows from (6.3) that

(8.4) $$\alpha_j(\lambda) = \sum_{r=0}^{j} a_{j-r} \beta(\lambda + r).$$

This variation may now be described as follows. Compute the $\beta(j)$ up to $\beta(\lambda + n - 1)$ using (8.2) and (8.3) and compute $\alpha_j(\lambda)$ using (8.4). This gives an *explicit* formula for $G(\lambda, t)$ and hence for $\phi(\lambda, t)$.

Observe that this variation consists of a Bernoulli calculation followed by iteration.

The second variation is based on the fact that in the iteration

$$t_{i+1} = \phi(\lambda, t_i)$$

only the numbers $G(\lambda, t_i)$, not $G(\lambda, t)$ itself, are required. We form the $\beta(j)$ up to $\beta(\lambda - 1)$ using (8.2) and (8.3). Then form the sequence of numbers

(8.5) $$G(j+1, t_0) = t_0 G(j, t_0) - \beta(j) P(t_0), \qquad j = 0, 1, \cdots, \lambda - 1,$$

and use $G(\lambda, t_0)$ to calculate t_1. Then use (8.5) with t_0 replaced by t_1, and so on.

9. An iteration function for the smallest zero. The iteration function $\phi(\lambda, t)$ is used to calculate the largest zero of P. To calculate the smallest zero, we could calculate the largest zero of $t^n P(1/t)$. We introduce a sequence of polynomials $H(\lambda, t)$ which may be used to construct iteration functions for the smallest zero directly.

It is convenient in this section to assume that $p(t)$, the polynomial whose smallest zero we seek to calculate, is normalized so that $p(0) = 1$.*
Let the zeros of $p(t)$ be $\alpha_1, \alpha_2, \cdots, \alpha_n$ with $|\alpha_1| < |\alpha_i|$, $i > 1$. Let $b(t)$ be an arbitrary polynomial of degree at most $n - 1$ such that $b(\alpha_1) \neq 0$. Define

(9.1)
$$H(0, t) = b(t),$$
$$H(\lambda + 1, t) = (H(\lambda, t) - \delta_0(\lambda) p(t))/t$$

where

$$\delta_0(\lambda) = H(\lambda, 0).$$

An approximating sequence is defined by

(9.2)
$$t_{i+1} = \Phi(\lambda, t_i)$$

where

(9.3)
$$\Phi(\lambda, t) = \frac{t}{1 - p(t)/\widetilde{H}(\lambda, t)}$$

with

$$\widetilde{H}(\lambda, t) = H(\lambda, t)/\delta_0(\lambda).$$

From (9.1), we also have

(9.4)
$$\Phi(\lambda, t) = H(\lambda, t)/H(\lambda + 1, t).$$

10. Properties of the H polynomials. From the defining recursion for the H polynomials,

(10.1)
$$H(0, t) = b(t),$$
$$H(\lambda + 1, t) = (H(\lambda, t) - \delta_0(\lambda) p(t))/t,$$

we obtain the representation

(10.2)
$$H(\lambda, t) = \sum_{i=1}^{n} q_i \alpha_i^{-\lambda} \frac{p(t)}{t - \alpha_i}, \qquad q_i = \frac{b(\alpha_i)}{p'(\alpha_i)}.$$

It follows that

(10.3)
$$\delta_0(\lambda) = - \sum_{i=1}^{n} q_i \alpha_i^{-\lambda - 1}$$

Note Added in Proof. Additional thought has led to the realization that in the case of a smallest zero, the polynomial should be monic just as in the case of a largest zero. The results are then entirely analogous to those for a largest zero.

and hence that $\delta_0(\lambda)$ does not vanish for λ sufficiently large. From (10.2) and (10.3) we conclude that

$$(10.4) \qquad \lim_{\lambda \to \infty} \widetilde{H}(\lambda, t) = \lim_{\lambda \to \infty} \frac{H(\lambda, t)}{\delta_0(\lambda)} = \frac{p(t)}{1 - t/\alpha_1}.$$

for all finite t.

The H polynomials possess a property which is analogous to a G polynomial property discussed in §6. We expand $H(\lambda, t)/p(t)$ into a Taylor series around the origin. Let

$$(10.5) \qquad \frac{H(\lambda, t)}{p(t)} = \sum_{k=0}^{\infty} e_k(\lambda) t^k.$$

Let

$$\gamma(\lambda) = \sum_{i=1}^{n} q_i \alpha_i^{-\lambda}.$$

Clearly, $e_0(\lambda) = \delta_0(\lambda) = -\gamma(\lambda + 1)$. Write the recurrence for $H(\lambda, t)$ as

$$(10.6) \qquad \frac{H(\lambda + 1, t)}{p(t)} = \frac{1}{t}\left[\frac{H(\lambda, t)}{p(t)} - \delta_0(\lambda) \right].$$

Then we conclude that

$$(10.7) \qquad e_{k+1}(\lambda) = e_k(\lambda + 1).$$

Hence the right side of (10.6) may be viewed as the operation of performing a left shift upon the vector of coefficients of the Taylor series. From (10.7)

$$e_k(\lambda) = e_0(\lambda + k) = -\gamma(\lambda + k + 1).$$

Hence

$$\frac{H(\lambda, t)}{p(t)} = t^{-\lambda}\left[\frac{b(t)}{p(t)} + \sum_{k=0}^{\lambda-1} \gamma(k + 1) t^k \right].$$

Thus, except for a factor of $t^{-\lambda}$, $H(\lambda, t)/p(t)$ is just the remainder of the series for $H(0, t)/p(t)$ after λ terms.

11. Calculation of multiple zeros. Until now we have restricted ourselves to polynomials all of whose zeros are simple. We turn to the case where the polynomial has multiple zeros. There are no essential difficulties. If the dominant zero is multiple, $P(t)$ can only be evaluated to a certain accuracy but this is common to all iterative methods which require the evaluation of $P(t)$.

We first prove a fundamental

THEOREM. *Let P have n distinct zeros ρ_i where the multiplicity of ρ_i is m_i. Let $B(t) = P'(t)$. Then for all λ*

(11.1) $$\frac{G(\lambda, t)}{P(t)} = \sum_{i=1}^{n} \frac{m_i \rho_i^{\lambda}}{t - \rho_i}.$$

PROOF. We proceed by induction on λ. If $\lambda = 0$, the result is well known. Assuming it holds for λ and substituting (11.1) into the recursion formula for the G polynomials yields the result immediately.

Observe that (11.1) implies that for all λ, $G(\lambda, t)$ has zeros of multiplicity $m_i - 1$ at ρ_i. Furthermore,

$$\lim_{\lambda \to \infty} \bar{G}(\lambda, t) = \frac{P(t)}{t - \rho_1}.$$

Hence, for λ sufficiently large, the remaining $n - 1$ zeros of $\bar{G}(\lambda, t)$ lie arbitrarily close to the subdominant zeros of P. Thus the iteration function will have no poles in the neighborhood of ρ_1.

Observe that the theorem is based on the choice $B(t) = P'(t)$. This shows that the restriction $B(\rho_1) \neq 0$ is not the appropriate condition in the case of a multiple zero. The reason for this is apparent if one compares the partial fraction expansion of $G(\lambda, t)/P(t)$ in the simple and multiple zero cases.

A detailed analysis of the multiple zero case will appear elsewhere.

12. **Calculation of complex conjugate zeros.** So far we have dealt with polynomials which have a zero of largest modulus or a zero of smallest modulus. We turn to the case of equimodular dominant zeros. Fortunately in the case of polynomial zeros it is sufficient to consider the case of either one zero of largest modulus or of a pair of complex conjugate zeros of largest modulus for the following reason.

A translation in the t plane replaces zeros of equal modulus by zeros of unequal modulus. In the case of a polynomial with real coefficients, a real translation will remove all zeros of equal modulus except for a pair of complex conjugate zeros. Hence only the two cases mentioned need be considered.

A discussion of how to effect the translation so as not to damage the zeros of P will appear elsewhere.

We turn to the calculation of a pair of complex conjugate zeros. In [17] we recently announced a theorem on global convergence of an iterative method for calculating complex zeros. In this section we describe one method for calculating complex zeros and state the theorem of global convergence. Variations on and extensions of this method as well as proofs of our results will be published in a forthcoming paper.

The theory holds no matter what the relation between ρ_1 and ρ_2 requiring only $|\rho_1| > |\rho_i|$ and $|\rho_2| > |\rho_i|$, $i > 2$. Here we restrict ourselves to ρ_1 and ρ_2 complex conjugate.

If $|\rho_1| = |\rho_2|$, then the normalized G polynomials do not converge. Let

(12.1)
$$I(\lambda, t) = \beta(\lambda) G(\lambda + 1, t) - \beta(\lambda + 1) G(\lambda, t),$$
$$J(\lambda, t) = \beta(\lambda) G(\lambda + 2, t) - \beta(\lambda + 2) G(\lambda, t).$$

Then

$$\overline{I}(\lambda, t) \rightarrow P(t)/(t - \rho_1)(t - \rho_2),$$
$$\overline{J}(\lambda, t) \rightarrow P(t)/(t - \rho_1)(t - \rho_2).$$

Recursions involving only the I and J polynomials and not depending on the G polynomials have been developed. These recursions may be of advantage in numerical calculations.

From the I and J polynomials an iteration function may be constructed as follows. We define a polynomial which is quadratic in u and has coefficients which are polynomials in t of degree at most $n - 2$,

$$F_2(u, \lambda, t) = I(\lambda, t) u^2 - J(\lambda, t) u + I(\lambda + 1, t).$$

Let λ be a fixed integer and let t_0 be an arbitrary point in the extended complex plane not equal to a subdominant zero. Define an iteration by

$$F_2(t_{i+1}, \lambda, t_i) = 0.$$

(If $t_0 = \infty$, calculate t_1 by $F_2(t_1, \lambda, t_0)/I(\lambda, t_0) = 0$.) It can be shown that for all t_i, and for λ sufficiently large, this quadratic has a zero in the upper half plane and a zero in the lower half plane. Choose t_{i+1} as the zero in the upper half plane and define ψ by $t_{i+1} = \psi(\lambda, t_i)$. Label ρ_1 as the zero in the upper half plane. Then we have the following.

THEOREM. *Let the zeros ρ_i of the polynomial P be distinct with ρ_1 and ρ_2 complex conjugate and $|\rho_1| > |\rho_i|$, $i > 2$. Let t_0 be an arbitrary point in the extended complex plane such that $t_0 \neq \rho_3, \cdots, \rho_n$ and let $t_{i+1} = \psi(\lambda, t_i)$. Then for all λ sufficiently large but fixed, the sequence t_i is defined for all i and $t_i \rightarrow \rho_1$.*

13. **A numerical example.** For illustration of the method described in the previous section we calculate the dominant zero of

$$P(t) = t^4 - 4.2t^3 + 8.7125t^2 - 9.025t + 4.625.$$

Its zeros are

$$\rho_1 = 1.1 + 1.05i,$$
$$\rho_2 = 1.1 - 1.05i,$$
$$\rho_3 = 1 + i,$$
$$\rho_4 = 1 - i.$$

Note that the zeros are pairwise quite close together.

We choose $B(t) = P'(t)$, $\lambda = 96$, and choose our initial approximation as $t_0 = 1000$. We obtain the sequence of approximations exhibited in Table 2. In the right-hand column we exhibit the ratios of the moduli of the errors. As in the example of §3 we observe that all the ratios are small and that the initial ratio is particularly small. Again this can be quantitatively explained.

TABLE 2. Sequence of Approximants

i	t_i	$\|t_{i+1} - \rho_1\| / \|t_i - \rho_1\|$
0	1000.	
1	1.10009 $+ 1.04997i$	9.5×10^{-8}
2	1.10000003 $+ 1.04999992i$	9.0×10^{-4}
3	1.09999999997 $+ 1.04999999992i$	9.0×10^{-4}

$$\rho_1 = 1.1 + 1.05i$$

14. Calculation of zeros of analytic functions. Let

$$f(t) = \sum_{j=0}^{\infty} a_j t^j, \qquad a_0 = 1$$

be a power series which converges in a circle about the origin. Suppose that $f(t)$ has a zero of smallest magnitude. Then we can define analytic functions $H(\lambda, t)$ by the recursion of (9.1). Results analogous to those in the polynomial case can be developed here.

Since we cannot actually form the analytic functions $H(\lambda, t)$, we cannot use the basic method. There are a number of other possibilities and we merely sketch two of them.

The first takes a section of the power series of degree n and uses it instead of f itself. A section of degree 1000 would offer no difficulties. The size of λ which is needed to separate out the effect of the dominant zero depends on the ratio of dominant to subdominant zero and not on the degree of the section one takes. Hence quite a modest choice of λ, much smaller than the degree of the section, should be sufficient. Since $G(\lambda, t)$ can be formed in λn multiplications and since each iteration takes about $2n$ multiplications, the process is reasonably economical even for large values of n.

A second possibility is to use the second variation of the basic method as described in §8. The variation is used with the H recursion rather than the G recursion. The constants appearing in the H recursion can be precomputed by an appropriate generalization of (8.2) and (8.3) which amounts to calculating the coefficients of the Taylor series for $H(0, t)/f(t)$. This last mentioned process is just the computation required for the application of König's method [10].

15. **Computer implementation.** In the computer implementation of the type of methods described here, the program should decide automatically on the value of λ at which to start iteration, and as to whether or not there is a zero of largest modulus. Such decisions should be made by monitoring the numbers produced during the calculation of the G polynomials. A number of strategies are available and will be discussed elsewhere.

16. **Bibliographic remarks.** Schröder [12] in his classic 1870 paper introduced certain symmetric functions of zeros. These symmetric functions are just the derivatives of the rational functions $G(\lambda, t)/P(t)$. He derived a number of the properties of these functions. Since Schröder restricted himself to low values of λ for which explicit formulas could be obtained, he did not find globally convergent iteration functions.

In 1941, Sebastião e Silva [13] defined G polynomials as the remainder of the division of t^λ by $P(t)$ and gave a long proof that the normalized G polynomials converge to $P(t)/(t - \rho_1)$. His work has been continued by Aparo [1], [2].

G polynomials are used by Bauer [3], [4] in an important series of papers which appeared in the mid-1950's. H polynomials appear in a paper by Bauer and Samelson [5].

Sebastião e Silva, Aparo, and Bauer are concerned with quadratically convergent versions of Bernoulli-Jacobi-Aitken type methods for the factorization of polynomials. Thus they continue the first stage of our two-stage process to the limit.

Underlying many of the methods for calculating zeros are theorems concerning the coefficients of a function which has poles on its circle of convergence. Papers by König [10] and Hadamard [7] are classic. A perceptive account is given by Householder [9], Chapter 3. The method we have discussed here may be incorporated in this framework.

Our work has links with the QD algorithm (Rutishauser [11], Henrici [8]) which will be explored elsewhere.

Finally we note a different application of G polynomials. Traub [15] uses G polynomials with the variable t replaced by the translation operator E, to give a new derivation of the formula for the general solution of a linear inhomogeneous difference equation with constant coefficients.

Additional bibliographic references may be found in Traub [16] and in the papers by Bauer.

ACKNOWLEDGEMENT. I would like to thank my colleague Professor W. Kahan of the University of Toronto, who was a visiting professor at Stanford University, for many stimulating conversations.

References

1. E. Aparo, *Applicazione di un nuovo metodo per la risoluzione numerica delle equazioni algebriche*, Bol. Soc. Portuguesa Mat. Sér. A **1** (1948), 49-57.

2. _____, *Un procedimento iterativo per la risoluzione numerica delle equazioni algebriche*, Ricerca Sci. **24** (1954), 1003-1005.

3. F. L. Bauer, *Beiträge zur Entwicklung numerischer Verfahren für programmgesteuerte Rechenanlagen*. I, *Quadratisch konvergente Durchführung der Bernoulli-Jacobischen Methode zur Nullstellenbestimmung von Polynomen*, Bayer. Akad. Wiss. Math.-Nat. Kl. S.-B. **1954** (1955), 275-303; II: *Direkte Faktorisierung eines Polynoms*, Bayer. Akad. Wiss. Math.-Nat. Kl. S.-B. **1956** (1957), 163-203.

4. _____, *Das Verfahren der abgekürtzen Iteration für algebraische Eigenwertprobleme, inbesondere zur Nullstellenbestimmung eines Polynoms*, Z. Angew. Math. Phys. **7** (1956), 17-32.

5. F. L. Bauer and K. Samelson, *Polynomkerne und Iterationsverfahren*, Math. Z. **67** (1957), 93-98.

6. G. E. Forsythe, *Singularity and near singularity in numerical analysis*, Amer. Math. Monthly **65** (1958), 229-240.

7. J. Hadamard, *Essai sur l'étude des functions données par leur développement de Taylor*, J. Math. Pures Appl. (4) **8** (1892), 101-186.

8. P. Henrici, *The quotient-difference algorithm*, NBS Appl. Math. Ser. **49** (1958), 23-46.

9. A. S. Householder, *Principles of numerical analysis*, McGraw-Hill, New York, 1953.

10. J. König, *Über eine Eigenschaft der Potenzreihen*, Math. Ann. **23** (1884), 447-449.

11. H. Rutishauser, *Der Quotienten-Differenzen-Algorithmus*, Mitt. Inst. Angew. Math. Zurich no. 7 (1957).

12. E. Schröder, *Über unendlich viele Algorithmen zur Auflösung der Gleichungen*, Math. Ann. **2** (1870), 317-365.

13. J. Sebastião e Silva, *Sur une méthode d'approximation semblable à celle de Gräffe*, Portugal. Math. **2** (1941), 271-279.

14. J. F. Traub, *Iterative methods for the solution of equations*, Prentice-Hall, Englewood Cliffs, N. J., 1964.

15. _____, *Solution of linear difference and differential equations*, Bull. Amer. Math. Soc. **71** (1965), 538-541.

16. _____, *A class of globally convergent iteration functions for the solution of polynomial equations*, Math. Comp. **20** (1966), 113-138.

17. _____, *Proof of global convergence of an iterative method for calculating complex zeros of a polynomial*, Notices Amer. Math. Soc. **13** (1966), 117.

STANFORD UNIVERSITY
STANFORD, PALO ALTO, CALIFORNIA

BELL TELEPHONE LABORATORIES
MURRAY HILL, NEW JERSEY

Michael O. Rabin[1]

MATHEMATICAL THEORY
OF AUTOMATA

Introduction. The purpose of this article is to survey the most important developments and trends in automata theory. No attempt was made to give an exhaustive enumeration of all results and methods in this field. Still, it is hoped that even the uninitiated reader will get an idea of the basic and typical concepts and results.

The term "automaton" is quite elastic and has been stretched to cover all sorts of mathematical machines. Thus one hears about push-down store automata, linearly bounded automata, etc. In the present survey, we shall restrict ourselves exclusively to finite automata. It will be seen that the restriction to finite machines (as opposed to, say, push-down store automata, which are in effect growing machines), leads to a uniformity of definitions and to a theory which is very algebraic in nature.

Numerous open problems and suggestions of lines for further research appear at the appropriate places throughout this survey.

I. FINITE AUTOMATA

I.0. **Basic definitions.** Let Σ be a set. By a *word on* Σ we shall understand a finite sequence x,

$$x = \sigma_0\sigma_1 \cdots \sigma_{n-1}, \qquad \sigma_i \in \Sigma$$

of elements of Σ. The *length* $l(x)$ of x is, by definition, the number n of elements in the sequence x. The (unique) word x for which $l(x) = 0$, will be denoted by Λ. Let $y = \tau_0\tau_1 \cdots \tau_{m-1}$ be any other word on Σ then xy, the result of *concatenating* x with y, is defined by

$$xy = \sigma_0\sigma_1 \cdots \sigma_{n-1}\tau_0\tau_1 \cdots \tau_{m-1}.$$

The set of all words on Σ will be denoted by Σ^*. Note that Σ^* is a free

---

[1] Preparation of this lecture was supported in part by Navy Contract N 63558-4695 at the Hebrew University of Jerusalem.

semigroup under the operation of concatenation, that Λ is the unit element and the $\sigma \in \Sigma$ are the free generators of this semigroup. Subsets of Σ^* are sometimes called *events*. For subsets $A \subseteq \Sigma^*$, $B \subseteq \Sigma^*$ define

$$AB = \{xy \mid x \in A, \ y \in B\}.$$

For $0 \le n$ define $A^0 = \{\Lambda\}$ and, inductively, $A^{n+1} = A^n A$. Finally,

$$A^* = A^0 \cup A \cup A^2 \cup \cdots.$$

From now on Σ will denote a fixed *finite* set which will sometimes be referred to as the *alphabet*.

DEFINITION 1. *A finite automata (f.a.) over* Σ *is a system* $\mathfrak{A} = \langle S, M, s_0, F \rangle$ *where* S *is a finite set (the set of states), $M : S \times \Sigma \to S$ (the table of transitions of $\mathfrak{A}$), $s_0 \in S$ (s_0 is the initial state), $F \subseteq S$ (F is the set of designated final states).*

The function M can be uniquely extended to a function $M^* : S \times \Sigma^* \to S$ by the following inductive definition

$$M^*(s, \Lambda) = s, \qquad s \in S,$$

$$M^*(s, x\sigma) = M(M^*(s, x), \sigma), \quad s \in S, \quad \sigma \in \Sigma, \quad x \in \Sigma^*.$$

Intuitively speaking, the function M describes the state-transitions of $\mathfrak{A}$. If $\mathfrak{A}$ is in s and has input $\sigma \in \Sigma$, then it will go into state $s' = M(s, \sigma)$. Similarly M^* describes the state-transitions under input *words* $x \in \Sigma^*$.

DEFINITION 2. The set

$$T(\mathfrak{A}) = \{x \mid x \in \Sigma^*, \ M^*(s_0, x) \in F\}$$

is the *set* (event) *defined* by $\mathfrak{A}$. A set $A \subseteq \Sigma^*$ is called a *regular event* if for some finite automaton $\mathfrak{A}$, $A = T(\mathfrak{A})$.

I.1. **F.a. mappings.** Some emphasis has been put on the distinction between automata as introduced by Definition 1, where they serve as "recognition devices," and automata which yield a mapping from input sequences to output sequences. Actually, this distinction is rather superficial. For we can associate with each state $s \in F$ the output 1 and with each $s \in S - F$ the output 0. With $\mathfrak{A}$ we then associate the mapping $T : \Sigma^* \to \{0, 1\}^*$ such that

$$T(\sigma_0 \sigma_1 \cdots \sigma_{n-1}) = \tau_0 \tau_1 \cdots \tau_{n-1}$$

where, for $0 \le i \le n - 1$, $\tau_i = 1$ if $M^*(s_0, \sigma_0 \cdots \sigma_i) \in F$ and $\tau_i = 0$ otherwise.

Several generalizations are possible. We can partition S into the (disjoint) union of k sets, $S = F_0 \cup \cdots \cup F_{k-1}$, and obtain a mapping $T : \Sigma^* \to \{0, 1, \cdots, k - 1\}^*$ into words on a k-letter alphabet. Furthermore, we can take the output corresponding to F_i, $0 \le i \le k - 1$, to be a word w_i on some alphabet Ω. In this way we obtain a mapping $T : \Sigma^* \to \Omega^*$ which is not even length-preserving. Finally, the output may be made into a function $f(s, \sigma)$ of both the current state and the current input of $\mathfrak{A}$ (*Mealy automata* [20]). All of these formulations are, however, mutually transformable into each other and lead to the same mathematical theory. In order to have as simple a notation as possible we shall adhere to the formulation in Definition 1 (Rabin-Scott [33]).

I.2. **Nondeterministic automata.** The definition of f.a. can be generalized by allowing $\mathfrak{A}$, when in state s and having input σ, to go into any one of a number of states $s' \in S'$, where $S' \subseteq S$ is a set depending on s and σ.

Thus in Definition 1 we understand M to be a function $M : S \times \Sigma \to P(S)$ where $P(S)$ is the power set of S. Also, the element s_0 is replaced by a set $S_0 \subseteq S$ of initial states. The resulting system is called a *nondeterministic automaton*.

If $x = \sigma_0 \sigma_1 \cdots \sigma_{n-1}$ then the sequence $s_0, s_1, \cdots, s_n$ of states is called *compatible* with x if $s_0 \in S_0$ and for $0 \leq i \leq n - 1$, $s_{i+1} \in M(s_i, \sigma_i)$. We say that $\mathfrak{A}$ *accepts* x if for some sequence $s_0, \cdots, s_n$ compatible with x, $s_n \in F$. The set $T(\mathfrak{A})$ consists of all words accepted by $\mathfrak{A}$. The main result about nondeterministic automata is the following.

THEOREM 1 [33]. *For every nondeterministic automaton $\mathfrak{A}$ there exists a f.a. $\mathfrak{B}$ such that $T(\mathfrak{A}) = T(\mathfrak{B})$. If $\mathfrak{A}$ has n states, then $\mathfrak{B}$ may be taken to have fewer than 2^n states.*

It is not known whether the bound of 2^n on the number of states of $\mathfrak{B}$ may be considerably improved.

The notion of nondeterministic automaton and Theorem 1 are useful in showing that certain sets are regular. The reader may test this by proving that if $A \subseteq \Sigma^*$ and $B \subseteq \Sigma^*$ are regular (f.a. definable) then so are A^* and AB.

I.3. **Regular expressions and events.** Let $Y_1, Y_2, \cdots$ be variables ranging over subsets of Σ^*. The set $\mathbf{R}$ of *regular terms* (in $Y_1, Y_2, \cdots$) is the smallest set satisfying the conditions (1) $Y_n \in \mathbf{R}$, $1 \leq n < \infty$ and (2) if $R_1 \in \mathbf{R}$ and $R_2 \in \mathbf{R}$ then $(R_1 \cup R_2) \in \mathbf{R}$, $(R_1 R_2) \in \mathbf{R}$, $R_1^* \in \mathbf{R}$. Every element $R \in \mathbf{R}$ is called a regular term. Thus, for example, $((Y_3(Y_2 \cup Y_5))^* \cup Y_1^*)$ is a regular term.

If we now take a regular term $R(Y_1, \cdots, Y_n)$ and replace each Y_i, $1 \leq i \leq n$, by a singleton set $\{\sigma_i\}$ where $\sigma_i \in \Sigma$, we get what Kleene calls a *regular expression* $R(\sigma_1, \cdots, \sigma_n)$ (here and elsewhere we omit the curly brackets from singleton sets). Thus under the assignment $Y_1 \to 0$, $Y_2 \to 1$, $Y_3 \to 0$, $Y_5 \to 1$, the previously defined term becomes $((0(1 \cup 1))^* \cup 0^*) = (01)^* \cup 0^*$.

There seems to be in the literature some confusion between the two notions of regular term and regular expression considered here. The regular terms are, of course, generalized polynomials in the algebra with operations XY, $X \cup Y$ and X^*. The regular expressions, on the other hand, are just ways of describing particular (regular) subsets of Σ^*. We feel that some of the problems described in the sequel are best formulated using the notion of regular terms.

Kleene [17] introduced the notion of regular expression and proved the following.

THEOREM 2. *A set $T \subseteq \Sigma^*$ is f.a. definable (regular) if and only if there exists a regular expression $R(\sigma_1, \cdots, \sigma_k)$ where $\sigma_i \in \Sigma$, $1 \leq i \leq k$, such that $T = R(\sigma_1, \cdots, \sigma_k)$.*

In [33] it is shown how to derive this result by applying nondeterministic automata.

The fact that every regular event is representable by a regular expression gives rise to some natural questions concerning regular terms and expressions. Two regular terms $R(Y_1, \cdots, Y_n)$ and $Q(Y_1, \cdots, Y_n)$ (this notation means that R and Q contain no variables other than $Y_1, \cdots, Y_n$) are called *equivalent*, $R \equiv Q$, if for all events $A_1 \subseteq \Sigma^*, \cdots, A_n \subseteq \Sigma^*$,

$$R(A_1, \cdots, A_n) = Q(A_1, \cdots, A_n).$$

Thus, for example, $(Y_1(Y_2 \cup Y_3))^* \equiv ((Y_1 Y_2) \cup (Y_1 Y_3))^*$.

The following remark, which seems to belong to the folklore of automata theory, was brought to our attention by C. C. Elgot and J. B. Wright. *Assume that Σ has at least two letters. Two terms $P(Y_1, \cdots, Y_n)$ and $Q(Y_1, \cdots, Y_n)$ are equivalent if and only if, when interpreting $Y_1, \cdots, Y_n$ as single letters taken from an alphabet $\Omega = \{Y_1, \cdots, Y_n\}$, the regular expressions $P(Y_1, \cdots, Y_n)$ and $Q(Y_1, \cdots, Y_n)$ represent the same regular event on Ω.* The proofs that regular expressions yield f.a. definable sets are effective in the sense that the automaton in question can be effectively constructed from the regular expression. Furthermore, the problem whether two automata $\mathfrak{A}$ and $\mathfrak{B}$ define the same set is decidable. Combining all of these remarks, it follows that *the problem of equivalence of regular terms is effectively solvable.*

Several authors (Aanderaa [1], Redko [35], Salomaa [36], [37], Janov [16]) have treated the problem of axiomatization of equations between regular *expressions*. Thus Redko shows that there is no finite system of identities from which all equations between regular expressions can be derived by the rules of substitution and replacement of equals by equals. Janov constructed a finite system of identities from which all equations between regular expressions containing Λ follow by the above rules. Salomaa and Aanderaa constructed complete systems using additional rules of deduction.

In the present author's view, the subject of identities is still not exhausted.

Let us extend the notion of regular term by allowing fixed letters of Σ to be used in term formation. This means that in the definition of terms previously given Clause 1 is replaced by: ($1'$) $Y_n \in \mathbf{R}'$, $\sigma \in \mathbf{R}'$, $n = 1, 2, \cdots$, $\sigma \in \Sigma$. J. B. Wright raised the following problem concerning identities between these terms: *To decide for $P \in \mathbf{R}'$, $Q \in \mathbf{R}'$ whether $P \equiv Q$.* The simple remark which was previously used for settling the equivalence problem does not apply here.

Many of the above questions change completely upon adding further operations to our formalism. Thus we can consider terms involving also $\cap$ (boolean intersection) or—(complementation). As far as we know, the decision problem for equivalence between such terms has not been handled.

Eggan [9] has defined the notion of star-height of a regular event and has proposed the problem whether there exist regular events of arbitrary large star-height. This was answered in the affirmative independently by McNaughton and the present author (unpublished) and by Dejan and Schützenberger [7].

There still remains the problem whether the same result holds if we extend the notion of regular expression by allowing the use of intersection or of complementation.

I.4. **Algebraization of f.a.** There are several algebraic characterizations of regular events which are of great importance both in leading to interesting concepts and results within classical automata theory and in pointing the way to generalizations of the classical theory. Some researchers would go as far as to completely algebrize the theory of automata and do everything from the algebraic point of view. It is the present author's view that some intermediate position is preferable. The algebraic notions were, after all, suggested by a certain model of automaton. Keeping this model in mind should continue to guide us as to which questions and notions are natural and profitable. Also, proofs and constructions which are complicated and even artificial in the algebraic formulations often become simple and transparent when thought about in the context of machines.

An equivalence relation E on Σ^* is called *right-invariant* if xEy implies $xzEyz$ for all x, y, z, $\in \Sigma^*$. The notion of a *left-invariant* equivalence is defined in an analogous fashion.

An equivalence relation which is both left-invariant and right-invariant is called a *congruence* on Σ^*.

Given a set $T \subseteq \Sigma^*$ one can define two relations E_T and $\equiv_T$ by

$$xE_Ty \leftrightarrow \text{for all } v \in \Sigma^*, \ xv \in T \text{ iff } yv \in T,$$

$$x \equiv_T y \leftrightarrow \text{for all } u, v \in \Sigma^*, \ uxv \in T \text{ iff } uyv \in T.$$

The index, $index(E)$, of an equivalence relation is the number of equivalence classes into which E divides Σ^*.

The following two characterizations of regular events are due, respectively, to Nerode [26] and Myhill [25] (see also [33] for proofs).

THEOREM 3. *A set $T \subseteq \Sigma^*$ is regular if and only if it is the union of equivalence classes of a right-invariant relation E (on Σ^*) with finite index.*

In particular, T is regular if and only if the relation E_T has a finite index. There exists an automaton $\mathfrak{A}$ with index(E_T) states such that $T = T(\mathfrak{A})$. No automaton with fewer than index(E_T) states defines T.

The previous theorem is very useful in showing that certain sets $T \subseteq \Sigma^*$ are or are not regular. Thus Shepherdson [39] used a version of this result to prove that two-way automata are equivalent to ordinary automata; Rabin [34] applied this criterion to show that, under a certain natural condition, probabilistic automata are equivalent to ordinary automata.

THEOREM 4. *A set $T \subseteq \Sigma^*$ is regular if and only if it is a union of equivalence classes of a congruence $\equiv$ (on Σ^*) with finite index.*

In particular, T is regular if and only if index$(\equiv_T)$ is finite.

Given a congruence relation $\equiv$ on Σ^*, we can make the set $\Sigma^*/\equiv$ of equivalence classes of Σ^* with respect to $\equiv$, into a semigroup in such a way that the mapping $\phi\colon x \to [x]$ of each $x \in \Sigma^*$ into its equivalence class is a homomorphism of Σ^* onto $\Sigma^*/\equiv$. Conversely, to each homomorphism $\phi\colon \Sigma^* \to M$ of Σ^* onto a semigroup M there corresponds a congruence $\equiv$ defined by $x \equiv y$ if and only if $\phi(x) = \phi(y)$.

Bearing these remarks in mind, we see that the previous theorem can be restated as follows. *A set $T \subseteq \Sigma^*$ is regular if and only if there exist a finite semigroup M, a set $H \subseteq M$ and a homomorphism $\phi\colon \Sigma^* \to M$ such that $T = \phi^{-1}(H)$.* The semigroup $\Sigma^*/\equiv_T$ occupies, in this approach, the position of a canonical semigroup associated with the regular event T.

The work of Krohn and Rhodes [18] centers around the semigroup approach to automata. They define ways of decomposing automata into simpler automata. These decompositions are interpreted by appropriate decompositions of the corresponding semigroups. Algebraic methods and results are then used to obtain interesting information concerning existence and uniqueness of decompositions of automata into simple basic automata.

Another set of problems arises from the semigroup approach to automata theory by considering finite semigroups with special properties and examining the associated regular events (see Schützenberger [38]).

We shall finish this section with yet another characterization of regular events. Associate with each $\sigma \in \Sigma$ a unary operation (function) symbol F_σ. A system $\langle A, a_0, f_\sigma \rangle_{\sigma \in \Sigma}$ is called an *algebra of type* Σ if $a_0 \in A$ and every f_σ, $\sigma \in \Sigma$, is a function from A into A. In particular, we have the *free-algebra F_Σ of type* Σ which is defined as follows. Let v_0 be a fixed symbol. Let

V be the smallest set such that $v_0 \in V$ and, for all t, if $t \in V$ then $F_\sigma(t)$ $\in V$, $\sigma \in \Sigma$. Now, $F_\Sigma = \langle V, v_0, f_\sigma \rangle_{\sigma \in \Sigma}$ where $f_\sigma \colon V \to V$ is defined by $f_\sigma(t)$ $= F_\sigma(t)$, $t \in V$. There is a natural one-to-one correspondence ϕ between words $x \in \Sigma^*$ and terms $t \in V$ given by the recursion

$$\phi(v_0) = \Lambda, \quad \phi(F_\sigma(t)) = \phi(t)\sigma, \quad \sigma \in \Sigma, \quad t \in V.$$

The characterization reads as follows.

THEOREM 5. *A set* $T \subseteq \Sigma^*$ *is regular if and only if there exist a finite algebra* $F = \langle A, a_0, \bar{f}_\sigma \rangle_{\sigma \in \Sigma}$ *of type* Σ, *a homomorphism* $\psi \colon F_\Sigma \to F$ *and a subset* $H \subseteq A$ *such that* $T = \phi(\psi^{-1}(H))$.

This may seem to be a very roundabout way of looking at regular events. It does, however, lead directly to the tree-automata of §III.

I.5. **Decision problems and algorithms.** A central topic in theory of automata is the effective (in the sense of recursive-function theory) solution of various decision problems concerning automata. Typically, we are given a property P of automata and we are requested to either exhibit an effective procedure for deciding for every automaton $\mathfrak{A}$ whether $\mathfrak{A}$ has property P, or else to prove that no such procedure exists. Sometimes the property in question may involve pairs (or triplets, etc.) of automata. Thus the *equivalence problem* for automata involves pairs $(\mathfrak{A}, \mathfrak{B})$ and the property in question is $T(\mathfrak{A}) = T(\mathfrak{B})$. In other cases we may have mappings from automata to automata. In the *state-minimization problem* we want to construct an algorithm for passing from every automaton $\mathfrak{A}$ to the (unique) automaton $\mathfrak{B}$ with least number of states such that $T(\mathfrak{A}) = T(\mathfrak{B})$.

It turns out that all the natural decision problems one can formulate for automata are effectively solvable (see Rabin-Scott [33]). Despite this, there still remain interesting and important questions concerning the existence of "practical" algorithms for various decision problems. In the following we shall consider an algorithm to be practical if, for automata with n states, it requires at most cn^k (k is a fixed integer and c a fixed constant) computational steps. This stipulation is, admittedly, both vague and arbitrary. We do not, in fact cannot, define what is meant by a computational step, thus have no precise and general measure for the complexity of algorithms. Furthermore, there is no compelling reason to classify algorithms requiring cn^k steps as practical.

Several points may be raised in. defense of the above stipulation. In every given algorithm the notion of a computational step is quite obvious. Hence there is not that much vagueness about the measure of complexity of existing algorithms. Another significant pragmatic fact is that all existing algorithms either require up to about n^4 steps or else require 2^n or worse steps. Thus drawing the line of practicality between algorithms requiring n^k steps and algorithms for which no such bound exists seems to be reasonable. Assume, for example, that algorithm A for decision problem P_1 requires n^3 steps for automata with n states, and that algorithm B for decision problem P_2 requires 2^n steps. The basic steps of A and B are assumed to require comparable time in actual computation. Let n_0 be the largest value of n for which algorithm A is still practical with present-date computing devices. Under these conditions, algorithm B will be practical only for automata with up to $m_0 = 3 \log_2 n_0$ states. Furthermore, if the speed of computing devices will be improved by a factor of ten then algorithm A will be applicable to values of n up to $2n_0$, whereas the range of applicability of B will extend only to $m_0 + 3$.

All the above considerations were just heuristic in nature. There is no doubt that these questions concerning complexity of algorithms, and not only algorithms having to do with automata, but algorithms for combinatorial problems in general, are of paramount importance. Setting up proper definitions of complexity of algorithms and creation of a mathematical machinery for proving significant statements about complexity will be a major breakthrough.

Let us now return to specific problems about automata. The practical algorithms concerning automata are usually variations of the "merging procedure" initiated by Moore [23]. By way of illustration, we shall treat the equivalence problem for automata.

Let $\mathfrak{A} = \langle S, M, s_0, F \rangle$, $\mathfrak{B} = \langle \bar{S}, \bar{M}, \bar{s}_0, \bar{F} \rangle$ be two automata over Σ. We wish to determine whether $T(\mathfrak{A}) = T(\mathfrak{B})$. As usual, $A \times B$ denotes the set of all pairs (a, b), $a \in A$, $b \in B$. Define inductively a sequence H_i, $i = 0, 1, 2, \cdots$ of subsets of $S \times \bar{S}$ as follows:

$$H_0 = \{ (s_0, \bar{s}_0) \},$$

(1) $$H_{i+1} = \{ (M(s, \sigma), \bar{M}(t, \sigma)) \mid (s, t) \in H_i, \ \sigma \in \Sigma \}.$$

It can be readily proved, by induction on i, that $(s, t) \in H_i$ if and only if there exists a word $x \in \Sigma^*$ such that $l(x) = i$, $M^*(s_0, x) = s$, and $\bar{M}^*(\bar{s}_0, x) = t$.

Now let $|S| = n$ (S has n elements), $|\bar{S}| = m$, $|\Sigma| = k$. The sequence H_i, $0 \leq i < \infty$, has the property that once

$$H_{j+1} \subseteq H_0 \cup \cdots \cup H_j = U_j$$

occurs for some j, then also

$$H_{j+p} \subseteq H_0 \cup \cdots \cup H_j, \qquad 1 \leq p < \infty.$$

Thus the sequence of the unions U_i has the form

$$U_0 \subset \cdots \subset U_j = U_{j+1} = U_{j+2} = \cdots$$

where $\subset$ denotes strict inclusion. Since $U_i \subseteq S \times \bar{S}$, $i = 0, 1, 2, \cdots$ and the latter set has exactly nm elements, it follows that $j \leq nm$. Now, $T(\mathfrak{A}) \neq T(\mathfrak{B})$ if and only if there exists a word $x \in \Sigma^*$ such that $M^*(s_0, x) = s \in F$ and $\bar{M}^*(\bar{s}_0, x) = t \notin \bar{F}$ or vice versa; in set theoretical notation this condition reads

(2) $$(s, t) \in [F \times (\bar{S} - \bar{F})] \cup [(S - F) \times \bar{F}].$$

The decision procedure will proceed as follows. Check whether $(s_0, \bar{s}_0)$ satisfies (2); if it does, then $T(\mathfrak{A}) \neq T(\mathfrak{B})$. If not, define $H_0 = \{ (s_0, \bar{s}_0) \} = U_0$. At the $(i + 1)$th stage of the procedure, H_i and U_i are given. Calculate H_{i+1} according to formula (1). Check whether H_{i+1} contains a pair (s, t) satisfying (2). If it does, then $T(\mathfrak{A}) \neq T(\mathfrak{B})$. Otherwise, check whether $H_{i+1} \subseteq U_i$, if this occurs, then $T(\mathfrak{A}) = T(\mathfrak{B})$ and we are through. If neither case occurred, then form $U_{i+1} = U_i \cup H_{i+1}$ and proceed to stage $i + 2$.

We know that the procedure will terminate at some stage $k \leq mn$. It is an easy matter to estimate the number of computational steps involved at each stage. Thus, for example, to calculate H_{i+1}, if we count a computation of $(M(s, \sigma), \bar{M}(t, \sigma))$ as a "step," then we have at most nmk steps (because $|H_i| \leq nm$, $|\Sigma| = k$). Hence it is easy to obtain a good bound on the total number of steps required to solve our problem.

As a byproduct of the above discussion, we have the following result. If $T(\mathfrak{A}) \neq T(\mathfrak{B})$ then there exists a word x with $l(x) \leq nm$ such that $x \in T(\mathfrak{A})$ and $x \notin T(\mathfrak{B})$ or vice versa (for a different proof see [33], p. 120). This result in itself suffices to show that the equivalence problem is effectively solvable. In order to check whether $T(\mathfrak{A}) = T(\mathfrak{B})$, we have to only look at words x with $l(x) \leq nm$ of which there are only finitely many. This proposed procedure is of course impractical, for the number of steps involved may be k^{nm}. The construction of the set H_i in the previous discussion amounts to merging, for every pair $(s, t) \in S \times \bar{S}$, the many words x with $l(x) = i$ for which $(M(s_0, x), M(\bar{s}_0, x)) = (s, t)$ into one equivalence class. This reduces the number of objects to be considered at this stage from k^i to at most nm.

The state-minimization problem mentioned before can also be handled by a merging procedure (Moore [23]). Here one successively merges the states $s \in S$, $t \in S$ which lead from s_0 to the same states under the same words x. Again we have a practical procedure.

The situation changes completely upon passing to the related and superficially very similar problem of state minimization of an incomplete automaton.

The system $\mathfrak{A} = \langle S, M, s_0, F \rangle$ is an *incomplete automaton* if M is a function from a (possibly proper) subset $H \subseteq S \times \Sigma$ into S. Thus the state transition $s \to M(s, \sigma)$ may be undefined for certain pairs (s, σ). The function $M^*(s, x)$

may also be undefined for certain pairs (s, x), $s \in S$, $x \in \Sigma^*$. For an incomplete $\mathfrak{A}$ we say that $x \in \Sigma^*$ is *accepted* by $\mathfrak{A}$ $(x \in T(\mathfrak{A}))$ if $M^*(s_0, x)$ is defined and an element of F. Similarly, x is *rejected* by $\mathfrak{A}$ $(x \in R(\mathfrak{A}))$ if $M^*(s_0, x)$ is defined and an element of $S - F$. For incomplete automata $R(\mathfrak{A}) \cup T(\mathfrak{A})$ may be unequal to Σ^*.

An automaton $\mathfrak{B}$ is said to *include* $\mathfrak{A}$ if $T(\mathfrak{A}) \subseteq T(\mathfrak{B})$ and $R(\mathfrak{A}) \subseteq R(\mathfrak{B})$. The state-minimization problem for incomplete automata is to find, for a given incomplete $\mathfrak{A}$, an incomplete $\mathfrak{B}$ which includes $\mathfrak{A}$ and has the smallest possible number of states.

Several authors, among them Ginsburg [12], [13], [14], Beatty and Miller [2], Miller [22] (this also contains additional references), Paull and Unger [28], have treated this question. No practical algorithm exists for this problem. In fact, estimates made by Miller [22] show that the existing procedures could require up to 2^{2^n} steps. This state of affairs shows once more that even for decision problems which are trivial from the point of view of recursive function theory (as this problem is) there may remain difficult questions concerning existence of "practical" algorithms.

I.6. Finite automata and infinite sequences. Büchi [5] was the first to notice that one can extend the notion of a f.a. $\mathfrak{A}$ accepting a word, to the case where $x = \sigma_0 \sigma_1 \cdots \sigma_n \cdots$ is a *denumerable* sequence of letters $\sigma_n \in \Sigma$. The need for this extension arose in a natural way in connection with applications of automata to logic which will be described later.

Let $\mathfrak{A} = \langle S, M, S_0 F \rangle$ be a nondeterministic atuomaton. A denumerable sequence $\mathbf{s} = s_0, s_1, \cdots$ of states is called *compatible* with x if $s_0 \in S_0$ and $s_{n+1} \in M(s_n, \sigma_n)$, $0 \leq n < \infty$.

Following Büchi we define

DEFINITION 3. $\mathfrak{A}$ *accepts* x if for some sequence $\mathbf{s}$ compatible with x, the set $\{n \mid s_n \in F\}$ is infinite. The set of all denumerable sequences accepted by $\mathfrak{A}$ will be denoted by $T_\infty(\mathfrak{A})$.

Denote by Σ_∞ the set of all denumerable sequences on Σ. Call a subset $H \subseteq \Sigma_\infty$ *f.a. definable* if for some $\mathfrak{A}$, $H = T_\infty(\mathfrak{A})$. The following theorem is due to Büchi.

THEOREM 6. *If $H_1 \subseteq \Sigma_\infty$ and $H_2 \subseteq \Sigma_\infty$ are f.a. definable then so are $H_1 \cup H_2$, $H_1 \cap H_2$ and $\Sigma_\infty - H_1$. Thus the definable sets are a boolean algebra of subsets of Σ_∞.*

It is easy to show that $H_1 \cup H_2$ and $H_1 \cap H_2$ are f.a. definable. The result concerning $\Sigma_\infty - H_1$ lies much deeper and requires interesting new ideas.

Elgot and Rabin [11] raise in connection with f.a. on infinite sequences a new kind of decision problem. Given a *fixed* infinite sequence $x \in \Sigma_\infty$, to either give an effective procedure for deciding, for every $\mathfrak{A}$, whether $x \in T_\infty(\mathfrak{A})$, or else prove that no such procedure exists. They prove, for example, that *for* $\Sigma = \{0,1\}$ *and the sequence* x_A *which is the characteristic function of the set* $A = \{n! \mid n = 0, 1, 2, \cdots\}$ *this problem is recursively solvable.*

It seemed for a while that a reasonable theory of f.a. on denumerable sequences could be developed only for nondeterministic automata. D. Muller has shown [24] how to formulate the definition of acceptance of a sequence $x \in \Sigma_\infty$ by a (deterministic) f.a. so as to get a notion which is, in fact, coextensive with Büchi's.

Let $\mathfrak{A} = \langle S, M, s_0, \mathbf{F} \rangle$ be a (deterministic) f.a. except that here $\mathbf{F}$ is a set of subsets of S ($\mathbf{F} \subseteq P(S)$). For a sequence $x = \sigma_0 \sigma_1 \cdots \sigma_n \cdots$, define $F(x)$ by $F(x) = \{s \mid s \in S, \ M^*(s_0, \sigma_0 \cdots \sigma_n) = s \ \text{for infinitely many } n\}$.

DEFINITION 4. $\mathfrak{A}$ is said to *accept* x (*in Muller's sense*) if $F(x) \in \mathbf{F}$. The set of all sequences accepted by $\mathfrak{A}$ will be denoted by $T_\infty^M(\mathfrak{A})$.

Again we have the notion of a *f.a. definable* subset $H \subseteq \Sigma_\infty$. The main result is that *every H f.a. definable in Büchi's sense is f.a. definable in Muller's sense and vice versa.* Muller's original proof seems to contain an error. R. McNaughton [19] gave another proof involving some new constructions with automata.

Büchi has recently [6] generalized the Muller definition and McNaughton's methods to automata on transfinite sequences.

I.7. F.A. and mathematical logic. One of the finest applications of automata theory is to the decision problem of second-order theory of successor. We shall give just a brief description of these problems. The reader not interested or not acquainted with mathematical logic may skip this section.

Consider the structure $\langle N, 0, S \rangle$ where N is the set of nonnegative integers and S is the successor function $S(x) = x + 1$. We define two monadic second-order applied languages. The first of these is a weak second-order language, WS, which has, besides the nonlogical constants $\mathbf{0}$ and $\mathbf{S}$ which will be interpreted as the zero and the successor function, set variables $\alpha, \beta, \cdots$ which are intended to range over *finite* subsets of N. In forming formulas of WS we allow quantification over set variables as well as over individual variables. Thus

$$\forall \alpha [\ \forall z [\mathbf{S}(z) \in \alpha \to z \in \alpha] \wedge y \in \alpha \to x \in \alpha]$$

is a formula of WS. In fact, denoting this formula by $\mathbf{F}(\mathbf{x}, \mathbf{y})$ and having the usual notion of numeral, $F(\mathbf{n}, \mathbf{m})$ is true in $\langle N, 0, S \rangle$ if and only if $n \leq m$ holds.

The strong second-order language, SS, is like WS except that we have set variables $\mathbf{A}, \mathbf{B}, \cdots$ intended to range over arbitrary subsets of N.

The decision problem of WS (SS) is to find an effective procedure of deciding, for every sentence of WS (SS) whether it is true in $\langle N, 0, S \rangle$.

Büchi and Elgot [3], [4], [10] solved the decision problem of WS using methods of automata theory. Büchi [5] used a far-reaching extension of these ideas (see §I.6) to solve the decision problem of SS. Elgot and Rabin [11] give further applications of automata to the solution of decision problems.

To see the connection of WS and SS with automata, we shall describe the application to SS. In solving the decision problem for SS it is enough to deal with formulas containing no free individual variables, i.e., all free variables (if there are any) are set variables.

Let $A = (A_1, \cdots, A_n)$, $A_i \subseteq N$, $1 \leq i \leq n$ be an n-tuple of sets. We wish to describe this n-tuple by an infinite sequence x on a suitable alphabet. Let $\Sigma = \{0, 1\}$; Σ^n is the alphabet of the 2^n sequences on 0 and 1 of length n. Define $x_A \in \Sigma^n_\infty$ by

$$\sigma_k = (\chi_{A_1}(k), \cdots, \chi_{A_n}(k)), \qquad k = 0, 1, 2, \cdots,$$

$$x_A = \sigma_0 \sigma_1 \cdots \sigma_k \cdots$$

where χ_S denotes the characteristic function of S. This definition sets up a one-to-one correspondence between n-tuples of subsets of N and Σ^n_∞. Büchi's main result is

THEOREM 7. *For every formula* $F(A_1, \cdots, A_n)$ *of SS there exists a (non-deterministic) f.a.* $\mathfrak{A}_F$ *over* Σ^n *such that* $A = (A_1, \cdots, A_n)$ *satisfies* $F(A_1, \cdots, A_n)$ *in* $\langle N, 0, S \rangle$ *if and only if* $x_A \in T(\mathfrak{A}_F)$.

This result is proved by induction on formulas. Theorem 6 is used to take care of the propositional connectives. The reader may try to treat the case of an existential set quantifier. The fact that we are dealing with nondeterministic automata makes this step a very simple one.

The construction of $\mathfrak{A}_F$ from $F(A_1, \cdots, A_n)$ is effective. Thus Theorem 7 leads immediately to a decision procedure for SS.

II. PROBABILISTIC AUTOMATA

II.0. **Definitions.** The idea of introducing probabilities into the state-transitions of an automaton lies near at hand. Rabin [34] developed a systematic theory of probabilistic automata (p.a.). In particular, he introduced the notion of an isolated cut-point for p.a. and proved that, under certain natural conditions, p.a. are equivalent to ordinary automata.

P.a. automata in the sense of [34] were subsequently studied by Paz [29], [31], Page [27], and Salomaa (references unavailable).

We shall now define probabilistic automata. It will be seen that probabilistic automata are like the usual automata except that now the transition table M assigns to each pair $(s, \sigma) \in S \times \Sigma$ certain transition probabilities.

DEFINITION 5. A *probabilistic automaton* (p.a.) over the alphabet Σ is a system $\mathfrak{A} = \langle S, M, s_0, F \rangle$ where $S = \{s_0, \cdots, s_n\}$ is a finite set (the set of *states*), M is a function from $S \times \Sigma$ into $[0, 1]^{n+1}$ (the *transition proba-*

bilities table) such that for $(s, \sigma) \in S \times \Sigma$

$$M(s, \sigma) = (p_0(s, \sigma), \cdots, p_n(s, \sigma)), \quad 0 \leq p_i(s, \sigma), \quad \sum_i p_i(s, \sigma) = 1,$$

$s_0 \in S$ (the *initial state*), and $F \subseteq S$ (the set of *designated final states*).

Probabilistic automata are models for systems (such as sequential circuits) having a finite number of states $s_0, \cdots, s_n$. The system may receive inputs $\sigma \in \Sigma$. When in state s and if the input is σ then the system can go into any one of the states $s_i \in S$ and the probability of going into s_i is the $(i+1)$th coordinate $p_i(s, \sigma)$ of $M(s, \sigma)$. These transition probabilities $p_i(s, \sigma)$ are assumed to remain fixed and be independent of time and previous inputs. Thus the system also has definite transition probabilities for going from state s to state s_i by a *sequence* $x \in \Sigma^*$ of inputs. These probabilities are calculated by means of products of certain stochastic matrices.

For $\sigma \in \Sigma$ and $x = \sigma_1 \sigma_2 \cdots \sigma_m$ define the $n+1$ by $n+1$ matrices $A(\sigma)$ and $A(x)$ by

$$A(\sigma) = [p_j(s_i, \sigma)]_{0 \leq i, j \leq n},$$

$$A(x) = A(\sigma_1) A(\sigma_2) \cdots A(\sigma_m) = [p_j(s_i, x)]_{0 \leq i, j \leq n}.$$

An easy calculation (involving induction on m) will show the $(i+1, j+1)$ element $p_j(s_i, x)$ is the probability of $\mathfrak{A}$ for moving from state s_i to state s_j by the input sequence x.

If $\mathfrak{A} = \langle S, M, s_0, F \rangle$ and $F = \{s_{i_0}, \cdots, s_{i_r}\}$, $I = \{i_0, \cdots, i_r\}$, define

$$p(x) = \sum_{i \in I} p_i(s_0, x).$$

$p(x)$ clearly is the probability for $\mathfrak{A}$, when started in s_0, to enter into a state which is a member of F by the input sequence x.

A p.a. $\mathfrak{A}$ may be used to define sets of words in a manner similar to that of deterministic automata except that now the set of words will depend not just on $\mathfrak{A}$ but also on a parameter λ.

DEFINITION 6. Let $\mathfrak{A}$ be p.a. and λ be a real number, $0 \leq \lambda < 1$. The set of words $T(\mathfrak{A}, \lambda)$ is defined by

$$T(\mathfrak{A}, \lambda) = \{x \,|\, x \in \Sigma^*, \quad \lambda < p(x)\}.$$

If $x \in T(\mathfrak{A}, \lambda)$ we say that x is *accepted* by $\mathfrak{A}$ with *cut-point* λ. $T(\mathfrak{A}, \lambda)$ will also be called the set *defined by* $\mathfrak{A}$ *with cut-point* λ.

Deterministic automata can be considered as a special case of p.a. Namely, if in Definition 1 $M(s, \sigma) = s_i$, then we can view this as if $\mathfrak{A}$ will enter state s_i with probability 1. Thus in rewriting the deterministic automaton as a p.a. the stochastic vectors $M(s, \sigma) = (p_0, \cdots, p_n)$ will have exactly one coordinate 1 and all the others 0. It is readily seen that in this case $p(x) = 1$, for $x \in \Sigma^*$, if and only if $x \in T(\mathfrak{A})$. Hence for any λ, $0 \leq \lambda < 1$, we have $T(\mathfrak{A}) = T(\mathfrak{A}, \lambda)$. Thus every set definable by a deterministic automaton is trivially definable by some p.a. We shall see that the converse is not true and that, therefore, p.a. give a strictly larger class of definable sets.

The following matrices were suggested by E. F. Moore:

$$P_0 = \begin{bmatrix} 1 & 0 \\ \frac{1}{2} & \frac{1}{2} \end{bmatrix}, \qquad P_1 = \begin{bmatrix} \frac{1}{2} & \frac{1}{2} \\ 0 & 1 \end{bmatrix}.$$

It can be readily verified that if

$$P_{\delta_1} \cdot P_{\delta_2} \cdot \cdots \cdot P_{\delta_n} = \begin{bmatrix} m & p \\ q & r \end{bmatrix}, \qquad \delta_i \in \{0,1\},$$

then $p = \cdot \delta_n \delta_{n-1} \cdots \delta_1$ where p is written in binary expansion.

THEOREM 8. *Let* $\mathfrak{A} = \langle S, M, s_0, F \rangle$ *be an automaton over* $\Sigma = \{0,1\}$ *such that* $S = \{s_0, s_1\}$, $A(0) = P_0$, $A(1) = P_1$, $F = \{s_1\}$. *There exists a* $0 \leq \lambda < 1$ *such that* $T(\mathfrak{A}, \lambda)$ *is not definable by a deterministic automaton (is not a regular event).*

PROOF. If $x = \delta_1 \delta_2 \cdots \delta_n \in \Sigma^*$, then by the above, $p(x) = \cdot \delta_n \delta_{n-1} \cdots \delta_1$.

The values $p(x)$ are dense in the whole interval $[0,1]$. This implies that if $0 \leq \lambda < \lambda_1 < 1$ then $T(\mathfrak{A}, \lambda_1) \subset T(\mathfrak{A}, \lambda)$ where the inclusion is proper. The sets $T(\mathfrak{A}, \lambda)$, $0 \leq \lambda < 1$, therefore form a nondenumerable pairwise different collection of sets. But there is only a denumerable collection of regular events. Therefore, there exists a λ such that $T(\mathfrak{A}, \lambda)$ is not regular.

II.1. **Isolated cut-points.** Let $\mathfrak{A}$ be a p.a. and $0 \leq \lambda < 1$. Given a word $x \in \Sigma^*$ we devise the following probabilistic experiment E to test whether $x \in T(\mathfrak{A}, \lambda)$. We run x through $\mathfrak{A}$ a large number N of times and count the number $m(E)$ of times that $\mathfrak{A}$ ended in a state in F. If $\lambda < m(E)/N$ we accept x and otherwise we reject it. Because of the probabilistic nature of the experiment it is of course possible that we sometimes accept x even though $x \notin T(\mathfrak{A}, \lambda)$ or reject it even though $x \in T(\mathfrak{A}, \lambda)$. By the law of large numbers, however, there exists for each x such that $p(x) \neq \lambda$ and each $0 < \epsilon$ a number $N(x, \epsilon)$ such that

$$\Pr(E | \lambda < m(E)/N(x, \epsilon) \leftrightarrow x \in T(\mathfrak{A}, \lambda)) \geq 1 - \epsilon.$$

That is, the probability of obtaining the *correct* answer by the experiment E (consisting of running x $N(x, \epsilon)$ times through $\mathfrak{A}$ and counting successes) is greater than $1 - \epsilon$.

To perform the above stochastic experiment we must know $N(x, \epsilon)$ which depends on $|p(x) - \lambda|$. Thus we have actually to know $p(x)$ in advance if we want to ascertain whether $x \in T(\mathfrak{A}, \lambda)$ with probability greater than $1 - \epsilon$ of being correct. Once we know $p(x)$, however, the whole experiment E is superfluous.

The way out is to consider values λ such that $|p(x) - \lambda|$ is bounded from below for all $x \in \Sigma^*$.

DEFINITION 7. A cut-point λ is called *isolated* with respect to $\mathfrak{A}$ if there exists a $0 < \delta$ such that

(3) $$\delta \leq |p(x) - \lambda| \quad \text{for all} \quad x \in \Sigma^*.$$

It is readily seen that there exists an integral valued function $N(\delta, \epsilon)$ such that for an isolated λ and *any* $x \in \Sigma^*$

$$\Pr(E | \lambda < m(E)/N(\delta, \epsilon) \leftrightarrow x \in T(\mathfrak{A}, \lambda)) \geq 1 - \epsilon.$$

Thus the proposed stochastic experiment for determining whether $x \in T(\mathfrak{A}, \lambda)$ can be performed without any a priori knowledge of $p(x)$. This fact makes it natural to consider isolated cut-points.

The concept of isolated cut-point plays a fundamental role in the theory of probabilistic automata. Can one devise an algorithm for deciding for every given p.a. $\mathfrak{A}$ (the automaton is given by the matrices $A(\sigma)$, $\sigma \in \Sigma$, and we assume for the sake of simplicity that these matrices have rational coordinates) and every (rational) λ whether λ is an isolated cut-point of $\mathfrak{A}$? Another problem is to decide for every given p.a. $\mathfrak{A}$ whether it has *any* isolated cut-points. Are these problems perhaps recursively unsolvable?

II.2. The reduction theorem.

THEOREM 9. *Let $\mathfrak{A}$ be a probabilistic automaton and λ be an isolated cut-point satisfying (3). Then there exists a deterministic automaton $\mathfrak{B}$ such that $T(\mathfrak{A}, \lambda) = T(\mathfrak{B})$. If $\mathfrak{A}$ has n states then $\mathfrak{B}$ can be chosen to have e states where*

$$e \leq [1 + (1/\delta)]^{n-1}$$

The proof of this theorem uses certain ideas from geometric number theory. It does not seem to yield an effective way of constructing the f.a. $\mathfrak{B}$ from the p.a. $\mathfrak{A}$. Neither is it clear whether the bound $[1 + (1/\delta)]^{n-1}$ on the number of states of $\mathfrak{B}$ is reasonably close to the best possible bound.

In [34] an example is given of a p.a. $\mathfrak{A}$ with 2 states and an isolated cut-point λ for which the least number of states of a f.a. $\mathfrak{B}$ with $T(\mathfrak{A}, \lambda) = T(\mathfrak{B})$ is $m + 1$. In this case $\delta = 3^{-m-1}$ so that $[1 + (1/\delta)]^{n-1} \geq 1 + 3^{m+1}$. It would be of interest to see whether the bound in Theorem 9 can be considerably improved.

II.3. The stability problem.
Consider a p.a. $\mathfrak{A}$ and an isolated cut-point λ. It is natural to ask whether the set $T(\mathfrak{A}, \lambda)$ remains unchanged (*stable*) under small perturbations of the transition probabilities of $\mathfrak{A}$. Results along this line we shall call *stability theorems*.

One motivation for the study of stability comes from considering probabilistic automata as models for sequential circuits built from unreliable components. Suppose that we are synthesizing a sequential circuit which is intended to have a certain behavior, from unreliable components having certain probabilities of misfiring. We surely want the behavior of the whole circuit (i.e., the event defined by it) to be independent of small fluctuations in the failure probabilities.

The exact notion of stability is given by the following

DEFINITION 8. Let $\mathfrak{A} = \langle S, M, s_0, F \rangle$ be a p.a. with transition matrices $A(\sigma)$, $\sigma \in \Sigma$, and let λ be an isolated cut-point of $\mathfrak{A}$. $\mathfrak{A}$ is called *stable for cut-point* λ, if there exists an $\epsilon > 0$ such that for every p.a. $\mathfrak{A}' = \langle S, M', s_0, F \rangle$ with transition matrices $A'(\sigma)$, $\sigma \in \Sigma$ satisfying

$$(4) \qquad\qquad \| A(\sigma) - A'(\sigma) \| \leq \epsilon, \qquad \sigma \in \Sigma,$$

we have that λ is an isolated cut-point of $\mathfrak{A}'$ and $T(\mathfrak{A}, \lambda) = T(\mathfrak{A}', \lambda)$.

In the above definition, the norm $\| A \|$ of a matrix is the maximum of the absolute values of its elements.

A p.a. $\mathfrak{A}$ with transition matrices $A(\sigma)$, $\sigma \in \Sigma$, is called an *actual* p.a. if all elements of $A(\sigma)$ are strictly positive for every $\sigma \in \Sigma$. In [34] it is shown that *if $\mathfrak{A}$ is an actual p.a. and λ is an isolated cut-point then $T(\mathfrak{A}, \lambda)$ is a definite event.* For a discussion of definite events, see Perles, Rabin, and Shamir [32].

We have the following stability result.

THEOREM 10. *If $\mathfrak{A}$ is an actual p.a. and λ is an isolated cut-point then $\mathfrak{A}$ is stable for cut-point λ.*

The condition of strict positivity of the matrices $A(\sigma)$ can be somewhat relaxed. Paz [30] noticed that if the set $\{ A(\sigma) \mid \sigma \in \Sigma \}$ of transition matrices of $\mathfrak{A}$ satisfies a certain condition of Wolfowitz [42] then (for isolated cut-points) $\mathfrak{A}$ defines a definite event and is stable.

One can hope for stability in the most general sense of Definition 8 only in the case that $T(\mathfrak{A}, \lambda)$ is a definite event. For if $\mathfrak{A}$ is stable for cut-point λ there are, for every $\epsilon > 0$, matrices $A'(\sigma)$, $\sigma \in \Sigma$, which are strictly positive and satisfy (4). Thus $\mathfrak{A}'$ is an actual p.a. and λ an isolated cut-point so that $T(\mathfrak{A}, \lambda) = T(\mathfrak{A}', \lambda)$ is a definite event. Hence *if $\mathfrak{A}$ is stable at isolated cut-point λ then $T(\mathfrak{A}, \lambda)$ is a definite event.*

Thus to have stability theorems for the general case, where $T(\mathfrak{A}, \lambda)$ is regular but not necessarily definite, one would have to impose on the perturbed matrices $A(\sigma)$ conditions which are more stringent than (4). One possible conjecture is: If $\mathfrak{A}$ is a p.a. and λ is an isolated cut-point then there exists a $0 < \epsilon$ such that for every automaton $\mathfrak{A}'$ with conditions as in Definition 8 and such that the matrices $A'(\sigma)$ *have zeros where $A(\sigma)$ had zeros*, λ is an isolated cut-point of $\mathfrak{A}'$ and $T(\mathfrak{A}', \lambda) = T(\mathfrak{A}, \lambda)$. H. Kesten (private communication) constructed a neat counterexample to this conjecture. Thus the problem of giving suitable stability results for nondefinite $T(\mathfrak{A}, \lambda)$ is completely open.

III. Tree-Automata

III.0. **Background and motivation.** This last chapter is devoted to a new development in theory of automata; namely, the generalization from automata having (linear) sequences for inputs to automata having trees for inputs. We shall call these new automata *tree-automata* (this name seems to have originated with the present author who takes full responsibility should it be considered inadequate).

Tree-automata were discovered by Doner [8] who first applied them to solve the decision problem of the weak monadic second-order theory of several successor functions. Thatcher and Wright [40], [41] independently developed tree-automata and then noticed the same application. Mezei and Wright [21] apply a version of tree-automata to context-free languages; their work was influenced by certain ideas of D. Muller.

We attach great importance to these generalizations and, in our opinion, this new notion will completely change and revive the study of finite automata. In the following sections we list numerous open problems and possible applications.

Finite tree-automata (f.t.a.) will be introduced by an approach which, we hope, will bring out the fact that they are a natural and one-step generalization of f.a.

Our discussion, here and throughout Chapter III is limited to binary trees. The generalization to trees with higher (but bounded) branching is immediate. These generalizations also carry over to the algebraic formulations (§III.4), where we consider algebras with just binary functions, whereas the general formulation would require algebras of arbitrary type or *species* (see [41]). The special binary case considered here is, however, typical and all notions and results are immediately extendable to the general case.

Consider first ordinary automata. Let $\mathfrak{A} = \langle S, M, s_0, F \rangle$ be a f.a. over Σ, let $x = \sigma_0 \sigma_1 \sigma_2 \in \Sigma^*$. One can view x as a linear graph with nodes valued by elements $\sigma \in \Sigma$. Thus to x there corresponds the valued linear graph (a) of Figure 1.

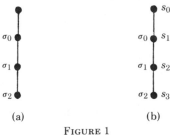

(a)   (b)

FIGURE 1

The lowest node is *the root* of the graph and the highest node is the *terminal node*. Note that the terminal node is not valued. If $M(s_i, \sigma_i) = s_{i+1}$,

$i = 0, 1, 2$, then Figure 1(b) describes the behavior of $\mathfrak{A}$ on x (except for the initial state s_0, the elements of S are not indexed which enables us to write, say, $M(s_1, \sigma_1) = s_2$ without implying anything special about M).

We now change the definition of an automaton by making M a function $M: S \times S \times \Sigma \rightarrow S$. Thus $M(s_1, s_2, \sigma) \in S$ for $s_1, s_2 \in S$, $\sigma \in \Sigma$. Whereas the basic transition of a f.a. is depicted by Figure 2(a), the basic transition of a f.t. a. is depicted by Figure 2(b) where two states are combined into a new state at a lower node.

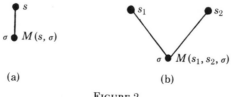

(a)   (b)

FIGURE 2

Let $\mathfrak{A}$ now be a tree automaton. Inputs for $\mathfrak{A}$ will be finite binary trees with nodes valued by Σ. Figure 3 describes the behavior of $\mathfrak{A}$ on a valued tree (note that the terminal nodes are not valued). Here $M(s_0, s_0, \sigma_1) = s_1$, $M(s_2, s_0, \sigma_5) = s_5$, $M(s_3, s_5, \sigma_4) = s_4$, etc.

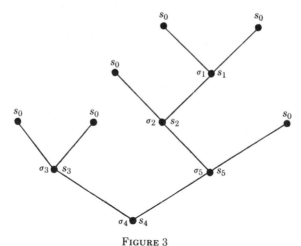

FIGURE 3

III.1. **Binary trees.** In order to give a precise description of f.t.a. we need a convenient way of defining binary trees. In fact, we have to define trees in such a manner that not only their topological structure, but also their left-right structure will be determined. (This distinction was pointed out to me by J. B. Wright.) We shall define trees as sets of words on the alphabet $\Omega = \{0, 1\}$.

Let $x, y \in \Omega^*$, x is called a *prefix* of y if for some $z \in \Omega^*$ $y = xz$. A subset $H \subseteq \Omega^*$ is *prefix closed* if $y \in H$ and x prefix of y imply $x \in H$. The *prefix* *closure* of a set $G \subseteq \Omega^*$ is the smallest prefix closed set H such that $G \subseteq H$. Every prefix closed set contains Λ.

A (*binary*) *tree* is a prefix-closed subset $H \subseteq \Omega^*$. The elements $x \in H$ are the *nodes* of H. The node $\Lambda \in H$ is the *root* of the tree. If $x \in H$ and $x0 \notin H$, $x1 \notin H$, then x is called a *terminal* node. H is a *frontiered tree* if for every nonterminal node $x \in H$ we have $x0 \in H$ and $x1 \in H$.

It is quite clear how these trees $H \subseteq \Omega^*$ represent the geometric trees. Let us make the (arbitrary) stipulation that 0 represents "left" and 1 represents "right." The tree in Figure 3 is given by the prefix closure H of the set $G = \{00, 01, 100, 1010, 1011, 11\}$; H is frontiered.

From now on we shall restrict ourselves to finite frontiered trees $H \subset \Omega^*$. For such a tree H, denote by $Ft(H)$ the set of all terminal nodes of H.

III.2. **Tree-automata.** A Σ-*valued* tree is a pair (v, H) where H is a finite frontiered tree and v is a function $v: (H - Fr(H)) \to \Sigma$ assigning to each nonterminal $x \in H$ a symbol $v(x) \in \Sigma$. Denote the set of all valued trees by $V(\Sigma, \Omega)$.

DEFINITION 9. A *finite tree-automaton* (f.t.a.) is a system $\mathfrak{A}_t = \langle S, M_t, s_0, F \rangle$ where S, s_0, F are as in Definition 1, and M_t is a function $M_t: S \times S \times \Sigma \to S$.

DEFINITION 10. The f.t.a. $\mathfrak{A}_t$ is said to *accept* $(v, H) \in V(\Sigma, \Omega)$ if there exists a function $\phi: H \to S$ satisfying: (1) $\phi(x) = s_0$ for $x \in Fr(H)$, (2) if $x \in H - Fr(H)$ (hence $x0, x1 \in H$) then $\phi(x) = M_t(\phi(x0), \phi(x1), v(x))$, (3) $\phi(\Lambda) \in F$.

The set of all valued trees accepted by $\mathfrak{A}_t$ is denoted by $T(\mathfrak{A}_t)$ and called the set *defined by* $\mathfrak{A}_t$. A set $T \subseteq V(\Sigma, \Omega)$ is *f.t.a. definable if for some* $\mathfrak{A}_t$, $T = T(\mathfrak{A}_t)$.

Note the role played in clause (2) of the above definition by the fact that H is frontiered. The function ϕ satisfying (1)—(3) is, of course, unique.

The reader may look again at Figure 3 which illustrates our general definition. In this case we have, for example, $v(10) = \sigma_2$, $\phi(10) = s_2$, $v(\Lambda) = \sigma_4$, $\phi(\Lambda) = s_4$, etc.

The notion of a *nondeterministic f.t.a.* is defined in complete analogy with the corresponding notion for f.a. (§I.2). By using an appropriate notion of a $\phi: H \to S$ *compatible with* (v, H), we can again introduce the set $T(\mathfrak{A}_t)$ *defined* by a nondeterministic f.t.a. $\mathfrak{A}_t$.

The basic results about f.a. carry over, word by word, to the case of f.t.a. (see [41]). In fact, the same proofs (e.g., those in [33]) generalize to f.t.a. Thus we have the following results.

The class of all f.t.a. definable subsets $T \subseteq V(\Sigma, \Omega)$ *is a boolean algebra.*

For every nondeterministic f.t.a. $\mathfrak{A}_t$ *there exists a (deterministic) f.t.a.* $\mathfrak{B}_t$ *such that* $T(\mathfrak{A}_t) = T(\mathfrak{B}_t)$.

The emptiness and equivalence problems for f.t.a. are solvable.

III.3. **Valued trees and terms.** There exists a well-known analysis of algebraic terms by means of trees. This procedure yields a one-to-one correspondence between terms and valued trees which we shall now describe.

Let $T_0 = (v_0, H_0)$ and $T_1 = (v_1, H_1)$ be Σ-valued trees and let $\sigma \in \Sigma$. The trees H_0, H_1 can be combined into a tree $H = \{\Lambda\} \cup 0H_0 \cup 1H_1$. The *combined valued tree* $C(\sigma, T_0, T_1)$ is defined to be (v, H) where H is as above and $v(\Lambda) = \sigma$, $v(0x) = v_0(x)$ for $x \in H_0$, $v(1x) = v_1(x)$ for $x \in H_1$.

Associate with each $\sigma \in \Sigma$ a binary function (operation) symbol F_σ and let u_0 be a fixed symbol. The set V_2 of all *terms* is defined as the smallest set such that $u_0 \in V_2$, if $t_0 \in V_2$, and $t_1 \in V_2$ then $F_\sigma(t_0, t_1) \in V$ for $\sigma \in \Sigma$.

The one-to-one correspondence ϕ between $V(\Sigma, \Omega)$ and V_2 is given by the recursive definition

$$\phi(\Lambda) = u_0, \quad \phi(C(\sigma, T_0, T_1)) = F_\sigma(\phi(T_0), \phi(T_1)), \quad \sigma \in \Sigma, \; T_0, T_1 \in V(\Sigma, \Omega).$$

The term corresponding to the valued tree of Figure 3 is (we write i instead of σ_i, $1 \leq i \leq 5$)

$$F_4(F_3(u_0, u_0), F_5(F_2(u_0, F_1(u_0, u_0)), u_0)).$$

A set $K \subseteq V_2$ of terms is called *f.t.a. definable* if for some definable $T \subseteq V(\Sigma, \Omega)$ we have $K = \phi(T)$.

If we consider the terms $t \in V_2$ as words on the alphabet $\{F_\sigma | \sigma \in \Sigma\} \cup \{u_0, ",", (,)\}$, then we see that we have definable sets of terms which are not always regular events in the sense of Definition 2. Terms and sets of terms play an important role in programming languages such as ALGOL. We therefore propose an application of f.t.a. and of f.t.a. definable sets of terms to serve as means of computationally defining subsets of the set of all terms. The implementation of this algorithm for defining a subset may be quite feasible if the automaton $\mathfrak{A}$ is not too large. The term t is often stored in memory in tree (list) form and the evaluation of the state $\phi(x)$ assigned to each node is done successively, starting from the terminals for which $\phi(x) = s_0$, and ending with $\phi(\Lambda)$.

III.4. **Algebraization of f.t.a.** We can now give an algebraic version of the theory, which is completely analogous to Theorem 5.

A system $\langle A, a_0, f_\sigma \rangle_{\sigma \in \Sigma}$ is *an algebra of type* Σ_2 if $a_0 \in A$ and every f_σ, $\sigma \in \Sigma$, is a function $f_\sigma: A \times A \to A$.

In particular, we have the free algebra $F_{\Sigma 2} = \langle V_2, u_0, f_\sigma \rangle_{\sigma \in \Sigma}$ where f_σ is defined by $f_\sigma(t_0, t_1) = F_\sigma(t_0, t_1)$, $t_0, t_1 \in V_2$.

THEOREM 11. *A set $K \subseteq V_2$ is f.t.a. definable if and only if there exists a finite algebra $F = \langle A, a_0, \bar{f}_\sigma \rangle_{\sigma \in \Sigma}$ of type Σ_2, a homomorphism $\psi: F_{\Sigma 2} \to F$ and a subset $H \subseteq A$ such that $K = \psi^{-1}(H)$.*

III.5. **Further problems.** The theory of f.t.a. is in its beginnings and there are still many problems and directions of research. We list a few proposals which seem to us to be fruitful.

Establish fully the connection between f.t.a. and context-free and related languages.

Find for f.t.a. definable sets a characterization similar to Kleene's characterization by means of regular expressions. On both this and the previous problem there is some information, but the picture is not complete.

Study the minimal automaton $\mathfrak{A}_t$ defining a given definable set T (is $\mathfrak{A}_t$ unique?). State-minimization problems.

Develop for f.t.a. a theory of decomposition similar to the classical Krohn-Rhodes theory. Here the starting point may be Theorem 11.

Develop a theory of *probabilistic* f.t.a. It is quite clear how the definitions will go. How about the analogue of Theorem 9?

Is it possible to develop for finite automata operating on infinite trees a theory similar to Büchi's theory of automata over infinite sequences (§I.6)? This is of particular interest because if it were possible to develop a satisfactory theory, it would have as a consequence the solvability of Büchi's [5] decision problem of monadic second-order theory of two successor functions. The present author has found a reduction of Grzegorczyk's decision problem of the theory of the lattice of all closed subsets of the real line (see [15]) to Büchi's problem. We also have reductions of many known and new decision problems to Grzegorczyk's problem. Thus a successful extension of the theory of f.t.a. along the above mentioned lines will have far reaching consequences.

Bibliography

1. S. Aanderaa, *On the algebra of regular expression*, Mimeographed Notes, Harvard Computation Laboratory, 1965.

2. J. Beatty and R. E. Miller, *Some theorems for incompletely specified sequential machines with applications to state minimalization*, AIEE Proc. Third Annual Sympos. of Switching Circuit Theory and Logical Design, Chicago, Ill., 1962, pp. 123-136.

3. J. R. Büchi and C. C. Elgot, *Decision problems of weak second-order arithmetics and finite automata.* Part I, Abstract 553-112, Notices Amer. Math. Soc. 5 (1958), 834.

4. J. R. Büchi, *Weak second order arithmetic and finite automata*, Z. Math. Logic Grundlagen Math. 6 (1960), 66-92.

5. ———, *On a decision method in restricted second order arithmetic*, Proc. Internat. Congr. Logic, Method. and Philos. Sci. 1960, Stanford Univ. Press, Stanford, Calif., 1962, pp. 1-11.

6. ———, *Decision methods in the theory of ordinals*, Bull. Amer. Math. Soc. 71 (1965), 767-770.

7. F. Dejan and M. P. Schützenberger, *On a question of Eggan*, Information and Control 9 (1966), 23-25.

8. J. E. Doner, *Decidability of the weak second-order theory of two successors*, Abstract 65T-468, Notices Amer. Math. Soc. 12 (1965), 819.

9. L. C. Eggan, *Transition graphs and the star height of regular events,* Michigan Math. J. **10** (1965), 385-395.

10. C. C. Elgot, *Decision problems of finite automata design and related arithmetics,* Ph.D. Thesis, University of Michigan, 1959; Trans. Amer. Math. Soc. **98** (1961), 21-51.

11. C. C. Elgot and M. O. Rabin, *Decidability and undecidability of extensions of second (first) order theory of (generalized) successor,* J. Symbolic Logic **31** (1966), 169-181.

12. S. Ginsburg, *A synthesis technique for minimal state sequential machines,* IRE Trans. Electronic Computers EC-8 (1959), 13-24.

13. _____, *A technique for the reduction of a given machine to a minimal state machine,* IRE Trans. Electronic Computers EC-8 (1959), 346-355.

14. _____, *On the reduction of superfluous states in a sequential machine,* J. Assoc. Comput. Mach. **6** (1959), 259-282.

15. A. Grzegorczyk, *Undecidability of some topological theories,* Fund. Math. **38** (1951), 137-152.

16. J. I. Janov, *On identical transformations of regular expressions,* Soviet Math. **3** (1962), 1630-1634.

17. S. C. Kleene, "Representation of events in nerve nets and finite automata" in *Automata studies,* Ann. of Math. Studies, no. 34, Princeton Univ. Press, Princeton, N.J., 1956, pp. 3-41.

18. K. Krohn and J. Rhodes, *Algebraic theory of machines.* I: *Prime decomposition theorem for finite semigroups and machines,* Trans. Amer. Math. Soc. **116** (1965), 450-464.

19. R. McNaughton, *Testing and generating infinite sequences by a finite automaton,* Information and Control **9** (1966), 521-530.

20. G. H. Mealy, *A method for synthesizing sequential circuits,* Bell Systems Tech. J. **34** (1955), 1045-1079.

21. J. Mezei and J. B. Wright, *Generalized ALGOL-like languages,* IBM Res. Report, RC 1528, 1965.

22. R. E. Miller, *Switching theory.* Vol. II: *Sequential circuits and machines,* Wiley, New York, 1965.

23. E. F. Moore, "Gedanken-experiments of sequential machines" in *Automata studies,* Ann. of Math. Studies, no. 34, Princeton Univ. Press, Princeton, N.J., 1956, pp. 129-153.

24. D. E. Muller, *Infinite sequences and finite machines,* AIEE Proc. Fourth Annual Sympos. of Switching Circuit Theory and Logical Design, Chicago, Ill., 1963, pp. 3-16.

25. J. Myhill, *Finite automata and the representation of events,* WADC Tech. Report, 1957, 57-624.

26. A. Nerode, *Linear automaton transformation,* Proc. Amer. Math. Soc. **9** (1958), 541-544.

27. C. V. Page, *Equivalence between probabilistic and deterministic sequential machines,* Information and Control **9** (1966), 469-520.

28. M. C. Paull and S. H. Unger, *Minimizing the number of states in incompletely specified sequential switching functions,* IRE Trans. Electronic Computers EC-8 (1959), 356-367.

29. A. Paz, *Graph theoretic and algebraic characterizations of some Markov processes,* Israel J. Math. **1** (1963), 169-180.

30. _____, *Definite and quasidefinite sets of stochastic matrices,* Proc. Amer. Math. Soc. **16** (1965), 634-641.

31. _____, *Some aspects of probabilistic automata,* Information and Control **9** (1966), 26-60.

32. M. Perles, M. O. Rabin and E. Shamir, *The theory of definite automata,* IEEE Trans. Electronic Computers EC-12 (1963), 233-243.

33. M. O. Rabin and D. Scott, *Finite automata and their decision problems,* IBM J. Res. Develop. **3** (1959), 114-125; reprinted in *Sequential machines, selected papers,* edited by E. F. Moore, Addison-Wesley, Reading, Mass., 1964.

34. M. O. Rabin, *Probabilistic automata,* Information and Control **6** (1963), 230-245; reprinted in *Sequential machines, selected papers,* edited by E. F. Moore, Addison-Wesley, Reading, Mass., 1964.

35. V. N. Redko, *On the determining totality of relations of an algebra of regular events,* Ukrain. Mat. Z. **16** (1964), 120-126. (Russian)

36. A. Salomaa, *Axiom systems for regular expressions of finite automata,* Ann. Univ. Turku. Ser. AI **75** (1964), 5-26.

37. ———, *Two complete axiom systems for the algebra of regular events,* J. Assoc. Comput. Mach. **13** (1966), 158-169.

38. M. P. Schützenberger, "Sur certaines variétés de monoïdes finis" in *Automata theory,* edited by E. R. Caianiello, Academic Press, New York, 1966.

39. J. C. Shepherdson, *The reduction of two-way automata to one-way automata,* IBM J. Res. Develop. **3** (1959), 198-200; reprinted in *Sequential machines, selected papers,* edited by E. F. Moore, Addison-Wesley, Reading, Mass., 1964.

40. J. W. Thatcher and J. B. Wright, *Generalized finite automata,* Abstract 65T-469, Notices Amer. Math. Soc. **12** (1965), 820.

41. ———, *Generalized finite automata theory with an application to a decision problem of second-order logic,* IBM Res. Report, RC 1713, 1966.

42. J. Wolfowitz, *Products of indecomposable, aperiodic, stochastic matrices,* Proc. Amer. Math. Soc. **14** (1963), 733-737.

THE HEBREW UNIVERSITY OF JERUSALEM
JERUSALEM, ISRAEL

IBM RESEARCH CENTER
YORKTOWN HEIGHTS, NEW YORK

YALE UNIVERSITY
NEW HAVEN, CONNECTICUT

Marvin Minsky
Seymour Papert

LINEARLY UNRECOGNIZABLE PATTERNS[1]

Introduction. The central theme of this study is the classification of certain geometrical properties according to the type of computation necessary to determine whether a given figure has them. Consider, for example, the following algorithm to determine whether a figure X is *convex*. For each pair of points (p, q) we define the function

$$\phi_{pq}(X) = 1 \text{ if } (p \in X \text{ and } q \in X \text{ and midpoint } (p, q) \notin X)$$

$$= 0 \text{ otherwise.}$$

Then X is convex if and only if no $\phi_{pq}(X) = 1$ for any pair of points (p, q).

This shows, in a sense we shall presently define more precisely, that the "global" property of convexity can be determined by a simple computation from the "local" properties ϕ_{pq}.[2] Thus, if $\phi_{\text{convex}}(X)$ means that "X is convex," we have

$$\phi_{\text{convex}}(X) \Longleftrightarrow \sum_{\text{all } p, q} \phi_{pq}(X) < 1.$$

Now we generalize this. We say that a *property ψ is of order k* if k is the smallest integer for which there exists a family Φ of predicates each of which depends only on a subset of k points of the figure X, and real numbers α_ϕ associated with each member ϕ of Φ such that

$$\psi(X) \Longleftrightarrow \left(\sum_{\phi \in \Phi} \alpha_\phi \phi(X) > 0 \right)$$

In this sense, we can assert that *the order of ϕ_{convex} is at most* 3. The determination of the orders of simple geometrical properties turns out to be far from trivial and presents many surprises. In fact, the greater part of the following analysis seems to be needed to prove that *connectedness*

---

[1] This work was supported in part by Project MAC, and M.I.T. research project sponsored by the Advanced Research Projects Agency, Department of Defense, under Office of Naval Research contracts Nonr-4102(01) and (02).

[2] We identify "property" (or "predicate") with the characteristic function of the set of objects that have the property.

is not of any finite order, i.e.,

There is no k for which connectedness is of order k.

This remains true if we relax the definitions, as we shall, to make the sums finite by considering the plane as a fine-grained infinite chess-board, considering its squares to be points, and allowing only figures which contain each square entirely or not at all—that is, we will consider a discrete model of geometry.

Apart from the purely mathematical interest of the results that come from it, we consider the concept of *finite order* worthy of study for a number of reasons connected with the theories of computation and of pattern recognition. We shall briefly outline some of these reasons.

Motivation of This Study.

(a) *Local vs. global geometric properties.* In problems of geometric pattern recognition, one is led to ask: to what extent can one use "local" properties—evidence obtained from looking at small portions of an object—as a basis for judgements about the "global" character of the object. For example, one can distinguish "line" drawings from other pictures on the basis of the existence of no interior points in the drawing—and this can be determined by a simple combination of evidence obtained from examining arbitrary small neighborhoods. On the other hand, one cannot obtain "local" evidence in favor of a drawing being "connected"—or so one might suspect—without having to combine such collections of evidence by a very complicated procedure.

Our first attempt to study this was based on the idea of *diameter-restricted predicates*, i.e., the restriction on the "local" properties is on the diameter of the set of points on which they depend rather than the number of points. The results of this study are summarized in §IX. However it soon became clear that the more interesting concept is order-restriction, and that the distinction we were seeking was not so much a question of geometry as a question about the theory of computation.

(b) *Serial vs. parallel computation.* What characterizes the extent to which an algorithm can have an essentially *serial*, as opposed to *parallel*, character? That is, to what degree can a computation be sped-up by doing several subcomputations at the same time? One would suspect, for example, that in many successive approximation computations there is little to be gained except, at great expense and redundancy, by parallel processing. We were led to suppose that the same is true for geometric connectedness recognition. One way to recognize that a set is disconnected (connected) is to find that there is a (no) curve dividing the set without intersecting it. One could therefore examine in parallel all possible separating curves, rather than serially trace through the paths within the set. But it would seem that the price of speeding-up the computation this way is superbly costly, and one looks for a way to get theoretical estimates of what is the exchange rate between the minimal serial and parallel amounts of computation. (The goal must be an exchange-cost curve.) One might hope that study of a particular problem, e.g., connectedness, would yield some insight into this general question of computation complexity for finite problems comparable with, say, that achieved in the theory of complexity of the recursive functions (Blum).

(c) *Theory of perceptrons and linear separability.* The pattern-recognition scheme known as the *perceptron* (Rosenblatt [6]) is known to be capable of learning to make any pattern discrimination which is within the scope of its potential ability—that is, if there is a set of parameter values that will suffice, it will find them. Thus, a good deal is known about this system's learning ability, and therefore one is particularly interested to know what is the scope of potential ability. Curiously enough, there seems to be nothing in the large perceptron literature on this question, and the present paper seems to be the first to link the linear-separation problem with the geometric-property problem.

The perceptron (and its derivatives) are of considerable interest mathematically because they are perhaps the simplest nontrivial parallel machines. One therefore ought to understand them thoroughly—as a sort of "linear case"—if one is to get any satisfactory theory of "higher-order" parallel computation schemes.

(d) *Mathematical aspects.* Linear separation computations have considerable mathematical significance in themselves. For example, if we ask for a maximum likelihood decision process based on Bayesian use of the results of statistically independent experiments, one obtains (Minsky and Selfridge [8]) a linear separation procedure. For another example, the generalization (in §1) of Boolean disjunctive normal form appears to yield surprising and fruitful results. Finally, the combination of group theory and linear inequalities seems to promise some new combinatorial techniques.

I. **Theory of linear Boolean separation functions.** In this section we shall confine ourselves to the analysis of the linear representation of predicates defined on an abstract set R, without any additional mathematical structure. The theorems proved here will be applied in later sections to sets with geometrical or topological structures. When necessary for truth R must be taken as finite.

Our theory deals with predicates defined on subsets of a given base space which we shall consistently denote by R. We use the following notational conventions:

(i) Let R be an arbitrary set and $\mathscr{F}$ a family of subsets of R. Using the letters $X, Y, Z, \cdots$ for subsets of R it is natural to associate with $\mathscr{F}$ a predicate $\phi_{\mathscr{F}}(X)$ which is **TRUE** if and only if $X \in \mathscr{F}$.

(ii) We shall use the letters ϕ and ψ to denote predicates defined on the set of subsets of R.

We shall use the notation $\psi(X)$ sometimes to mean the predicate whose value for a given X is **TRUE** or **FALSE**, sometimes to mean a binary set function whose value is 1 or 0. When we wish to employ the two senses in the same context we adapt the notation $\lceil \psi(X) \rceil$ for the binary function whose value is 1 if $\psi(X)$ is **TRUE** and 0 if $\psi(X)$ is **FALSE**. We will usually use this only when there is a possibility of ambiguity, e.g., to distinguish between $\lceil 3 < 5 \rceil = 1$, which is true, and $3 < \lceil 5 = 1 \rceil$, which is false.

(iii) Occasionally it will be convenient in examples to use the traditional representation of $\psi(X)$ as a function of n "Boolean variables" where $n = |R|$. If the elements of R are $x_1, \cdots, x_n$, it is traditional to think of a subset X of R as an assignation of the values 1 or 0 to x_i according to whether the point x_i is in X or not, i.e., "x_i" is used ambiguously to stand for the ith point in the given enumeration of R, and for the set function $\lceil x_i \in X \rceil$. This notation is particularly convenient when ψ is represented in the form of a standard Boolean function of two variables. Thus $x_i \vee x_j$ is a way of writing the set function

$$\phi(x) = \lceil x_i \in X \text{ or } x_j \in X \rceil.$$

(iv) We need to express the idea that a function may depend only on a subset of the points of R. We denote by $S(\phi)$ the smallest subset S of R with the property that, for any subset X,

$$\phi(X) = \phi(X \cap S).$$

We call $S(\phi)$ the *support* of ϕ.

(v) Let Φ be a set of binary set-functions on R. We say that ψ is a *linear threshold function with respect to* Φ if to each member ϕ of Φ there corresponds a real number α_ϕ such that, for some real number θ:

$$\psi(X) = \lceil \sum_{\phi \in \Phi} \alpha_\phi \phi(X) > \theta \rceil.$$

This is often written more briefly as

$$\psi = \lceil \sum \alpha_\phi \phi > \theta \rceil.$$

We denote by $L(\Phi)$ the set of functions ψ expressible in this way.

(vi) We now introduce the central concept of *order*. The *order* of ψ is the smallest k for which there is a Φ satisfying

$$\psi \in L(\Phi),$$

$$\phi \in \Phi \Rightarrow |S(\phi)| \leq k$$

where $|S(\phi)|$ is the cardinality of $S(\phi)$.

Functions of order 1 appear in the literature under the name of "linear threshold functions." It should be noted that the order of a constant function is zero, hence the number θ in the definition of $L(\Phi)$ can be replaced by 0 (or any other number) without changing the definition of order. Note also that the definition is unchanged if we use "$\geq$," "$\leq$," or "$<$" instead of "$>$" (assuming, when necessary, that R is finite).

(vii) ϕ is called a *mask* if there is a set A such that

$$\phi(X) = \lceil X \supset A \rceil.$$

We denote this function by ϕ_A.

In point-function notation a mask is a function of the form:

$$y_1 \wedge y_2 \wedge \cdots \wedge y_t$$

where $\{y_i\}$ is the subset A of R. In particular constant functions are masks.

Linear Representation.

PROPOSITION. *All masks are of order* 1.

PROOF. For each $x \in A$ define $\phi_x(X)$ as $\lceil x \in X \rceil$. Then

$$\phi_A = \lceil \sum_{x \in A} \phi_x \geq |A| \rceil.$$

In particular the functions ϕ_x and ϕ_y are of order 1. Similarly the functions $x \vee y$, $x \wedge y$, $x \supset y$ are of order 1. But the "exclusive or," $x \oplus y$, and its complement, $x \equiv y$, are of order 2.

EXAMPLE (i). $x_1 \vee x_2 \vee x_3$ is of order 1:

$$\lceil x_1 + x_2 + x_3 > 0 \rceil.$$

$x_1 \wedge x_2 \wedge x_3$ is also of order 1:

$$\lceil x_1 + x_2 + x_3 > 2 \rceil.$$

$x_1 \bar{x}_2 = \lceil x_1 + (1 - x_2) > 1 \rceil = \lceil x_1 - x_2 > 0 \rceil$ is of order 1.
$x_2 \vee \bar{x}_1 = \lceil x_2 + (1 - x_1) > 0 \rceil = \lceil x_2 - x_1 > -1 \rceil$, which is also $x_1 \supset x_2$, is of order 1.

EXAMPLE (ii). $x_1 \equiv x_3$, which is

$$x_1 x_2 \vee \bar{x}_1 \bar{x}_2 = \lceil x_1 x_2 + (1 - x_1)(1 - x_2) > 0 \rceil$$

$$= \lceil 2 x_1 x_2 - x_1 - x_2 > -1 \rceil$$

is of order 2. (Proof that it is not order 1 is in §II.)

EXAMPLE (iii). Let M be an integer $0 < M < |R|$. Then the "counting function"

$$\psi^M(X) = \lceil |X| = M \rceil,$$

which recognizes when X contains *exactly* M points, is of order 2.

PROOF. Consider the representation

$$\psi^M(X) = \lceil (2M - 1) \sum_{\text{all } i} x_i + (-2) \sum_{i \neq j} x_i x_j \geq M^2 \rceil.$$

For any figure X there will be $|X|$ terms x_i with value 1, and $|X| \cdot (|X| - 1)/2$ terms $x_i x_j$ with value 1. Then the predicate is equal to

$$\psi^M(X) = \lceil (2M - 1) \cdot |X| - |X| \cdot (|X| - 1) + 1 - M^2 > 0 \rceil$$

and the only (integer) value of $|X|$ for which this is true is $|X| = M$.

Note that the linear form for the counting function does not contain R explicitly. Hence it works as well for an infinite space R. Q.E.D.

EXAMPLE (iv). The functions $\lceil |X| \geq M \rceil$ and $\lceil |X| \leq M \rceil$ are of order 1 because they are represented by $\lceil \sum x_i \geq M \rceil$ and $\lceil \sum x_i \leq M \rceil$.

EXAMPLE (v). We can obtain an arbitrary function $f(|X|)$ of the area of a figure from the predicates used in (iv) above by writing

$$f(X) = f(0) + \sum_{k=1}^{R} (f(k) - f(k - 1)) \cdot \lceil |X| > k \rceil.$$

The order of a function can be determined by examining its representation as a linear threshold with respect to sets of masks. To prove this we first show

THEOREM (POSITIVE NORMAL FORM THEOREM). *Every ψ is a linear threshold function with respect to the set of all masks.*

PROOF. The well-known disjunctive-normal-form theorem for Boolean functions tells us that any Boolean function $\psi(x_1, \cdots, x_n)$ can be written in the form (DNF)

$$\psi(X) = \bigvee_{i \in I} \psi_i(X)$$

where

$$\psi_i(X) = y_{i_1} y_{i_2} \cdots y_{i_n}$$

where for each i and j, $y_{ij} = x_j$ or $y_{ij} = \bar{x}_j$.

We can write this in linear form as:

$$\psi(X) = \lceil \sum_{i \in I} \psi_i > 0 \rceil$$

because, for any X, at most one term of the DNF is nonzero. Hence, we can replace logical "$\vee$" by arithmetic "$+$." Furthermore, since numerically $\bar{x}_i = 1 - x_i$, each ψ_i can be written in the form

$$\psi_i(X) = x_{i_1} \cdots x_{i_m}(1 - x_{i_{m+1}}) \cdots (1 - x_{i_n}),$$

supposing that the negative terms are at the right. Multiplying this out, we obtain an expression of the form

$$\psi_i(X) = \sum \beta_j Z_j$$

where Z_j is of the form

$$x_{i_1} \cdots x_{i_m} x_{h_1} \cdots x_{h_{m'}}, \text{ with } \{h_1, \cdots, h_{m'}\} \subset \{i_{m+1}, \cdots, i_n\}.$$

But such Z_j are masks, so that ψ_i is a linear combination of masks. It follows immediately that $\sum_{i \in I} \psi_i$ is itself a linear combination of masks

$$\psi = \sum \alpha_i Z_i$$

where each α_i is an integer and each Z_i a mask. Q.E.D.

REMARK. The above construction shows not only that any Boolean function is "linear" in the set of masks in the "$\psi = \lceil \sum \alpha_i \phi_i > \theta \rceil$" sense, but is also linear in a stronger "$\psi = \sum \alpha_i \phi_i$" sense. It is interesting that this form is unique, and is therefore entitled to be called a "normal form." We call it a "positive normal form." To see the uniqueness, suppose that

$$\psi = \sum \alpha_i Z_i = \sum \beta_i Z_i$$

and consider the difference

$$\phi = (\sum \alpha_i Z_i - \sum \beta_i Z_i) = \sum (\alpha_i - \beta_i) Z_i = \sum \gamma_i Z_i.$$

Now $\phi(X)$ must be identically zero. To see this, consider first any set X of one element x_i. Then

$$\phi(X) = \phi(\{x_i\}) = \gamma_{\{x_i\}} x_i = \gamma_{\{x_i\}} \cdot 1 = 0$$

so $\gamma_{\{x_i\}} = 0$. Next, consider any two-element $X = \{x_i x_j\}$; then

$$\phi(\{x_i, x_j\}) = \gamma_{\{x_i, x_j\}} x_i x_j + \gamma_{\{x_i\}} x_i + \gamma_{\{x_j\}} x_j$$

$$= \gamma_{\{x_i, x_j\}} \cdot 1 = 0$$

so all two-element $\gamma_{\{x_i, x_j\}}$'s are zero. Similarly, by induction, all the γ's can be seen to vanish.

The proof of the positive normal form theorem implies also the

THEOREM. *ψ is of order k iff k is the smallest number for which there exist a set Φ of masks satisfying*

$$\phi \in \Phi \Rightarrow |S(\phi)| \leq k$$

and

$$\psi \in L(\Phi).$$

EXAMPLE (vi). A "Boolean form" has order no higher than the degree in its disjunctive normal form. Thus

$$\sum \alpha_{ijk} x_i x_j \overline{x_k} = \sum \alpha_{ijk} x_i x_j - \sum \alpha_{ijk} x_i x_j x_k$$

so that the negations can be removed without raising order. This particular order-3 form appears later in a perceptron that recognizes convex figures. Using this result we develop some more examples of the use of the concept of order.

THEOREM. *If* ψ_1 *has order* O_1 *and* ψ_2 *has order* O_2, *then* $\psi_1 \oplus \psi_2$ *and* $\psi_1 \equiv \psi_2$ *have order* $\leq O_1 + O_2$.

PROOF. The idea is to multiply together the positive mask representations $\lceil (\Sigma_1 \phi - \theta_1)(\Sigma_2 \phi - \theta_2) > 0 \rceil$ to get a positive form of order $\leq O_1 + O_2$. (Use ">" for $\equiv$ and "<" for $\oplus$.) This may not work in some cases where $\Sigma_1 = \theta_1$ or $\Sigma_2 = \theta_2$. In such cases, it is always possible to replace θ_1 and θ_2 by slightly different values, algebraically independent of the coefficients of Σ_1 and Σ_2, so that the predicates are unchanged but exact equality never holds.

Application.

EXAMPLE (vii). Since $\psi^M(X) = \lceil \lceil |X| \geq M \rceil \equiv \lceil |X| \leq M \rceil \rceil$, we conclude that ψ^M has order ≤ 2, the result of Example (iii).

Question. What can be said about the orders of $\lceil \psi_1 \wedge \psi_2 \rceil$ and $\lceil \psi_1 \vee \psi_2 \rceil$? The answer to this question may be surprising, in view of the simple result of the previous theorem: it is shown in §V that for any order n, there exists a pair of predicates ψ_1 and ψ_2 both of order 1 for which $(\psi_1 \wedge \psi_2)$ and $(\psi_1 \vee \psi_2)$ have order $> n$. In fact suppose that $R = A \cup B \cup C$ where A, B, and C are large disjoint subsets of R. Then $\psi_1 = \lceil |X \cap A| > |X \cap C| \rceil$ and $\psi_2 = \lceil |X \cap B| > |X \cap C| \rceil$ each have order 1 because they are represented by

$$\left\lceil \sum_{x_i \in A} x_i - \sum_{x_i \in C} x_i > 0 \right\rceil \quad \text{and} \quad \left\lceil \sum_{x_i \in B} x_i - \sum_{x_i \in C} x_i > 0 \right\rceil$$

but, as shown in §V, $(\psi_1 \wedge \psi_2)$ and $(\psi_1 \vee \psi_2)$ have high orders.

II. **Group theory of linear inequalities.** In this section we consider linear threshold functions that are invariant under groups of permutations of the points of the base-space R. The purpose of this, realized finally in §V, is to establish a connection between the geometry of R and the question of when a geometric predicate can be a linear threshold function.

As an introduction to the methods introduced in this section we first consider a simple, almost trivial example. Suppose we wish to prove that the function $x_1 x_2 \vee \overline{x_1}\overline{x_2}$ is not of order 1. To do so we might try to deduce a contradiction from the hypothesis that numbers α, β and θ can be found for which

(1) $$\psi(x_1, x_2) = x_1 x_2 \vee \bar{x}_1 \bar{x}_2 = \lceil \alpha x_2 + \beta x_1 > \theta \rceil.$$

We could proceed directly by writing down the conditions on α and β:

$$x_1 = 0, \quad x_2 = 0 \Rightarrow 0 > \theta,$$
$$x_1 = 1, \quad x_2 = 0 \Rightarrow \alpha \leq \theta,$$
$$x_1 = 0, \quad x_2 = 1 \Rightarrow \beta \leq \theta,$$
$$x_1 = 1, \quad x_2 = 1 \Rightarrow \alpha + \beta > \theta.$$

In this simple case it is easy enough to deduce the contradiction.

But arguments of this sort are hard to generalize to more complex situations involving many variables. On the other hand the following argument, though it may be considered more complicated in itself, leads to elegant generalizations. First observe that the value of ψ is invariant under permutation of x_1 and x_2, that is,

$$\psi(x_1, x_2) = \psi(x_2, x_1).$$

Thus

$$\alpha x_1 + \beta x_2 > \theta,$$
$$\alpha x_2 + \beta x_1 > \theta;$$

yields

$$((\alpha + \beta)/2) x_1 + ((\alpha + \beta)/2) x_2 > \theta$$

by adding the inequalities.

Similarly

$$\alpha x_1 + \beta x_2 \leq \theta,$$
$$\alpha x_2 + \beta x_1 \leq \theta$$

yields

$$((\alpha + \beta)/2) x_1 + ((\alpha + \beta)/2) x_2 \leq \theta.$$

It follows that if we write γ for $(\alpha + \beta)/2$, then

$$\psi(x_1, x_2) = \lceil \gamma x_1 + \gamma x_2 > \theta \rceil;$$

i.e., we can assume that the coefficients of x_1 and x_2 in the linear representation of ψ are equal. It follows that

$$\psi(X) = \lceil \gamma |X| > \theta \rceil \quad \text{or} \quad \lceil \gamma |X| - \theta > 0 \rceil$$

(if we assume that the space X has only the two points x_1 and x_2).

Now consider three values of X,

$$X_0 = \Lambda, \qquad |X_0| = 0, \quad \gamma|X| - \theta \leqq 0,$$
$$X_1 = \{x_2\}, \qquad |X_1| = 1, \quad \gamma|X| - \theta > 0,$$
$$X_2 = \{x_1, x_2\}, \quad |X_2| = 2, \quad \gamma|X| - \theta \leqq 0.$$

Since X_0 and X_2 *satisfy* ψ, and X_1 does not, *the first-degree polynomial* $\gamma|X| - \theta$ *in* $|X|$ *would have to change direction twice, from positive to negative and back to positive as* $|X|$ *increases from 0 to 2.* This is clearly impossible. *Thus we learn something about* ψ *by averaging it over the permutations that leave it invariant.* The method is similar to that used in Haar measure theory. In fact, for order 1, it is the same method.

The generalization of this procedure involves consideration of groups of permutations on the set R and functions ψ invariant under these groups of permutations. In anticipation of application to geometrical problems, we recall the mathematical viewpoint from which every interesting geometrical property is an invariant of some natural transformation group.

Let G be a group of permutations of R; $g \in G$ and $X \subset R$, and define

$$X_g = {}_{df} \{ y \mid y = xg, \ x \in X \},$$
$$\psi^g(X) = {}_{df} \psi(X_g),$$
$$\psi \equiv {}_G \phi = {}_{df} (\exists g \in G)(\psi = \phi^g).$$

Thus we define an equivalence relation of ϕ's with respect to a group G.

THE GROUP INVARIANCE THEOREM. *Let*
(i) G *be a finite group of permutations of* R;
(ii) Φ *be a set of predicates on* R *closed under* G, *i.e.,* $\phi \in \Phi, g \in G \Rightarrow \phi^g \in \Phi$;
(iii) ψ *be in* $L(\Phi)$ *and invariant under* G.
Then there exists a linear representation of ψ,

$$\psi = \left\lceil \sum_{\phi \in \Phi} \beta_\phi \phi > 0 \right\rceil$$

for which the coefficients β_ϕ *depend only on the G-equivalence class of* ϕ, *i.e.,*

$$\phi \equiv {}_G \phi' \Rightarrow \beta_\phi = \beta_{\phi'}.$$

PROOF. Divide Φ into equivalence classes by the relation $\equiv_G$:

$$\Phi = \Phi_1 \cup \cdots \cup \Phi_k.$$

Now let $\psi = \left\lceil \sum_{\phi \in \Phi} \alpha_\phi \phi(X) > 0 \right\rceil$ be any linear representation of ψ and choose X such that $\psi(X)$ i.e., $\sum_{\phi \in \Phi} \alpha_\phi \phi(X) > 0$.

Since $\psi(X) = \psi(X_g)$, it follows that for each $g \in G$,

$$\sum_{\phi \in \Phi} \alpha_\phi \phi(X_g) = \sum_{\phi \in \Phi} \alpha_\phi \phi^g(X) > 0.$$

Since the sum of positive quantities is positive we can sum all such equations:

$$\sum_{g \in G} \sum_{\phi \in \Phi} \alpha_\phi \phi^g(X) > 0.$$

Since $\Phi = \bigcup_{i=1}^k \Phi_i$, the expression on the left can be written:

$$\sum_{g \in G} \sum_{i=1}^k \sum_{\phi \in \Phi_i} \alpha_\phi \phi^g = \sum_{i=1}^k \sum_{g \in G} \sum_{\phi \in \Phi_i} \alpha_\phi \phi^g.$$

Hence,

$$\sum_{i=1}^k \sum_{\phi \in \Phi_i} \left(\sum_{g \in G} \alpha_\phi \phi^g(X) \right) > 0.$$

Now observe that the set

$$\Phi_i g = \{ \phi g \mid \phi \in \Phi_i \} = \{ \phi \mid \phi \in \Phi_i \} = \Phi_i$$

because any g just permutes members of an equivalence class. Then also,

$$\Phi_i = \Phi_i g^{-1}.$$

Hence for any g

$$\sum_{\phi \in \Phi_i} \alpha_\phi \phi^g = \sum_{\phi \in \Phi_i g^{-1}} \alpha_\phi \phi^g = \sum_{\phi \in \Phi_i} \alpha_{\phi g} \phi.$$

So

$$\sum_g \sum_{\phi \subset \Phi_i} \alpha_\phi \phi^g = \sum_g \sum_{\phi \in \Phi_i} \alpha_{\phi g^{-1}} \phi = \sum_{\phi \in \Phi_i} \left(\sum_g \alpha_{\phi g^{-1}} \right) \phi.$$

Since as g runs over G, ϕ^g "covers" $\Phi_{E(\phi)}$, then $\sum_{g \in G} \alpha_{\phi g^{-1}}$ has the same value for all equivalent ϕ's, i.e., if $\phi \in \Phi_i$, $\sum_{g \in G} \alpha_{\phi g^{-1}}$ depends only on i. Therefore we can denote $\sum_{g \in G} \alpha_{\phi g^{-1}}$ by β_i obtaining:

$$\sum_{i=1}^k \sum_{\phi \subset \Phi_i} \beta_i \phi(X) > 0$$

or

$$\sum \beta_{E(\phi)} \phi(X) > 0,$$

where $E(\phi)$ denotes "the equivalence class containing ϕ."

A similar argument shows that if $\sum \alpha_\phi \phi(X) < 0$, then $\sum \beta_{E(\phi)} \phi(X) < 0$. Thus $\psi = \lceil \sum \alpha_\phi \phi > 0 \rceil = \lceil \sum \beta_{E(\phi)} \phi > 0 \rceil$. We shall most often use this theorem in the following form:

COROLLARY 1. *Any function ψ, of order k has a linear representation*

$$\psi = \left\lceil \sum_\Phi \alpha_\phi \phi > 0 \right\rceil$$

where Φ is the set of masks of degrees $\leq k$ and $\alpha_\phi = \alpha_{\phi'}$ wherever $S(\phi)$ can be transformed into $S(\phi')$ by an element of G.

PROOF. The corollary follows immediately from the theorem and the observation that, for masks, $\phi_A \equiv_G \phi_B$ if and only if $A = B_g$ for some $g \in G$.

COROLLARY 2. *Let $\Phi = \Phi_1 \cup \cdots \cup \Phi_m$ be the decomposition of Φ into equivalence classes by the relation $\equiv_G$. Then if ψ is in $L(\Phi)$ and Φ is closed under G, ψ can be written in the form*

$$\psi = \lceil \sum \alpha_i N_i(X) > 0 \rceil$$

where $N_i(X) = |\{\phi \,|\, \phi \in \Phi_i; \; \phi(X)\}|$, i.e., $N_i(X)$ is the number of ϕ's of the i-th type, equivalent under the group, that "fit" the argument X.

PROOF. ψ can be represented as

$$\psi = \lceil \sum_{\phi \in \Phi} \alpha_\phi \phi > 0 \rceil$$

$$= \lceil \sum_i \sum_{\phi \in \Phi_i} \alpha_\phi \phi > 0 \rceil$$

$$= \lceil \sum_i \alpha_i \sum_{\phi \in \Phi_i} \phi > 0 \rceil = \lceil \sum_i \alpha_i N_i(X) > 0 \rceil.$$

COROLLARY 3. (THE TRIVIALITY OF INVARIANT PREDICATES OF ORDER 1). *Let G be any transitive group of permutations on R (transitive means: for every pair $p, q \in R$ there is a $g \in G$ such that $pg = q$). Then the only first-order predicates invariant under G are of the forms:*

or
$$\psi(X) = \lceil |X| > m \rceil,$$
$$\psi(X) = \lceil |X| < m \rceil, \quad \text{for some m.}$$

PROOF. Since the group is transitive all the one-point predicates $\phi_{\{p\}}$ are equivalent. Thus we can assume that

$$\psi(X) = \lceil \sum_{p \in X} \alpha \phi_{\{p\}} > \theta \rceil \quad \text{(or with some other inequality sign)}$$

i.e., the coefficient α is independent of p. But $\sum_{p \in X} \alpha \phi_{\{p\}} > \theta$ can be transformed into $\sum_{p \in X} \phi_{\{p\}} > \theta/\alpha$ (for $\alpha > 0$; for $\alpha \leq 0$ a similar argument proves the corresponding assertion). But $\sum_{p \in X} \phi_{\{p\}} = |X|$. Thus order-1 invariant predicates can do nothing more than define a count on the cardinality or "area" of figures. In fact, an order-1 predicate is a measure, and the order-1 invariant predicate is the Haar measure.

III. **Applications of the group-invariance theorem.**
The Parity Function. In this section we develop in some detail the analysis of the particular predicate ψ_{PAR} defined by

$$\psi_{\text{PAR}}(X) = \lceil |X| \text{ is odd} \rceil.$$

Our interest in ψ_{PAR} is threefold: it is interesting in itself; it will be used for the analysis of other more important functions; and, especially, it illustrates our mathematical methods and the kind of question they enable us to discuss.

THEOREM. ψ_{PAR} *is of order* $|R|$.

That is, to compute ψ_{PAR} requires at least one predicate whose support covers the *whole space* R!

PROOF. Let G be the group of all permutations of R. Clearly ψ_{PAR} is invariant under G.

Now suppose that $\psi_{PAR} = \lceil \sum \alpha_i \phi_i > 0 \rceil$ where the ϕ_i are masks with $|S(\phi_i)| \leq K$ and the α_i depend only on the equivalence classes defined by $\equiv_G$. Since masks with the same support are identical,

$$\phi_i \equiv_G \phi_j \Longleftrightarrow |S(\phi_i)| = |S(\phi_j)|.$$

Thus

$$\psi_{PAR} = \left\lceil \sum_{j=0}^{K} \left(\alpha_j \sum_{\phi \in \Phi_j} \phi \right) > 0 \right\rceil$$

where Φ_j is the set of masks whose supports contain exactly j elements. We now calculate for an arbitrary subset X of R,

$$C_j(X) = \sum_{\phi \in \Phi_j} \phi(X).$$

Since $\phi(X)$ is 1 if $S(\phi) \subset X$ and 0 otherwise, $C_j(X)$ is the number of subsets of X with j elements, i.e.,

$$C_j(X) = \binom{|X|}{j}$$

which is a polynomial of degree j in $|X|$.

It follows that

$$\psi_{PAR} = \sum_{j=0}^{K} \alpha_j C_j(X)$$

is a polynomial of degree K in $|X|$, say $P(|X|)$.

Now consider a sequence

$$\Lambda = X_0 \subset X_1 \subset \cdots \subset X_{|R|} = R$$

of $|R| + 1$ nested subsets of R, and the sequence of values

$$P(|X_0|) = 0, \ P(|X_1|) = 1, \ P(|X_2|) = 0, \cdots, P(|X_{|R|}|).$$

This implies that $P(|X|)$ changes direction $|R|$ times as $|X|$ increases from 0 to $|R|$. But since P is a polynomial of degree K, it follows that $K = |R|$. Q.E.D.

From this we obtain the

THEOREM. *If* $\psi_{PAR} \in L(\Phi)$ *and if* Φ *contains only masks, then* Φ *contains all the masks.*

PROOF. Suppose, if possible, that $\psi_{PAR} \in L(\Phi)$, that Φ contains only masks, and the mask whose support is A does not belong to Φ.

Let $\psi_{PAR} = \lceil \sum_{\phi \in \Phi} \alpha_\phi \phi > 0 \rceil$. Define, for any ψ, $\psi^A(X) = \psi(X \cap A)$. Clearly ψ_{PAR}^A, the parity function for subsets of A, is of order $|A|$ by the previous theorem.

Now consider ϕ^A for $\phi \in \Phi$. If $S(\phi) \subset A$, clearly $\phi^A = \phi$. If $S(\phi)$ is not a subset of A, ϕ^A is identically zero since

$$S(\phi) \not\subset A \Rightarrow S(\phi) \not\subset X \cap A \Rightarrow \phi(X \cap A) = 0 \Rightarrow \phi^A(X) = 0.$$

It follows that either $S(\phi^A)$ is a *proper* subset of A or ϕ^A is identically zero. Let Φ^A be the set of masks in Φ whose supports are subsets of A. Then $\psi_{PAR}^A = \lceil \sum_{\phi \in \Phi^A} \alpha_\phi \phi > 0 \rceil$. But for all $\phi \in \Phi^A$, $|S(\phi)| < |A|$. It would follow that the order of ψ_{PAR}^A is less than $|A|$, which is a contradiction. Thus the hypotheses are impossible and the theorem follows. Q.E.D.

COROLLARY 1. *If* $\psi_{PAR} \in L(\Phi)$, *then* Φ *must contain at least one* ϕ *for which*

$$|S(\phi)| = |R|.$$

The following theorem, also immediate from the above is of interest to students of threshold logic:

COROLLARY 2. *Let* Φ *be the set of all* ψ_{PAR}^A *for proper subsets* A *of* R. *Then* $\psi_{PAR}^R \notin L(\Phi)$.

The following theorem gives a hint that certain functions that might be recognizable, in principle, by a very large perceptron, might not actually be realizable in practice because of huge coefficients.

Coefficients of the Parity Function. Suppose that we have a $\lceil \sum \alpha_i \phi_i > 0 \rceil$ that recognizes Parity $(|X|)$ with masks. Let us suppose that the recognition is *reliable*, e.g., that $\sum \alpha_i \phi_i > 2$ for odd parity, and $\sum \alpha_i \phi_i < 0$ for even parity. If we apply the full permutation group, we obtain the same reliable discrimination with a set of "average coefficients" α_i all equal for ϕ's of the same order. Then we obtain the inequalities

$$\left. \begin{array}{r} \alpha_1 > 2 \\ \alpha_2 + 2\alpha_1 < 0 \\ \alpha_3 + 3\alpha_2 + 3\alpha_1 > 2 \end{array} \right\} \quad \text{or} \quad \sum_{i=1}^{n} \binom{n}{i} \alpha_i \begin{array}{l} > 2, \text{ if } n \text{ is odd,} \\ < 0, \text{ if } n \text{ is even.} \end{array}$$

$\cdot \quad \cdot \quad \cdot$

Subtracting successive inequalities, define

$$D_n = \sum_{1}^{n+1} \binom{n+1}{i} \alpha_i - \sum_{1}^{n} \binom{n}{i} \alpha_i$$

$$= \alpha_{n+1} + \sum_{1}^{n} \left[\binom{n+1}{i} - \binom{n}{i} \right] \alpha_i = \alpha_{n+1} + \sum_{1}^{n} \binom{n}{i-1} \alpha_i$$

$$= \sum_{0}^{n} \binom{n}{i} \alpha_{i+1}$$

so that for all n,

$$(-1)^n D_n > 2 \quad \text{or} \quad [(-1)^n D_n - 2] > 0.$$

Using these inequalities, we will obtain a bound on the coefficients $\{\alpha_i\}$. We will sum the inequalities with certain positive weights; choose any $M > 0$, and consider

$$\sum_{0}^{M} \binom{M}{i} [(-1)^i D_i - 2] > 0.$$

Then

$$\sum_{0}^{M} \binom{M}{i} (-1)^i D_i > 2 \sum_{0}^{M} \binom{M}{i} = 2^{M+1}.$$

The left-hand side is

$$\sum_{i=0}^{M} \sum_{k=0}^{i} (-1)^i \alpha_{k+1} \binom{i}{k} \binom{M}{i} = \sum_{k=0}^{M} \sum_{i=k}^{M} (-1)^i \alpha_{k+1} \binom{i}{k} \binom{M}{i}$$

$$= \sum_{k=0}^{M} \sum_{i=K}^{M} (-1)^i \alpha_{k+1} \left(\frac{i!}{k!\,(i-k)!} \right) \left(\frac{M!}{i!\,(M-i)!} \right)$$

$$= \sum_{k=0}^{M} \sum_{i=k}^{M} (-1)^i \alpha_{k+1} \left(\frac{M!}{k!\,(M-k)!} \right) \left(\frac{(M-k)!}{(i-k)!\,(M-i)!} \right)$$

$$= \sum_{k=0}^{M} \alpha_{k+1} \binom{M}{k} (-1)^k \sum_{j=0}^{M-k} \left(\frac{(M-k)!}{j!\,(M-k-j)!} \right) (-1)^j$$

$$= \sum_{k=0}^{M} \alpha_{k+1} \binom{M}{k} (-1)^k (1-1)^{M-k}$$

$$= \alpha_{M+1} (-1)^M$$

so we have the

THEOREM. *For each* M,

$$(-1)^M \alpha_{M+1} > 2^{M+1}.$$

These values hold for the average, so if the coefficients of each type are not equal, some must be even larger! This shows that it is impractical to use mask-like ϕ's to recognize parity-like functions: even if one could afford the huge number of ϕ's, one would have also to cope with huge ranges of their coefficients!

REMARK. This has a practically fatal effect on the corresponding learning machines. At least $2^{|R|}$ instances of just the maximal pattern is required to "learn" the largest coefficient; actually the situation is far worse because of the unfavorable interactions with lower order coefficients. It follows, moreover that the information capacity necessary to store the set $\{\alpha_i\}$ of coefficients is greater than that needed to store the entire set of patterns recognized by ψ_{PAR}—that is, the even subsets of R. For, any uniform representation of the α_i's must allow $|R|$ bits for each, and since there are $2^{|R|}$ coefficients the total number of bits required is $|R| \cdot 2^{|R|}$. On the other hand there are $2^{|R|-1}$ even subsets of R, each representable by an $|R|$-bit sequence, so that $|R| \cdot 2^{|R|-1}$ bits would suffice to represent the subsets.

It should also be noted that ψ_{PAR} is not very exceptional in this regard because the positive normal form theorem tells us that all possible $2^{2^{|R|}}$ Boolean functions can be so encoded as linear threshold functions in the set of all masks. Then, on the average, specification of the coefficients of each requires $2^{|R|}$ bits.

Another predicate of great interest is associated with the geometric property of "connectedness:" Its application and interpretation is deferred to §V; the basic theorem is proved now.

The "One-in-a-box" Theorem.

THEOREM. *Let $A_1, \cdots, A_m$ be disjoint subsets of R and define the predicate*

$$\psi(X) = \lceil (\forall i)(|X \cap A_i| > 0) \rceil$$

i.e., there is at least one point of X in each A_i. Then if for all i, $|A_i| = 4m^2$, the order of ψ is $\geq m$.

COROLLARY. *If $R = A_1 \cup A_2 \cup \cdots \cup A_m$, the order of ψ is at least the order of $(|R|/4)^{1/3}$.*

PROOF. For each $i = 1, \cdots, m$ let G_i be the group of permutations of R which permutes the elements of A_i but do not affect the elements of the complement of A_i. Let G be the group generated by all elements of the G_i. Clearly ψ is invariant with respect to G. Let Φ be the set of masks of degree K or less. To determine the equivalence class of any $\phi \in \Phi$ consider the ordered set of occupancy numbers

$$\{ |S(\phi) \cap A_i| \}.$$

Then $\phi_1 \equiv_G \phi_2$ if, for each i, $|S(\phi_1) \cap A_i| = |S(\phi_2) \cap A_i|$. Let $\Phi_1, \Phi_2, \cdots, \Phi_M$ be the equivalence classes.

Now consider an arbitrary set X and an equivalence class Φ_j. We wish to calculate the number $N_j(X)$ of members of Φ_j satisfied by X, i.e.,

$$N_j(X) = |\{\phi \mid \phi \in \Phi_j \wedge S(\phi) \subset X\}|.$$

A simple combinatorial argument shows that

$$N_j(X) = \binom{|X \cap A_1|}{|S(\phi) \cap A_1|} \binom{|X \cap A_2|}{|S(\phi) \cap A_2|} \cdots \binom{|X \cap A_M|}{|S(\phi) \cap A_M|}$$

where

$$\binom{y}{n} = \frac{y(y-1) \cdots (y = n + 1)}{n!}$$

and ϕ is an arbitrary member of Φ_j. Since the numbers $|S(\phi) \cap A_i|$ depend only on the classes Φ_j and add up to not more than K, it follows that $N_j(X)$ can be written as a polynomial of degree K or less in the numbers $x_i = |X \cap A_i|$

$$N_j(X) = P_j(x_1, \cdots, x_n).$$

Now let $\psi = \lceil \sum \alpha_\phi \phi > 0 \rceil$ be a representation of ψ as a linear threshold function in the set of masks of degree less than or equal to K. By the argument which we have already used several times we can assume that α_ϕ depends only on the equivalence class of ϕ and write

$$\sum \alpha_\phi \phi(X) = \sum_{j=1}^{M} \beta_j \sum_{\phi \in \Phi_j} \phi(X) = \sum_{j=1}^{M} \beta_j N_j(X)$$

$$= \sum_{j=1}^{M} \beta_j P_j(x_1, \cdots, x_m)$$

which, as a sum of polynomials of degree at most K, is itself such a polynomial. Thus we can conclude that there exists a polynomial of degree at most K,

$$Q(x_1, \cdots, x_m)$$

with the property that

$$\psi(X) = \lceil Q(x_1, \cdots, x_m) > 0 \text{ with } x_i = |X \cap A_i| \rceil$$

i.e., that for all i, $0 \le x_i \le 4m^2$

$$Q(x_1, \cdots, x_m) > 0 \Longleftrightarrow (\forall i)(x_i > 0).$$

In $Q(x_1, \cdots, x_m)$ make the formal substitution,

$$x_i = (t - (2i - 1))^2.$$

Then $Q(x_1, \cdots, x_m)$ becomes a polynomial of degree at most $2K$ in t. Now let t take on the values $t = 0, 1, \cdots, 2m$. By property (ψ) Q must be positive for even t and negative or zero for odd t. By counting the number of changes of sign it is clear that $2K \geq 2m$ i.e., $K \geq m$. This completes the proof.

IV. **The and/or theorem.** We have already remarked that if $R = A \cup B \cup C$ the predicate

$$\psi_1(X) = \lceil |X \cap A| > |X \cap C| \rceil \quad \text{is of order 1,}$$

and stated without proof that

$$\psi(X) = \lceil |X \cap A| > |X \cap C| \wedge |X \cap B| > |X \cap C| \rceil$$

is not of bounded order as $|R|$ becomes large. We shall now prove this assertion. We can assume without any loss of generality that $|A| = |B| = |C|$ and our formal statement is that if $\psi_k(X)$ is the predicate of the stated form for $|R| = 3k$, then the order of $\psi_k \to \infty$ as $k \to \infty$. The proof is similar to that used for the parity theorem. We shall assume that the order of (ψ_k) is bounded by N for all k and derive the contradiction by showing that the associated polynomials would have to satisfy inconsistent conditions. The first step is to set up the associated polynomials for a fixed k. We do this by choosing the group which permutes within the sets A, B, C. The equivalence classes of masks are then characterized by three numbers, i.e., $|A \cap S(\phi)|$, $|B \cap S(\phi)|$ and $|C \cap S(\phi)|$. The number $N_\phi(X)$ of masks in this equivalence class satisfied by a given set X is

$$N_\phi(X) = \binom{|A \cap X|}{|A \cap S(\phi)|} \times \binom{|B \cap X|}{|B \cap S(\phi)|} \times \binom{|C \cap X|}{|C \cap S(\phi)|}.$$

If $|S(\phi)| \leq N$ this is clearly a polynomial of degree at most N in the three numbers

$$x = |A \cap X|, \quad y = |B \cap X|, \quad z = |C \cap X|.$$

The group invariance theorem says that if

$$\psi_k = \lceil \sum_{\phi \in \Phi} \gamma_\phi \phi > 0 \rceil$$

when Φ is the set of masks with $|S(\phi)| \leq N$, then

$$\psi_k(X) = \lceil \sum \alpha_i N_i(X) > 0 \rceil$$

where i runs over the set of equivalence classes of ϕ. But $\sum \alpha_i N_i(X)$ is a polynomial of degree at most N in x, y and z. Call it $P_k(x, y, z)$.

Now, by definition, for possible values of x, y, z (i.e., nonnegative integers $\leq k$), $P_k(x, y, z) > 0$ if and only if $x > z$ **and** $y > z$. We shall show, through a series of lemmas, that this cannot be true for all k. The technical details of these lemmas are not essential for the subsequent sections.

LEMMA 1. *Let $P_k(x,y,z)$ be an infinite sequence of polynomials of fixed degree n, with the property that for all positive integers x, y, z less than k,*

(A)
$$x > z \text{ and } y > z \Longrightarrow P_k(x,y,z) \geq 0,$$
$$x \leq z \text{ or } y \leq z \Longrightarrow P_k(x,y,z) \leq 0.$$

Then there exists a nonzero polynomial $P(x,y,z)$ of the same degree n with the property that the implications (A) hold for all positive integral values of x, y, z. This follows from the following compactness argument: Write

$$P_k(x,y,z) = \sum_{i=1}^{r} C_{k,i} m_i(x,y,z)$$

where $m_i(x,y,z)$ is an enumeration of the monomials in variables x, y and z. We can assume $\sum C_{k,i}^2 = 1$ since the hypotheses remain true if P_k is divided by $\sum C_{k,i}^2$. Now the bounded sequence $C_{1,1}, C_{2,1}, \cdots, C_{k,1}, \cdots$ must contain an infinite convergent subsequence S_1 of the integers for which

$$\{C_{k,1} | k \in S_1\} \text{ converges to a limit, say } C_1.$$

Now consider $\{C_{k,2} | k \in S_1\}$. There must be an infinite subsequence of S_1, say S_2, on which this converges to a limit, say C_2. Continuing in this way we find a subsequence $S = S_r$ of the integers and a set of numbers $C_1 \cdots C_r$ such that $\{C_{k,i} | k \in S\}$ converges to C_i for all $i \leq r$. But then, for $k \in S$, $P_k(x,y,z)$ converges to the polynomial

$$P(x,y,z) = \sum_{i=1}^{r} C_i m_i(x,y,z) \quad \text{for all } x,y,z.$$

To see that $P(x,y,z)$ has the required properties, choose any positive integers x_0, y_0, z_0. For values of k smaller than the largest of these numbers, nothing can be said about $P_k(x_0,y_0,z_0)$. But for all sufficiently large k, $P_k(x_0,y_0,z_0)$ must be nonnegative if $x_0 > z_0$ and $y_0 > z_0$ (and nonpositive if $x_0 < z_0$ or $y_0 < z_0$). It follows immediately that $P(x_0,y_0,z_0)$ is nonnegative (nonpositive) under the same conditions. To see that P is nonzero note that $\sum c_i^2 = 1$.

LEMMA 2. *If a polynomial $f(\alpha,\beta)$ satisfies the following conditions for all integral values of α and β, then it is identically zero:*

(B)
$$\alpha > 0 \text{ and } \beta > 0 \Longrightarrow f(\alpha,\beta) \geq 0,$$

(C)
$$\alpha \leq 0 \text{ or } \beta \leq 0 \Longrightarrow f(\alpha,\beta) \leq 0.$$

PROOF. Suppose that a polynomial of degree N, $f(\alpha,\beta)$, satisfies the conditions (B) and (C) and is not identically zero. Without loss of generality we can suppose that

$$f(\alpha,\beta) = \alpha^N g(\beta) + r(\alpha,\beta)$$

where $g(\beta)$ is not identically zero and $r(\alpha,\beta)$ has degree less than N in α.

For any β for which $g(\beta) \neq 0$, there is an $\alpha_0 > 0$ such that

$$|\alpha_0^N g(\beta)| > |r(\alpha_0, \beta)|.$$

Thus $f(\alpha_0, \beta)$ has the same sign as $\alpha_0^N g(\beta)$, i.e., as $g(\beta)$ since α_0^N is positive. It follows from (B) and (C) that

(D)
$$\beta > 0 \Rightarrow g(\beta) \leq 0,$$
$$\beta < 0 \Rightarrow g(\beta) \leq 0.$$

(The conditions (D) hold for all β: if $g(\beta) \neq 0$ by preceding argument; if $g(\beta) = 0$, tautologously.) We now derive a contradiction by considering separately two cases:

(a) N *even*. Since $g(\beta)$ is not identically zero, there is some $\beta_0 > 0$ for which $g(\beta_0) \neq 0$. By (D), $g(\beta_0) > 0$. Thus $\alpha^N g(\beta_0) > 0$ so that for $|\alpha|$ sufficiently large

$$\alpha^N g(\beta_0) + r(\alpha, \beta_0) > 0$$

i.e., $f(\alpha, \beta_0) > 0$. But we are free to choose a negative value of α, i.e., we can find α_0, β_0 such that

$$\alpha_0 < 0 \quad \text{and} \quad f(\alpha_0, \beta_0) > 0$$

which contradicts (C).

(b) N *odd*. Choose $\beta_0 < 0$ for which $g(\beta_0) \neq 0$; then $g(\beta_0) < 0$, by (D). Choose negative α_0 as before. Then $\alpha_0^N g(\beta_0) > 0$ and $f(\alpha_0, \beta_0) > 0$, again contradicting (C). Q.E.D.

LEMMA 3. *No nonzero polynomial $P(x, y, z)$ can satisfy the following conditions for all positive integral values of x, y, z:*

$$x > z \quad \text{and} \quad y > z \Rightarrow P(x, y, z) \geq 0,$$
$$x \leq z \quad \text{or} \quad y \leq z \Rightarrow P(x, y, z) \leq 0.$$

PROOF. Suppose that $P(x, y, z)$ has these properties. Define $Q(\alpha, \beta, z) \equiv P(z + \alpha, z + \beta, z)$. Let M be the highest power of z in Q so that

$$Q(\alpha, \beta, z) = z^M f(\alpha, \beta) + R(\alpha, \beta, z)$$

where R is of degree less than M in z.

Now choose any α_0 and β_0 for which $f(\alpha_0, \beta_0) \neq 0$. For sufficiently large z, say z_0

(a) $z_0 + \alpha_0 > 0$ and $z_0 + \beta_0 > 0$,
(b) $|z_0^M f(\alpha_0, \beta_0)| > |R(\alpha_0, \beta_0, z_0)|$.

It follows that

$$f(\alpha_0, \beta_0) \geq 0 \Leftrightarrow Q(\alpha_0, \beta_0, z_0) \geq 0,$$
$$\Leftrightarrow P(z_0 + \alpha_0, z_0 + \beta_0, z_0) \geq 0.$$

Thus

$$\alpha_0 > 0 \quad \text{and} \quad \beta_0 > 0 \Rightarrow z_0 + \alpha_0 > z_0, \text{ and} \quad z_0 + \beta_0 > z_0$$
$$\Rightarrow P(z_0 + \alpha_0, z_0 + \beta_0, z_0) \geqq 0$$
$$\Rightarrow f(\alpha_0, \beta_0) \geqq 0$$

and similarly $\alpha_0 < 0$ or $\beta_0 < 0 \Rightarrow f(\alpha_0, \beta_0) \leqq 0$. But this is true for all α_0, β_0. Thus by the previous lemma, $f(\alpha, \beta) \equiv 0$. It follows that $P(x, y, z)$ is of degree zero in z, which is only possible if it is identically zero.   Q.E.D.

This concludes the proof of the AND-OR theorem. It is clear that the reason the theorem is true has to do with the algebraic geometry of the "occupancy" polynomials. If it were not for the constraints concerning integer values of the variables, the theorem would be an immediate consequence of Bezout's theorem.

V. The "order-limited" perceptron.

The Order of Some Geometrical Predicates. Now we consider the problem of computing the *order* of a number of interesting geometrical predicates. As a first step, we have to provide the underlying space R with the topological and metric properties necessary for defining geometrical figures; this was not necessary in the case of predicates like Parity and others related to counting, for these are not really geometric in character.

The simplest procedure that is rigorous enough yet not too mathematically fussy seems to be to divide the Euclidean plane, E^2, into squares as an infinite chess board. The set R is then taken as *the set of squares*. A figure X of E^2 is then identified with that set of elements of R—i.e., that collection of squares—that contain at least one point of X. Thus to any subset X of E^2 corresponds the subset $\hat{X}$ of R defined by

$$\hat{X} = \{\hat{x} \in R \mid \hat{x} \cap X \neq \Lambda\}.$$

Now, although X and $\hat{X}$ are logically distinct no serious confusion can arise if we identify them, and we shall do so from now on. Thus we refer to certain subsets of R as "circles," "triangles," etc., meaning that they can be obtained from real circles and triangles by the map $X \to \hat{X}$. Of course, this means that near the "limits of resolution" one begins to obtain apparent errors of classification because of the finite "mesh" of R. Thus a small circle

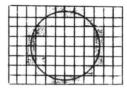

will not look very round.

When it is necessary to distinguish between F and F we will say that two figures X, X' of E^2 are in the same R-tolerance class if $\hat{X} = \hat{X}'$. In this we follow the general mathematical approach proposed by E. C. Zeeman for treating this kind of problem. To avoid inessential questions of how the group-invariance theorem applies to infinite groups, assume below when necessary that R has the toroidal topology.

We begin by listing some geometric predicates of rather small order.

(a) $k = 1$. When we say "geometric property" we mean something that is at least invariant under translation, usually also invariant under rotation, and often invariant under dilatation. The first two invariances combine to define the "congruence" group of transformations and all three the "similarity" group. For $k = 1$, just the translation group suffices for the Group Invariance Theorem to tell us that all coefficients are equal, hence the only patterns that can be of order 1 are those defined by a single cut in the cardinality or area of the set:

$$\psi = \lceil |X| > A \rceil \quad \text{or} \quad \psi = \lceil |X| < A \rceil.$$

Note: If translation invariance is *not* required, then order-1 can compute other properties, i.e., concerning *moments* about *particular* points or axes. However these are not "geometric."

(b) $k = 2$. For $k = 2$ things are more complicated. As shown in §I it is possible to make a double cut in the area of the set, hence we can do the counting trick, and recognize those figures whose areas are

$$\psi = \lceil A_1 < |F| < A_2 \rceil.$$

(In fact, in general we can always find a function of order k that recognizes the sets satisfied by any k inequalities concerning their cardinality.) Now consider only the group of translations and masks of order 2. Then two masks $x_1 x_2$ and $x_1' x_2'$ are equivalent if and only if the difference *vectors*

$$x_1 - x_2 \quad \text{and} \quad x_1' - x_2'$$

are equal. Then, with respect to the translation group, a figure is completely characterized (up to $k = 2$) by its "difference-vector spectrum," defined as the sequence of the numbers of pairs of points separated by each possible directed distance. The two figures:

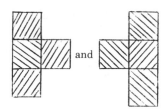

have the same difference-vector spectra, hence no order-2 predicate can make a classification which is both translation invariant and separates these two figures. Similarly,

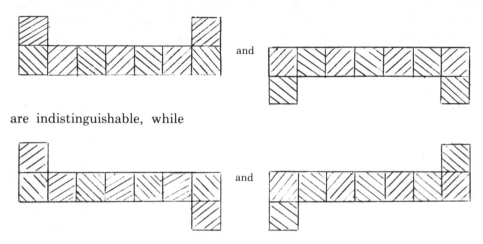

and

are indistinguishable, while

and

have different difference-vector spectra.

If we add the requirement of invariance under rotation, the last pair above becomes indistinguishable, for the spectra now relevant classify together all differences of the same length, whatever their orientation.[3] An interesting pair of figures rotationally distinct, but still indistinguishable, for $k = 2$, is the pair

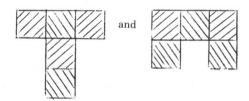

and

which have the same direction-independent distance-between-point-pair statistics. There is an interesting theoretical direction here, but we will not stop to look into it. Many interesting proposals for pattern recognition machines are related to the theory of these geometric spectra. The classic paper of Bledsoe and Browning [1] is related to this, as is the work on "integral geometry" of Novikoff [4].

(c) $k = 3$. As k increases, the class of realizable discriminations grows,

---

[3] Note that we did *not* allow reflections, yet these reflectionally opposite figures are now confused! One should be cautious about using "intuition" here. The theory of rotational invariance requires careful attention to the effect of the discrete retinal approximation, but can presumably be made consistent by application of Zeeman's methods; for the dilatation "group," there are serious difficulties.

and our detailed understanding wanes. It is interesting to discover that the predicate

$$\psi(X) = \lceil X \text{ is a single, solid, convex figure} \rceil$$

is of order ≤ 3, as noted in the Introduction, because

$$\psi_{\text{CONVEX}}(X) = \lceil \sum_{\text{all } a,b} \lceil a \in X \text{ and } b \in X \text{ and midpoint } (a,b) \notin X \rceil < 1 \rceil$$

is of order 3. Presumably this predicate cannot be realized with order 2. It is not difficult to show that the set of solid rectangles (with axis parallel to the mesh of R) can be recognized by a predicate of order 3. This is true also for the set of hollow rectangles (with borders one square thick). It is much more difficult to show, but true, that the set of hollow *squares* has order three! Intuitively one might suppose that at least order 4 is required to insure equality of side lengths.

Another example of a predicate that can be realized with $k = 3$, for any n, is

$$\lceil \text{the points of } X \text{ are collinear, and broken into}$$
$$\text{not more than } n \text{ segments} \rceil.$$

(d) $k = 4$. Using the fact that any three points determine a circle, we can make a perceptron with masks of order $k = 4$ for the following predicates:

$$\psi(X) = \lceil X \text{ is the perimeter of a complete circle} \rceil.$$

PROOF.[4] Define, for all concyclic quadruples of points in R; a, b, c, d

$$\phi_{abcd}(X) = \lceil a \in X \text{ and } b \in X \text{ and } c \in X \text{ and } d \notin X \rceil$$

and then realize ψ as

$$\psi = \lceil \sum_{a,b,c,d} \phi_{abcd} < 1 \rceil.$$

Many other curious and interesting predicates can be shown by similar arguments to have small orders. One should be careful not to conclude that this means that there are practical consequences of this, unless one is prepared to face the fact that

(a) large numbers of ϕ's are required, of the order of R^{k-1} for the examples given above.

(b) the threshold conditions are sharp, so that engineering considerations may cause difficulties in realizing the linear summation, especially if there is any problem of noise. Even with simple square-root noise, for $k = 3$ or larger, the noise grows faster than the retinal size.

---

[4] An alternative method is to integrate the curvature of line elements. This leads to interesting questions about the precision of global functions that can be approximated by summation of local elements with a given precision. Curvature requires order 4, in a sense. The predicate defined here admits a few uninteresting exceptions.

(c) a very slight change in the pattern-definition destroys the recognizability.

Furthermore, in most cases there will be more efficient machines, for the same amount of hardware, to realize these rather simply-defined patterns. Low-order recognition has often the character of a "trick," and one cannot generalize freely. The AND-OR order theorem tells us that some simple relations between simple properties of figures can be prohibitively hard to recognize.

VI. **Connectivity: A geometric property with unbounded order.** We define *connectedness* as follows:

Two points of R are *adjacent* if they are squares (in the map $F \rightarrow \hat{F}$) with a common edge. A figure is connected if, given any two points P_1, P_2 of the figure, we can find a path through adjacent squares from P_1 to P_2.

THEOREM. *The predicate*

$$\psi(X) = \lceil X \ is \ connected \rceil$$

has arbitrarily large orders as $|R|$ *grows in size.*

PROOF. Suppose that (X) could have order $< m$. Consider an array of $(2m + 1) \times 4m^2$ adjacent squares of R arranged in $2m + 1$ rows of $4m^2$ squares each. Let G_0 be the set of points shaded in the diagram below;

i.e., the array points whose row indices are odd, and let G_1 be the remaining squares of the array. Let $\mathscr{F}$ be the family of figures obtained from the figure G_0 by adding subsets of G_1. It is clear that if $F \in \mathscr{F}$ it is of the form $G_0 \vee F_1$, where $F_1 \subset G_1$. Now F will be connected if and only if its F_1 contains at least one square from each even row; that is, if the set F_1 satisfies the "one-in-a-box" condition (see end of §3). The theorem then follows from the One-in-a-Box Theorem.

To see the details of how the One-in-a-Box Theorem is applied, if it is not already clear, consider the figures of family $\mathscr{F}$ as a subset of all possible figures on R. Clearly, if we had an order-k predicate that could recognize connectivity on R, we could have one that worked on $\mathscr{F}$; namely the same predicate with constant zero inputs to all variables not in the small array. And since all points of the odd rows have always value 1 for figures in $\mathscr{F}$, this in turn means that we could have an order-k predicate to decide the one-in-a-box property on set G_1; namely the same predicate further restricted to having constant one inputs to the points in G_0. Thus each Boolean function of the original predicate is replaced by the function obtained by fixing some of its variables to zero and one; this operation can never increase the order of a function. But since this last predicate cannot exist, neither can the first.

An Example. Consider the special case for $k = 2$, and the equivalent one-in-a-box problem for a G_1-space of the form

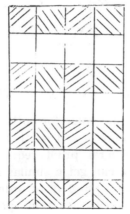

in which $m = 3$ and there are just 4 squares in each row. Now consider a ψ of degree 2; we will show that it cannot characterize the connectedness of pictures of this kind. Suppose that $\psi = \lceil \sum \alpha_i \phi_i > \theta \rceil$ and consider the equivalent form, symmetrized under the full group of permutations that interchange the rows *and* permute within rows.[5] Then there are just three equivalence-classes of masks of degree ≤ 2, namely:

single points: $\phi_i^1 = x_i,$

point-pairs: $\phi_{ij}^{11} = x_i x_j$ (x_i and x_j in same row),

point-pairs: $\phi_{ij}^{12} = x_i x_j$ (x_i and x_j in different rows);

---

[5] Note that this is not the same group used in proving the general theorem.

hence any order-2 predicate must have the form

(1) $$\psi = \alpha_1 N^1(X) + \alpha_{11} N^{11}(X) + \alpha_{12} N^{12}(X) > \theta$$

where N^1, N^{11}, and N^{12} are the numbers of point sets of the respective types in the figure X.

Now consider the two figures:

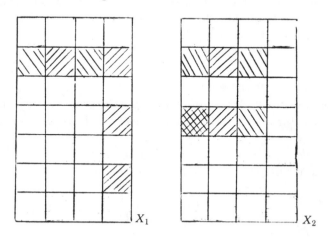

In each case one counts:

$$N^1 = 6, \qquad N^{11} = 6, \qquad N^{12} = 9;$$

hence the form (1) has the same value for both figures. But X_1 is connected while X_2 is not! Note that here $m = 3$ so that we obtain a contradiction with $|A_i| = 4$, while the general proof required $|A_i| = 4m^2 = 36$. It is known also that if $k = 6$, we can get a similar result with $|A_i| = 16$.

The case of $k = 2$, $m = 3$, $|A_i| = 3$ *is* of order 2, since one can in fact express the connectivity predicate for that space as

$$\psi = \lceil N^1(X) + N^{12}(X) - 2N^{11}(X) > 4 \rceil.$$

Cut-wise Connectivity. It should be observed that the proof of the previous theorem applies only to a property of connectivity in its classical sense but to the stronger predicate defined by:

A figure X is "cutwise disconnected" if there is a *straight line L* such that:

F does not intersect L and does not lie entirely to one side of L.

The general connectivity definition would have "curve" for L instead of "straight line," and one would expect that this would require a higher order for its realization.

Relations Between Perceptrons. The study of the order of predicates is often facilitated by the reduction of a given predicate to another simpler one. Although we do not have a satisfactory theory of any class of reductions, or even a clear enough insight into the nature of the relations which might play a role analogous to "homomorphism," "quotient" and so on in more developed areas of mathematics, the following examples are useful in particular applications and indicate an interesting area for future research.

(a) Let us say that a perceptron system, P, is defined by the basic set R and a set Φ of predicates on subsets of R. A second perceptron system, P', is a subperceptron system of P if the basic set R' is a subset of R and if its set of predicates Φ' is that obtained by relativising the members of Φ to R', i.e., all predicates $\phi' \in \Phi'$ satisfy

$$X \subset R' \Rightarrow \phi'(X) = \phi(X) \quad \text{for some} \quad \phi \in \Phi$$

and all predicates ϕ' satisfying this condition are in Φ'. Clearly the order of any predicate of the form ψ' for P' is at most that of ψ for P.

(b) Isomorphism must be given the following natural sense: Let P be defined by R and Φ and P' by R' and Φ'. Then an isomorphism, f, is an isomorphic map $f: R \to R'$ of the sets R with the property that for each $\phi \in \Phi$ there is exactly one $\phi' \in \Phi$ satisfying $\phi(x) = \phi'(f(x))$ (where $f(x)$ $= \{p \in R' \mid \exists q \in R; f(a) = p\}$).

(c) P' is obtained from P by a *collapsing operation* f, if f is a map from points of R' to disjoint sets of R, i.e.,

$$p \in R' \Rightarrow f(p) \subset R,$$
$$p \neq q \Rightarrow f(p) \cap f(a) = \Lambda.$$

A predicate ψ' on R' is obtained from a predicate ψ on R by the collapsing map f if $\psi'(X') = \psi(f(X'))$, for $x' \subset R'$.

THEOREM (COLLAPSING THEOREM). *If f is a collapsing map from R to R' and ψ' is obtained from a predicate ψ by f, then the order of ψ' is not greater than that of ψ.*

PROOF. Let $\psi = \lceil \sum_{\Phi} \alpha_\phi \phi > 0 \rceil$ where Φ is the set of masks of degree less than k on R. Now for any $X' \subset R'$,

$$\psi'(X') = \psi(f(X'))$$
(1)
$$= \lceil \sum_{\Phi} \alpha_\phi \phi(f(x')) > 0 \rceil.$$

We next observe that (1) remains true if Φ is replaced by the set $\hat{\Phi}$ of masks ϕ for which $s(\phi) \subset f(R')$, for if

$$s(\phi) \not\subset f(R'), \quad \phi(f(X')) = 0 \quad \text{for all } X' \subset R'.$$

Now for $\phi \in \tilde{\Phi}$ we have

$$s(\phi) \subset \bigcup \{ f(p) \mid p \in R' \},$$

in fact

$$s(\phi) \subset \bigcup \{ f(p) \mid f(p) \cap s(\phi) \neq \Lambda \}.$$

Thus,

$$X' \supset \{ p \mid f(p) \cap s(\phi) \neq \Lambda \}$$
$$\Rightarrow f(X') \supset \bigcup \{ f(p) \mid f(p) \cap s(\phi) \neq \Lambda \} \supset s(\phi)$$

i.e., $X' \supset \{ p \mid f(p) \cap s(\phi) \neq \Lambda \} \Rightarrow f(X') \supset s(\phi) \Rightarrow \phi(f(X'))$. On the other hand, if $\phi(f(X'))$, i.e., $f(X') \supset s(\phi)$, it follows that

$$f(p) \cap s(\phi) \neq \Lambda \Rightarrow p \in X'$$

since $f(p) \cap f(q) = \Lambda$ for $p \neq q$. Thus $\phi(f(x')) = \lceil X' \subset \{ p \mid f(p) \cap s(\phi) \neq \Lambda \} \rceil$. In other words $\phi(f(x'))$ is a mask on R' with support

$$\{ p \mid f(p) \cap s(\phi) \neq \Lambda \}.$$

But since the sets of the form $f(p)$ are disjoint, for different p, it follows that

$$|\{ p \mid f(p) \cap s(\phi) \neq \Lambda \}| \leq |s(\phi)| < k.$$

Going back to Equation (1) we see, then, that ψ' is represented as a linear function of masks of degree less than k.   Q.E.D.

Huffman's Construction for ψ_{con}. We shall illustrate the application of the preceding concept by giving an alternative proof that ψ_{con} has no finite order, based on a construction suggested to us by D. Huffman.

The intuitive idea is to construct a switching network which will be connected if an even number of its n switches are in the "on" position. Thus the connectedness problem is reduced to the parity problem. The network is shown in the diagram for $n = 3$.

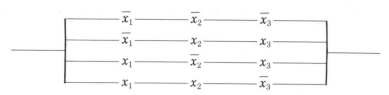

The interpretation of the symbols x_i and $\bar{x}_i$ is as follows: when x_i is in the "on" position contact is made whenever x_i appears, and broken whenever $\bar{x}_i$ appears; when x_i is in the "off" position contact is made where $\bar{x}_i$ appears and broken where x_i appears. It is easy to see that the whole net is connected in the electrical and topological sense if the number of switches in the "on" position is 0 or 2. The generalization to n is obvious:

(a) List the terms in the classical normal form for ψ_{PAR} considered as a point function, which in the case n *even* can be written:

$$\psi_{\text{PAR}}(x_1 \cdots x_n) = \bar{x}_1\bar{x}_2 \cdots \bar{x}_n \vee x_1 x_2 \bar{x}_3 \,\bar{x}_4 \cdots \bar{x}_n \vee \cdots \vee x_1 x_2 \cdots x_n.$$

(b) Translate this Boolean expression into a switching net by interpreting conjunction as series coupling and disjunction as parallel coupling.

(c) Construct a perceptron which "looks at" the position of the switches.

The reductive argument, in intuitive form, is as follows: the Huffman switching net can be regarded as defining a class $\mathscr{F}$ of geometric figures which are connected or not depending on the parity of a certain set, the set switches in "on" position. We thus see how a perceptron for ψ_{con} on one set, R, can be used as a perceptron for ψ_{PAR} on a second set R'. As a perceptron for ψ_{PAR}, it must be of order at least $|R'|$. Thus the order of ψ_{con} must be of order $|R'|$. We shall use the collapsing theorem to formalize this argument. But before doing so we note that a certain price has been paid for its intuitive simplicity: the set R is much bigger than the set R', in fact $|R|$ must be of the order of magnitude of $2^{|R'|}$, so that the best result to be obtained from the construction is that the order of ψ_{con} must increase with $|R|$ like $\log|R|$. This gives a weaker bound, $\log|R|$ compared with $|R|^{1/3}$, if we wish to estimate the order.

Connectivity on a Toroidal Space $|R|$. Our earliest attempts to prove that $\psi_{\text{connected}}$ has unbounded order led to the following curious result: The predicate $\psi_{\text{connected}}$ on an $2n \times 6$ *toroidally* connected space $|R|$ has order $\geq n$. The proof is by construction: consider the space

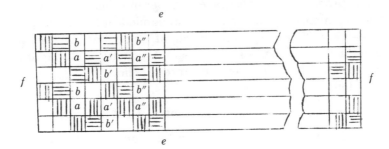

in which the edges e, e and f, f are identified. Consider the family of subsets of R that satisfy the conditions:

(i) All the shaded points belong to each $X \in \mathscr{F}$.

(ii) For each $X \in \mathscr{F}$ and each i, either both points marked $a^{(i)}$ or both points $b^{(i)}$ are in $\mathscr{F}$, but no other combinations are allowed.

Then it can be seen, for each $X \in \mathscr{F}$, that X is either one connected figure or X divides into two separate connected figures. Which case actually occurs depends only on the parity of $||\{i|a^{(i)} \in X\}||$. Then using the Collapsing Theorem and the order $(\psi_{\mathrm{PAR}}) = |R|$ theorem, we find that ψ_{con} has order $|R|/12$.

The idea of this proof came from the attempt to reduce *connectivity* to *parity* directly by representing the switching diagram:

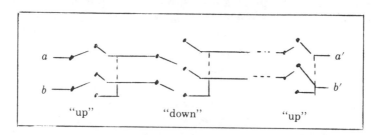

If an even number of switches are in the "down" position then a is connected to a' and b to b'. If the number of down switches is odd, a is connected to b' and a' to b. This diagram can be drawn in the plane by bringing the vertical connections around the end; then one finds that the predicate $\lceil a$ is connected to $a' \rceil$ has for order some constant multiple of $|R|$. If we put the toroidal topology on R, the order becomes $\geq$ constant times $|R|$; this is also true for a 3-dimensional nontoroidal R. Because of these results, we conclude that the order $\sim |R|^{1/3}$ obtained for $\psi_{\mathrm{connected}}$ is too low.

ADDED IN PROOF: We have since shown that the order is at least $\sim |R|^{1/2}$ in the plane.

Some Other Geometrical Predicates. A number of other important geometric predicates that almost certainly have unbounded orders are:

1. Symmetry: $\lceil X$ is a symmetric about some line in the plane. $\rceil$[6]
2. "Twins": $\lceil X$ consists of two disjoint congruent subfigures. $\rceil$
3. Concentricity: $\lceil X$ contains an interior hole. $\rceil$

Curiously enough, the predicate

$$\lceil X \text{ has a single connected comparent} \rceil \vee \lceil X \text{ contains a hole} \rceil$$

has order 2. This can be shown by a construction using the Euler relation, (Holes $= 1 +$ Edges $-$ Vertices $-$ Faces), even though each separately has unbounded order.

VII. **Connectivity and serial computation.** It seems intuitively clear that the reason that the abstract quality of connectivity cannot be captured by a machine of finite order is that it has an inherently serial character; one cannot conclude that a figure is connected by any simple order-

---

[6] But, if a *particular* axis line is chosen in advance, then only order 2 is required!

independent combination of simple tests. The same is true for the much simpler property of *parity*. In the case of parity, there is a stark contrast between our "worst possible" result for finite-order machines (§III) and the following "best possible" result for the *serial* computation of parity. Let $x_1, x_2, \cdots, x_n$ be any enumeration of the points of R and consider the following algorithm for determining the parity of $|X|$:

START: set i to 0

EVEN: add 1 to i
If $i = |R|$ then STOP; parity is EVEN
If $x_i = 0$, go to EVEN; otherwise go to ODD:

ODD: add 1 to i
If $i = |R|$ then STOP; parity is ODD
If $x_i = 0$, go to ODD; otherwise go to EVEN:

where "go to α" means continue the algorithm at the instruction whose name is α.

Now this program is "minimal" in two respects: first in the number of computation-steps per point, but more significant, in the fact that the program requires no temporary storage-place for partial information accumulated during the computation, other than that required for the enumeration variable i. (In a sense, the process requires one binary-digit of current information, but this can be absorbed [as above] into the algorithm-structure.)

This suggests that it might be illuminating to ask for connectivity: how much storage is required by the best serial algorithm? The answer, as shown below, is that it requires no more than about 2 times that for storing the enumeration variable alone! To study this problem it seems that the Turing machine framework is the simplest and most natural, because of its simple uniform way of handling information storage.

A Serial Algorithm for Connectivity. Connectivity of a geometric figure X is characterized by the fact that between any path (p, q) of points of X there is a path that lies entirely in X. An equivalent definition, using the enumeration $x_1, \cdots, x_{|R|}$ of the points of R is: X is connected if and only if for each point x_i after the first point in X, there is a path to some x_j in X for which $i > j$. (Proof: by recursion, then, each point of X is connected to the *first* point in X.) Using this definition of connectivity we can describe a beautiful algorithm to test whether X is connected. We will consider only figures that are "reasonably regular"—to be precise, we suppose that X is bounded by a number of oriented, simple, closed curves so that for each point x_i on a boundary there is defined a unique "next point" $x_{i\cdot}$ on that boundary. We choose $x_{i\cdot}$ to be the boundary point to the left of x_i when facing the complement of X. We will also assume that points x_i and x_{i+1} that are *consecutive* in the enumeration are *adjacent* in R. Finally, we will assume that X does not touch the edges of the space R.

START: Set i to 0 and go to **SEARCH**

SEARCH: Add 1 to i. If $i = |R|$, Stop and print "*X is NULL.*"

              If $x_i \in X$ then go to **SCAN**, otherwise go to **SEARCH**.

SCAN: Add 1 to i. If $i = |R|$, Stop and print "*X is connected.*"

              If $x_{i-1} \in X$ or $x_i \notin X$ go to **SCAN**, otherwise

              Set j to i and go to **TRACE**.

TRACE: Set j to j^*

              If $j = i$, Stop and print "*X is disconnected.*"

              If $j > i$, go to **TRACE**.

              If $j < i$, go to **SCAN**.

Notice that at any point in the computation, it is necessary to keep track of the indexes of just the two points x_i and x_j.

Analysis. **SEARCH** simply finds the first point of X in the enumeration of R. Once such a point of X is found, **SCAN** searches through all of R, eventually testing every point of X. The current point, x_i, of **SCAN** is tested as follows: If x_i is not in X, then no test is necessary and **SCAN** goes on to x_{i+1}. If the previous point x_{i-1} was in X (and, by induction, is presumed to have passed the test) then x_i, if in X, is connected to x_{i-1} by adjacency. Finally, if $x_i \in X$ and $x_{i-1} \notin X$, then x_i is on a boundary curve B. **TRACE** circumnavigates this boundary curve. Now if B is a boundary curve it is either (i) an exterior boundary of a previously encountered component of X, in which case some point of B must have been encountered before or (ii) B is an interior boundary curve, in which case a point of B must have been encountered before reaching x_{i-1} which is *inside* B or (iii) B is the exterior boundary curve of a never-before-encountered component of X, the only case in which **TRACE** will return to x_i without meeting an x_j for which $j < i$. Thus **SCAN** will run up to $i = |R|$ if and only if X has a single nonempty connected component.

Note that we can *count* the number of components of X by introducing K, initially zero, and adding 1 to K each time **TRACE** reaches the $i = j$ exit. Note also that the algorithm is quite efficient; the only points examined more than once are some of the boundary points, and none of them is examined more than three times (see figure below).

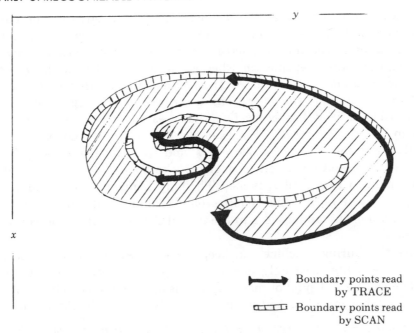

Boundary points read
by TRACE

Boundary points read
by SCAN

The Turing Machine Version of the Connectivity Algorithm. It is convenient to assume that R is a $2^n \times 2^n$ square array. Let $x_1, \cdots, x_{22n}$ be an enumeration of the points of R in the order

$$
\begin{array}{cccc}
1 & 2^n + 1 & \cdots & (2^n - 1)2^n + 1 \\
2 & 2^n + 2 & \cdots & (2^n - 1)2^n + 2 \\
\cdot & \cdot & \cdots & \cdot \\
\cdot & \cdot & \cdots & \cdot \\
\cdot & \cdot & \cdots & \cdot \\
2^n & 2 \cdot 2^n & \cdots & 2^n \cdot 2^n.
\end{array}
$$

This choice of dimension and enumeration makes available a simple way to represent the situation to a Turing machine. The Turing machine must be able to specify a point x_i of R, find whether $x_i \in X$, and in case x_i is a boundary point of X, find the index j^* of the "left neighbor" of x_i. The Turing Machine tape will have the form

I_y	$\cdot \cdot n \cdot \cdot$	I_x	$\cdot \cdot n \cdot \cdot$	J_y	$\cdot \cdot n \cdot \cdot$	J_x	$\cdot \cdot n \cdot \cdot$	K

where "$\cdot \cdot n \cdot \cdot$" denotes an interval of n blank squares. Then the intervals to the right of I_x and I_y can hold the x and y coordinates of a point of R.

We will suppose that the Turing machine is coupled with the outside world, i.e., the figure X, through an "oracle" that works as follows: certain internal states of the machine have the property that when entered, the resulting next state depends on whether the coordinates in the I (or J) intervals designate a point in X. It can be verified, though the details are tedious, that all the operations described in the algorithm can be performed by a fixed Turing machine that uses no tape squares other than those in "$\cdot\cdot n\cdot\cdot$" intervals. For example, "$i = |R|$" if and only if there are all zeros in the "$\cdot\cdot n\cdot\cdot$"s following I_x and I_y. "Add 1 to i" is equivalent to: "start at J_y and move left, changing 1's to 0's until a 0 is encountered and changed to 1 or until I_y is met. The only nontrivial operation is computing j^* given j. But this requires only examining the neighbors of x_j, and that is done by adding ± 1 to the J_x and J_y coordinates, and consulting the oracle.

Since the Turing machine can keep track of which "$\cdot\cdot n\cdot\cdot$" interval it is in, we really need only one symbol for punctuation, so the Turing machine can be a 3-symbol machine. By using a block encoding, one can use a 2-symbol machine, and, omitting details, we obtain the result:

THEOREM. *For any ϵ there is a 2-symbol Turing machine that can verify the connectivity of a figure X on any rectangular array R, using less than* $(2 + \epsilon) \log_2 |R|$ *squares of tape.*

For *convexity* there is a similar procedure that makes three tests:
    i. X is not disconnected by any vertical line that does not intersect X.
    ii. The intersection of X with any vertical line is a connected segment.
    iii. The outer boundary of X does not change the sign of its curvature.
    A detailed construction shows that each test requires only one index point, so that

THEOREM. *For any ϵ there is a 2-symbol Turing machine that can verify the convexity of a figure X on any rectangular array R, using less than* $(1 + \epsilon) \log_2 |R|$ *squares of tape.*

This last result is certainly minimal since $\log_2 R$ squares are needed just to indicate a point of R, and all points must be examined. We are quite sure that the connectivity algorithm is minimal, also, in its use of tape, but we have no proof. In fact, we do not know any method, in general, to show that an algorithm is minimal in storage, except when information-theoretic arguments can be used. Incidentally, it is not hard to show that $\lceil |X|$ is prime$\rceil$ requires no more than $(2 + \epsilon) \log_2 |R|$ squares (and presumably needs more than $(2 - \epsilon) \log_2 |R|$).

We do not definitely know any geometric predicates that require higher orders of storage, but we suspect that in an appropriate sense, the topological equivalence of two figures (e.g., two components of X) requires something more like $|R|$ than like $\log|R|$ squares. There are, of course, recursive function-theoretic predicates that require arbitrarily high, indeed non-computable, orders of storage, but none of these is known to have straight-forward geometric interpretations.

VIII. **Multi-layer perceptrons.** We have found a number of limitations of perceptrons, as defined above, and we have suggested that these may point toward as yet unknown theorems about parallel machines in general. On the other hand one suspects that some, at least, of the results above are not so general, and might not survive minor relaxations of the definitions. One direction of generalization that seems important is that of relaxing the constraint that the ϕ's be simply weighted and added. We have not found any particularly enlightening generalization on the lowest level—e.g., of replacing addition by an arbitrary commutative operation. An easier direction is to consider compositions of perceptrons. The remainder of this section explores some kinds of composite perceptrons. Unfortunately we do not understand them very well, so this section is more concerned with problem-posing than with problem-solving.

Gamba Machines. Consider functions of the form

$$\left\lceil \sum_j \beta_j \left\lceil \sum_i \alpha_{ij} x_i > \theta_j \right\rceil > \theta \right\rceil.$$

This form was proposed and realized in a series of machines built by A. Gamba [2]. It is essentially an order-1 composition of order-1 perceptrons, and is of interest to us for a number of reasons:

(i) The parity problem is solved neatly by

$$\left\lceil \sum_{j=0}^{|R|} (-1)^j \left\lceil \sum_{\text{all } i} x_i > j \right\rceil > 0 \right\rceil.$$

Thus only $|R|$ functions are needed, each itself of order 1 in the $\{x_i\}$. In fact, any predicate $f(|X|)$ that depends only on the area $|X|$ can be realized, as

$$f(|X|) = f(0) + \sum_{j=0}^{|R|} \left\lceil \sum x_i > j \right\rceil \cdot (f(j+1) - f(j)).$$

The problem that led to our formulation of the AND-OR theorem also is solved neatly:

$$\left\lceil \left\lceil \sum_{x \in A} x - \sum_{x \in C} x > 0 \right\rceil + \left\lceil \sum_{x \in B} x - \sum_{x \in C} x > 0 \right\rceil \geqq 2 \right\rceil$$

is 1 if and only if $|X \cap A| > |X \cap C|$ and $|X \cap B| > |X \cap C|$. This might suggest that this class of machines might transcend the other kinds of limitations we have found for machines of finite-order.[7]

We are quite certain that this impression is misleading; that the deeper geometric properties are still outside the reach of this kind of "2-layer" perceptron. The inclusion of AND and OR is due to the 2-layer construction; any Boolean function is obtainable, in such a manner, through its normal form, but for most functions there will still be too many terms for practical interest. The $\ulcorner \, |X \cap A| > |X \cap C| \, \urcorner$ type of predicates are within reach because they are simple area functions and hence fit precisely the inner $\sum \alpha_{ij}$ first-order predicate forms. In fact, *any* class $\mathscr{F}$ of figures can be recognized by a Gamba-machine because

$$\ulcorner \sum_{X \in \mathscr{F}} \ulcorner \sum_{x \in X} x_i \geq |X| \urcorner > 0 \urcorner$$

realizes it. But, this general form requires a special "Gamba-mask" for each $X \in \mathscr{F}$. Although the above examples show that in special cases more economical representations are possible, this is not true in general (as one can see by considering the number 2^{2^n} of possible functions). In particular we conjecture, for example, that for the Connectivity Predicate, the machine would require a number of masks of an order approaching the number of simple-closed-curves in R. Even for convexity, we doubt that that predicate can be realized with significantly fewer than the number of ϕ's needed for the order-3 1-layer machine.

(ii) In spite of its apparent simplicity, analysis of the geometric predicate problem for Gamba machines appears to require methods quite different from those we have used. First, because of the arbitrary order-1 predicate permitted in the inner sum, the notion of *order* does not seem to apply, and theorems must concern restrictions on the numbers of terms. Second, we have not found a way to carry the group-averaging methods into the inner α_{ij} coefficients, so that we cannot use the techniques that come from the group-invariance theorem. It is difficult to see how to analyse other multi-layer and composite perceptrons until this simple case is better understood. How much weaker are the machines with $\alpha_{ij} > 0$ or those with all $\theta = 0$? We have no characterization of what they can do.

(iii) The Gamba-machine is of considerable practical interest because of the possibility of realizing the inner, and even the outer, sums by inexpensive, highly parallel optical methods. Using coherent light and properly

---

[7] Note that the Gamba-machine can have order as large as $|R|$, in the $\{x_i\}$. If the inner predicate threshold were removed then, because

$$\sum_j \beta_j \sum_i \alpha_{ij} x_i = \sum_i \left(\sum_j \beta_j \alpha_{ij} \right) x_i,$$

one would have merely an order-1 function in the $\{x_i\}$.

prepared photographic transparencies, one can realize each inner sum (even with complex coefficients!) with a picture p_j whose density at point x_i is α_{ij}. By shrewd optics, one can even do this (with fixed p_j) for all translations of the source pattern X. Because of these technological possibilities it is important to have a better theory; we expect that the result will be favorable to problems like recognition of printed characters, but still very poor for the more abstract properties like detection of connectivity, symmetry, topological equivalence, and the like.

IX. **The diameter-limited perceptron.** In this section we discuss the power and limitations of the "diameter-limited" perceptrons: those in which each ϕ can see only a circumscribed portion of the retina R.

We consider a machine that sums the weighted evidence about a picture obtained by experiments ϕ_i each of which report on the state of affairs within a circumscribed region r_i of *diameter less than or equal to some length D*. That is, Diameter $(S(\phi)) < D$. We will suppose that D is uniform over the ϕ's of the machine (each actual region that affects a ϕ_i can be smaller, but not larger). We suppose also that in a practical sense D is small compared with the full dimensions of the space R. That is, D should be small enough that none of the ϕ's can see the whole of an interesting figure (or else we would not have an effective limited-diameter situation, and there would be no interesting theory) but D should be large enough that a ϕ_i has a chance to detect an interesting "local feature" of the figure.

We will consider first some things that a diameter-limited perceptron can recognize, and then some of the things it cannot.

(a) *Blank picture, or black picture.* A diameter-limited perceptron can tell when a picture is entirely black, or entirely white: suppose that the set of ϕ_i's is chosen to *cover* the retina in regions, that may overlap, and that we define ϕ_i to be zero when all the points it can see are white, otherwise its value is 1. Then $\sum \phi_i > 0$ if the picture has one or more black points, and not if the picture is blank. Similarly, we could define the ϕ_i's to be 1 when they see any white point, 0 otherwise, thus distinguishing the all-black picture from all others.

For later examples, it is important here to notice why these patterns can be recognized: it is not that any ϕ-unit can really say that there is strong evidence that the figure is all-white (although it has a slight correlation with this); but any ϕ can definitely say that it has conclusive evidence that the picture is *not* all white. Some interesting patterns have this character; that one can *reject* all pictures not in the class because each must have, somewhere or other, a local feature that is definitive and can be detected by what happens within a region of diameter D.

(b) *Area cuts.* We can distinguish, for any number S, the class of figures whose area is greater than S. To do this we define a ϕ_i for each point to be 1 if that point is black, 0 otherwise. Then $\sum x_i > S$ is a recognizer for the class in question. (One can do slightly better; if the ϕ's look at regions of area A, then one can recognize this pattern by using only of the order of $(R \log A)/A$ units.)

(c) *Nonintersecting lines.* One can say that a pattern is composed of nonintersecting lines if, in each small region, the pattern is composed of separate line-segments, or blank. Then, if we make each ϕ have value zero when this condition is met, unity when it is not, then $\sum \phi_i > 0$ will reject all figures not in the class.

(d) *Triangles.* We can make a diameter-limited perceptron recognize the figures consisting of exactly one triangle (either solid or outline) by the following trick: We use two kinds of ϕ's: the first has weight $+1$ if its field contains a vertex (two line segments meeting at an angle), otherwise its value is zero. The second kind, ϕ_i^*, has value zero if its field is blank, or contains a line segment, solid black area, or a vertex, but has value $+1$ if the field contains anything else, including the end of a line segment. Provide enough of these ϕ's so that the entire retina is covered, in nonoverlapping fashion, by both types. Finally assign weight 1 to the first type and a very large positive weight W to those of the second type. Then

$$\sum \phi_i - W \sum \phi_i^* < 4$$

will be a specific recognizer for triangles. (But also the null-picture is accepted.) Similarly, by requiring that the first kind of unit recognize right-angle vertices, the machine can be made to recognize the class of rectangles (setting the threshold to be < 5).

Note that this does not generalize to a very wide class of geometric recognition abilities. The triangle and rectangle cases are rather peculiar; the triangle because it is the simplest figure that has true vertices. The rectangle can be recognized because it has four equal angles; the system cannot be specialized to recognize, for example, exactly the squares. It is interesting, in view of the limitations we will establish shortly, to see why these patterns can be recognized by the diameter-limited machine; a rectangle is the only figure that has four *or fewer* right angles and no free line ends, etc.

(e) *Absolute template-matching.* Suppose that one wants the machine to recognize exactly a certain figure X_0 and no other. Then the diameter-limited machine can be made to do this by partitioning the retina into regions, and in each region a ϕ-function has a value 0 if that part of the retina is exactly matched to the corresponding part of X_0, otherwise the value is 1. Then

$$\sum \phi_i < 1$$

if and only if the picture is exactly X_0.

Note, however, that this scheme works just on a particular object in a particular position. It cannot be generalized to recognize a particular object in any position (or even, in general, in two positions). In fact we show in the next section that even the simplest possible figure, namely one that consists of just one point, cannot be recognized independently of position!

(f) *Convexity*. The remarks in §5, Example c, footnote apply to the diameter-limited case.

Limitations of Diameter-limited Perceptron. Now we consider some of the basic limitations of the diameter-limited perceptron, by exhibiting and analysing some patterns they cannot recognize.

(g) *The figure containing one single black point*. This is the fundamental counter-example. We want a machine

$$\sum \alpha_i \phi_i > 0$$

to accept figures with area 1, but reject figures with area 0 or area greater than 1. Clearly this can be defined by two area cuts (i.e., area > 0 AND area < 2), but it cannot be realized by a linear threshold function with the area-restriction.

To see that this cannot be done, suppose that $\{\phi_i\}$, $\{\alpha_i\}$ and θ have been selected. Present first the blank picture, X_0. Then, defining $f(X) = \sum \alpha_i \phi_i(x)$ we have $f(X_1) < \theta$. Now present a figure, X_1, containing only one point, x_1. We must then have

$$f(X_1) \geqq \theta.$$

The change in the sum must be due to a change in the values of some of the ϕ's. In fact, it must be due to changes only in ϕ's for which $x \in S(\phi)$, since nothing else in the picture has changed. In any case,

(1) $$f(X_1) - f(X_0) > 0.$$

Now choose another point x_2 which is farther than D away from x_1. Then no $S(\phi)$ can contain both x_1 and x_2. For the figure X_2 containing only x_2 we must also have

(2) $$f(X_2) = \sum \alpha_i \phi_i \geqq \theta.$$

Now consider the figure X_{12} containing both x_1 and x_2. The addition, to X_2, of the point x_1 can affect only ϕ's for which $x \in S(\phi)$, and these are changed exactly as they are changed when the all-blank picture X_0 is changed to the picture X_1. Therefore

$$f(X_{12}) = f(X_2) + [f(X_1) - f(X_0)]$$

and by (1) and (2),

$$f(X_{12}) > \theta,$$

but we require that

$$f(X_{12}) \leqq 0.$$

REMARK. Of course, this is the same phenomenon noted in the introduction to §II.

(h) *Area segments.* The diameter-limited perceptron cannot recognize the class of figures whose areas A lie between two bounds $A_1 \leqq A \leqq A_2$.

PROOF. This follows from the method of (a) above, which is a special case of this, with $A_1 = 1$ and $A_2 = 1$. But using the method of §I, Example (vii), this recognition is possible with order 2 if the diameter-limitation is relaxed.

(i) *Connectedness.* The diameter-limited perceptron cannot decide when the picture is a single, connected whole, as distinguished from two or more disconnected pieces.

PROOF. Consider the four pictures

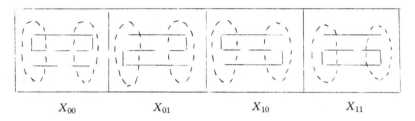

$$X_{00} \qquad\qquad X_{01} \qquad\qquad X_{10} \qquad\qquad X_{11}$$

and suppose that the diameter D is of the order indicated by the dotted circle. Now figures X_{01} and X_{10} are connected, but X_{00} and X_{11} are disconnected. Suppose that there were a set of ϕ's and α's and a such that

$$\sum \alpha_i \phi_i(X_{00}) < \theta, \qquad \begin{array}{c} \sum \alpha_i \phi_i(X_{01}) \geq \theta, \\ \sum \alpha_i \phi_i(X_{10}) \geq \theta, \end{array} \qquad \sum \alpha_i \phi_i(X_{11}) < \theta$$

so that these four figures were correctly separated. But then, just as in the previous argument we would have for all ϕ_i,

$$\phi_i(X_{11}) = \phi_i(X_{10}) + \phi_i(X_{01}) - \phi_i(X_{00})$$

because the two changing regions are more than D apart, hence

$$\sum \alpha_i \phi_i(X_{11}) \geq \theta + \theta - \theta = \theta$$

contradicting the separation requirement.

Acknowledgement: We would like to thank many students and associates, particularly William Henneman, Dona Strauss and John White, for their contributions to this work.

Bibliography

1. W. W. Bledsoe and I. Browning, *Pattern recognition and reading by machine*, Proc. Eastern Joint Computer Conference, 1959; reprint, *Pattern recognition*, Uhr, 1966.

2. A. Gamba, *Optimum performance of learning machines*, Proc. I.R.E. **49** (1961), 349; *Further experiments with PAPA*, Nuovo Cimento Suppl. Ser. X **20** (1961), 112-115.

3. N. Nilsson, *Learning machines*, McGraw-Hill, New York, 1965.

4. A. B. J. Novikoff, *Integral geometry as a tool in pattern perception*, Principles of self-organization, Pergamon, New York, 1961.

5. W. Pitts and W. S. McCulloch, *How we know universals*, Bull. Math. Biophys. **9** (1943), 127-147fl reprinted in *Embodiments of mind*, M.I.T. Press, Cambridge, Mass., 1965.

6. F. Rosenblatt, *Principles of neurodynamics*, Spartan, Washington, D.C., 1962.

7. C. J. Zeeman, "Topology of the brain" in *Topology of 3-manifolds*, M. K. Fort, ed., Prentice-Hall, Englewood Cliffs, N. J., 1961.

8. M. Minsky and O. G. Selfridge, *Learning in random nets*, Proc. London Information Theory Sympos., Butterworth, London, 1961.

Massachusetts Institute of Technology
Cambridge, Massachusetts

AUTHOR INDEX

Roman numbers refer to pages on which a reference is made to an author or a work of an author.

Italic numbers refer to pages on which a complete reference to a work by the author is given.

Boldface numbers indicate the first page of the articles in the book.

SUBJECT INDEX